THE LAND BETWEEN

Dad wants us to see
Beth - Sheenan

A REGIONAL STUDY GUIDE TO THE LAND OF THE BIBLE

JAMES M. MONSON

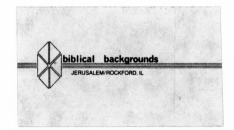

biblical backgrounds
JERUSALEM/ROCKFORD. IL

TO POLLY

companion, editor and patient wife, who by her
faith and actions demonstrates those qualities
needed to live in this *Land Between.*

PREFACE

The Land Between is a book of assignments for *Part A* of the *Student Map Manual* (Pictorial Archive, Jerusalem, 1979). It does not pretend to be a textbook on the subject of historical geography with proper footnotes and bibliography. Nor does it expose the student to the myriad of views on chronological questions, site identifications and archeological evidences. Its purpose is to introduce the land of the Bible to students of the Bible. If this study motivates students to exploit the expertise of their own teachers, a process will be initiated which will go far beyond the scope of this book. In this sense, the completion of these assignments is only *the end of a beginning.*

The approach used in *The Land Between* emerged over many years of interaction with students who came to the Institute of Holy Land Studies in Jerusalem, Israel, for serious study of Biblical backgrounds. As pre-Israel assignments, classroom lectures, visual aids and an intensive field trip program for these students were developed, a basis was laid for a more comprehensive study guide. All of this brought an ever-increasing awareness of what might be called *the dynamic of the land*, that sense of reality which comes from seeing the Biblical text continually *played out* on the actual terrain.

In Chapter One this *dynamic* is set within the larger geopolitical context of this *Land Between*. At the same time the chapter introduces highlights of a millennium of history. Each subsequent chapter presents a different region of the country and broadens Biblical horizons, allowing the history of the land to teach the land itself. In this way the Bible makes the land come alive. In turn, the complex historical background of the Bible is far easier to understand if it is placed within the geographical setting in which it actually occurred.

These assignments are not purely geographical nor purely historical. They represent the interplay of history and geography, disciplines which complement each other. The important supporting discipline of archeology is not treated seriously because of the limited scope and specific goal of this work. Therefore, recent excavations at sites such as Jerusalem, Lachish, Arad, Beer-sheba and Dan, as well as finds at other sites, are not discussed. This must wait for an on-the-scene study seminar in Israel or audio-visual presentations by each teacher.

Translations of Biblical quotations in *The Land Between* are those of the author. In this respect language is understood as having a definite geopolitical and geocultural context. Without reference to this context, the original writer's intent is not fully understood. If necessary, a paraphrase form of translation is used in order to communicate a concept. Parentheses indicate another possible translation, while a phrase included in brackets is not found as such in the original text but may have been what the writer was saying *between the lines.* Translations of extra-Biblical texts are taken from *Ancient Near Eastern Texts* (edited by J. B. Pritchard) and are used with the kind permission of Princeton University Press.

Finally, the Bible is far more than history and geography. It is God's message to His world, a world of real people and real places. For that reason *The Land Between* has a definite spiritual emphasis. This was included unashamedly, for otherwise the exercise would have been in vain.

ACKNOWLEDGEMENTS

Over the years there have been many who made this book of assignments possible. First and foremost was the late Dr. G. Douglas Young who, with his wife, Georgina, established the Institute of Holy Land Studies in Jerusalem in 1957. This institution provided a setting for serious study where graduate students, and later undergraduates, could gain an exposure to the land of the Bible and to the vitality of scholarship available in a reborn Israel. In the spring of 1960, my wife and I were among the seminary students who took advantage of this setting. This study experience changed our lives.

The program received added impetus and direction a few years later when Professor Anson Rainey joined the staff of lecturers at the Institute. The disciplines and methodology of historical geography, which he so ably controls, have provided the basis for many graduate students to continue their studies beyond the Institute's courses. Although *The Land Between* is not a formal textbook on historical geography, it nevertheless would have been wanting greatly without such firm foundations laid down by others.

Since 1965 it has been my privilege to become acquainted with hundreds of graduate and undergraduate students who have attended the annual course of study at the Institute of Holy Land Studies. In addition to this family of *long term* students, there are those many professors from colleges and seminaries who have brought thousands of *short term* students to Jerusalem for an intensive three to six week program of study. While taxing the energy of the Institute's small staff to the limit, these groups provided the *raison d'être* for study materials, of which *The Land Between* is a part. To these students, and to the faithful staff which has served them over the years, there is a deep sense of gratitude. As is often the case, the teacher has learned more than the students.

In the past seven years, a careful evaluation of what the student of the Bible should know about the temporal and spatial setting of the text has been especially important in the preparation of the historical sections of the *Student Map Manual* and supporting mapping (student and display maps and map slides). These, together with aerial photographs and other visual aids produced by Pictorial Archive, Est., are currently opening a new world to students and teachers alike. Being a part of these productions has been demanding, but it has also enforced an intensive reexamination of the primary sources as they relate to the land, for which I am now grateful.

In the actual production of this book over the past two years, there have been many helping hands. In addition to my wife, Polly, a number of graduate students have helped in the proofing and have worked on indexes, especially Merilyn Copland ('82) and Judy Hadley ('80). Ellen Hall checked marking instructions, while her husband, my teaching assistant, Stephen Hall ('82), worked through historical priorities, especially as they relate to Appendix II. The paste-up of final copy was done by William Lee, whose patient spirit always greeted my last minute changes with a smile. Thanks are also in order to Earl Hagar ('79) for handling the distribution of earlier editions of the *Guide* (as well as for helping in earlier proofing of the historical sections of the *Student Map Manual* with Judy Hadley).

Much of the encouragement in the production of *The Land Between* came from Michael and Audrey Rosenbaum ('80 and '78). Even Audrey's expert skills were pushed to the limit by the complicated typing of both the originals and the final copy with endless changes and additions. Her contribution went far beyond the call of duty and made the final result what it is. Mike's imprint, through his quiet and patient counsel, is evident on many pages. Indeed, it was he who suggested the title itself. As student, teaching assistant and advisor, he realized more than any other the need of this type of introductory study for students of the Bible.

As is often the case, one's wife and children are those who have to live with the added pressures involved in any effort like this. All that can be given in return for their help and encouragement in the face of these pressures is a hearty thanks.

Finally, in spite of the generous assistance of all mentioned above, there are no doubt mistakes to be found in the text and certainly suggestions for improvements in future editions. For the former I accept full responsibility. In regard to the latter, I look forward to hearing from those who share with me the joy of leading students into an appreciation of this *Land Between*, the land of the Bible.

James M. Monson
Jerusalem, 1982

CONTENTS

INTRODUCTION

This book (referred to below as the *Guide*) serves three categories of students. The first are those students who are required to complete these assignments in preparation for an intensive course of study at the Institute of Holy Land Studies in Jerusalem, Israel (address inside front cover). This independent study program is augmented by classroom and field study in the actual land of the Bible. Many who plan to teach this subject take advantage of this program.

The second group consists of students who are enrolled in a structured course of study with a teacher who uses the *Student Map Manual (SMM)* and *Student Map A (SMA)*. These students will receive the necessary preparation and follow-up to the assignments in this *Guide*. In some cases they may be able to accompany their teacher on a trip to the Middle East.

Finally, there are those students who are on their own, who may never attend a formal class on the subject. While their study is limited, it is hoped that these assignments will provide new insights into the world of the Bible and the message of the Scriptures.

For students in independent study programs (the first and third categories above) special preliminary instructions are given in Appendix I at the end of the *Guide*. It provides an explanation of the various sections of the *SMM* and outlines procedures, including what materials are needed to begin marking the maps of the *SMM*. These instructions are basic and should be read carefully before marking begins if no teacher is available to explain them.

The following pages are important for all students to read. They deal with general background to the study, introductory schematics and the general theme of the *Land Between*.

THE *SMM* AND THE *GUIDE*

The Bible is rooted in the geography and history of the Middle East, especially of that part of the Middle East known as the Holy Land (Palestine, Eretz Israel or Land of the Bible). Nineteenth and twentieth century scholars dedicated their lives to the exploration of this land, which witnessed most of the events recorded in the Bible. During the late 1970's the fruit of their efforts was incorporated in the *Student Map Manual (SMM)*.

The *SMM* is a workbook for students, a do-it-yourself atlas left uncompleted for each student to finish. It enables the student to interact seriously with the Bible and its related history on carefully prepared maps which must be marked with colored pens. The geographical context of these maps may be brought to life by a creative presentation of wide-screen color slides (The Wide-Screen Project) and a unique set of educational wall posters described on the inside cover of the *SMM*. Both the *SMM* and The Wide-Screen Project are produced by Pictorial Archive (Near East History) Est.

The assignments in this *Guide* are organized in such a way that the regional aspects of the land *(the playing board)* are brought to life by history *(the players and the game)*. The object of the assignments at this point is not to teach history. The goal is to help the student feel at home on *the playing board of Biblical history*. While this is in progress, background notes in each chapter acquaint the student with basic historical developments during a thousand year period of the country's history.

Of the 110 maps in the *SMM*, 78 deal with the history of the land. Of those 78 maps, 47 cover the Old Testament period. This period is presented on a full color map, *Student Map A (SMA)*. This *Guide* (to Part A of the *SMM*) contains directions for marking most of these 47 maps. The *Guide*, therefore, uses maps of the Old Testament period (including extra-Biblical events) to illustrate regional aspects of the land.

The task of the student is to follow the directions in the *Guide* for marking each *SMM* map. With a reasonable amount of effort the student can produce very effective graphics on the maps (individual *playing boards*) of the *SMM*. These, in turn, will help bring to life the Biblical text which may be assigned as reading for a particular map. Such a study stimulates the desire for visualization of the land itself. Schools and churches who have the programs of The Wide-Screen Project or its wall posters can satisfy this demand for reality without leaving their home institution. Those who can visit the Holy Land are prepared for what could be termed *intelligent viewing* rather than the simple tourist trip.

INTRODUCTORY SCHEMATICS

Students approach this subject from a wide range of backgrounds. In order to insure that all have the necessary historical and geographical basis, two schematics have been included at the end of this *Introduction*.

A. The Introductory Schematic for Periods from 1500 to 500 B.C.
This schematic serves as an historical reference for most maps studied in this *Guide*. The information on this schematic is not to be memorized but kept available for quick reference. The following markings on this schematic make it much more useful. (Instructions for marking can be reviewed in Appendix I.)
1. **Yellow HL** (highlight) =
   a. The dates 1500, 1000 and 500. (All dates are B.C.)

   b. The line joining these three dates.

   c. The headings **LOCAL** and **INTERNATIONAL** at the left side of the schematic.

2. **Large blue circle around names** (blue for non-Israelite nations) =
   a. EGYPTIAN DOMINANCE.

   b. ASSYRIAN DOMINANCE.

3. **Green box around name** (green for Israel) = DAVID/SOLOMON.

Note on this schematic that the *SMM* maps above the time line portray local events in the land, while those below are more international in character. The main period of Egyptian dominance in the land occurred prior to 1150 B.C. The study will begin by introducing you to some of the great pharaohs of Egypt who marched along the international highways of the land during these centuries. The Assyrian Empire's main period of greatness came in the late eighth century and early seventh century B.C. In these centuries the cruel army of the Assyrian Empire destroyed or annexed almost everything in its path, including the northern Israelite kingdom.

There was an international vacuum in the land between the Egyptian and Assyrian periods. In this vacuum local powers struggled for political, military and economic control of the main highways of the country. The schematic calls this a period when *the mice play while the cat's away*.

It is during this period that cooperation, competition and/or conflict between Phoenicians, Philistines, Arameans (Syrians), Ammonites, Moabites, Edomites and Israelites become common in the Biblical record. If properly understood these events provide some of the most interesting and illustrative *moves* on the *playing board of Biblical history*.

Each chapter of the *Guide* uses maps indicated on this schematic from one side to the other. Chapter One briefly discusses five maps beginning with 4-5 and ending with 9-4. Chapters Two through Four treat more maps in greater detail, each time beginning on the left side of the schematic and moving across it to the right.

It is helpful to refer often to this schematic, especially as you begin to work on each new map. If you check off each map as it is completed, you will note that only Maps 5-1 and 8-8 (as well as maps in Section Ten of the *SMM*) are left unmarked. The subjects of these maps do not lend themselves to marking at this level of study. Sections Ten through Thirteen will be discussed in another *Guide* for Part B of the *SMM*.

Appendix II of the *Guide* presents a slightly more detailed chronological introduction in chart form. Many students find this chart to be a useful reference as regional history becomes more complicated. You may want to glance at Appendix II now and refer to it when the need arises.

B. The Introductory Schematic of the Playing Board
The second schematic provides a simplified plan of the main routes in the country, or what can be termed a diagram of the *playing board*. The area covered by this schematic represents the same area seen in the overview maps for each section of the *SMM* (4-1, 5-1, 6-1, etc.). The top of the map is east, as is the case for all the maps used in this study. Many find it useful to remember that the bottom of the map is the Mediterranean Sea (in the west) while the top of the map is toward the rising sun. After you have marked the first few *SMM* maps, eastern orientation becomes second nature. If a map of the Eastern Mediterranean area is available, it might be helpful to turn it to the east and to orient this schematic to it. It should be possible to see the relationship of Egypt and Mesopotamia to this schematic.

As on the first schematic the various colors stand for certain ethnic or national distinctives. Blue signals all non-Israelite nations. Green is used for Israel when it is one nation or for Judah in the period of the Divided Kingdom when two Israelite kingdoms existed side by side. On the maps from the period of the Divided Kingdom orange is used to represent the Northern Kingdom, called *Israel* in this period (in contrast to Judah in the south). With the meaning of these colors in mind, complete the following marking.
1. **Yellow HL on name:**
   a. In the SW (southwest) corner of the schematic = EGYPT.

   b. In the NE corner of the schematic = MESOPOTAMIA (two times).

2. **Yellow HL on route** (the larger routes on this schematic) = The main route from Egypt to Mesopotamia via the International Coastal Highway and those routes which lead from this highway to Mesopotamia, both due N and via Aram-Damascus (Syria).

3. **Blue circle around name** (Do not mix with yellow.) = MESOPOTAMIA, EGYPT, PHOENICIA, PHILISTIA, ARAM-DAMASCUS, AMMON, MOAB and EDOM.

4. **Green circle around name** = JUDAH.

5. **Orange circle around name** = SAMARIA (Israel).

The chapters of the *Guide* follow a certain regional sequence. Chapter One introduces the **International Coastal Highway and its Northern Approaches.** Thus the chapter provides a general Introduction to the main route which runs through this *Land Between*, linking Egypt and Mesopotamia. Chapter Two concentrates on the region of **Galilee** as it is illustrated by its historical sequence. Studies in this chapter show both international priorities along main routes and cooperation or conflict between local powers during the period of international vacuum. Chapter Three discusses **Samaria** in its setting between the International Coastal Highway, the Transjordanian Highway, Galilee and Judah. Chapter Four treats **Judah** (Judea) and its position between Philistia, Transjordan, the Negev and Samaria.

The emphasis of these four chapters on these specific regions or nations does not mean that the histories of various surrounding nations are less important. Unfortunately, little is known about some of the smaller powers, except through Biblical texts and archeological evidences. On the other hand, much is known about great nations like Egypt and those of Mesopotamia. Such studies, however, go beyond the scope of this limited *Guide*.

THE LAND BETWEEN

Throughout this *Guide* the area represented on the *Introductory Schematic of the Playing Board* is referred to as the *land* or the *country*. The emphasis in the assignments upon this land must always be understood against the larger geographical and historical context of the Eastern Mediterranean, Egypt and Mesopotamia. In light of these larger forces the country which you are about to study is rather insignificant, except as a land bridge between greater powers.

The geographical nature and position of this land do not inherently encourage its independence nor its development as a natural center of political power. Geological forces have made it a mixture of mountains, canyons, passes and plains. Ripping through it from north to south is the Rift Valley, one of the great cleavages in the earth's crust. In this deep valley bodies of water, swamps or dry and inhospitable plains have produced regions through which travel was difficult. The slightest shift in world climatic conditions can render the country helpless, producing drought and famine. In this context there also exists an almost continual conflict between the herdsman and the farmer, between the desert and the sown.

To the west the land faces the Mediterranean Sea and the Coastal Plain with its International Coastal Highway. On the east, beyond the Rift Valley, the Transjordanian Highway links north and south. In the south, desert raiders posed a constant threat to settled populations, while in the north there was imminent danger of invasion along defined natural routes.

Such a land does not lend itself to unification or rule under any one government. Natural routes are constricted by uplifted limestone hills, deeply eroded canyons and sharp geological faults. At the same time the country lacks natural frontiers and is vulnerable to attack on all sides. These attacks came both from neighboring nations and from *the big powers* which regarded this land of transit as their private thoroughfare or as their first line of defense.

During periods of relative peace (due to weaker neighbors and/or a vacuum of international activity) a strong central government in the land was able to detach itself from the control of surrounding powers and to pursue an independent role. This has happened only three times in history: 1) in the period of the Israelite monarchies in Old Testament times, 2) in the period of the Maccabees/Hasmoneans in the late second and early first centuries B.C., and 3) in our day with the establishment of the State of Israel. In all three of these periods the land has been under an Israelite/Jewish government, and each time it has faced serious regional and international pressures of a political, economic and military nature.

It is to this *Land Between* that Abraham was first called. Following the Exodus, Moses and Joshua led the people of Israel back to this land. After the return from exile in Babylon, Ezra and Nehemiah helped restore a religious and political entity again in this land.

In all of these Biblical periods this land served as *God's testing ground of faith*. It was here, in this land where both personal and national existence were threatened, that Israel's leaders and people were called upon to learn the true meaning of security and well-being, of trust in the Lord their God. It was here that *God's weakness* was shown to be *stronger than men* (1 Corinthians 1.25).

It is this land that you are now called upon to study. Beyond the lessons of geography and history you may want to consider Biblical leaders and their responses to the threats of their time, both physical threats in times of distress and moral threats in times of affluency. After learning the conditions under which they lived, you may want to evaluate each of them according to their response to conditions in this *Land Between, God's testing ground of faith*.

In times of need the spiritual leaders of Israel often gave advice or passed judgment. Prophets spoke out against Israelite and non-Israelite alike (Jeremiah 9.23-26). Psalmists encouraged the people in their faith, in spite of conditions around them (Psalm 46). Two such pronouncements stand out among others. One was given by Moses on the eve of Israel's entry into the land (Map 5-3). At that important juncture, in the midst of an extended description of the nature of the land and warnings about its dangers, he admonished the people of Israel to fear the Lord their God and to love Him with heart, soul and might (Deuteronomy 6.1-4). In the following chapters this principle is summarized in the phrase *to recognize who God is* and to act accordingly.

Centuries later, in the closing decades of the Kingdom of Judah (in the late seventh century B.C.), another statement was made by the prophet Habakkuk. He knew how the land had suffered at the hands of the Assyrians during the previous century. In his day yet another *big power*, Babylonia, was marching into the *Land Between* (Map 9-7). He had difficulty understanding why God allowed such nations to overrun the land. In his short prophecy the answer is given to Habakkuk. His response is one of the Bible's prime examples of trust in God and living by faith in a time of utter despair (Habakkuk 2.1-4). In the writings of the Apostle Paul, Habakkuk's words are given added meaning to those living in Rome, the *big power* of his day (Romans 1.16-17).

Habakkuk closes his prophecy with a prayer of praise to the God of Israel, followed by his statement of faith. In his closing words paraphrased below the prophet alludes to the land's total ruin, including that of the farmer who loses the blessing of all the seasons and extending to the shepherd whose herds feed off the grass of the Wilderness.

> *I hear the news and my heart fails;*
> *The report leaves me speechless.*
> *My bones dissolve within me;*
> *I barely hold myself together.*
>
> *Yet I **calmly wait** for difficult times to overtake*
> *those who now attack us.*
>
> *For though the fig tree does not shoot forth its leaves [in the spring],*
> *Nor any fruit be on the vines [in the summer];*
> *Though the [supply of oil from the] olive harvest fail [in the fall],*
> *And the fields provide no food [due to the lack of winter rains];*
> *Though the pen be empty of sheep,*
> *And the stalls without cattle —*
>
> *Yet I will **rejoice** in the Lord,*
> *Yes, I will **rejoice** in the God of my salvation.*
> *The Lord, the Lord alone is my strength.*
> *He makes my legs as sure-footed as those of a doe;*
> *Over the mountains He keeps my paths.* (Habakkuk 3.16-19)

It is not difficult to understand why the Apostle Paul, in prison in Rome toward the close of a ministry in which he and his message were constantly threatened, thinks of the words of Habakkuk. As in the case of the prophet Habakkuk, Paul is assured that *the One who began a good work . . . will complete it* (Philippians 1.6). The Apostle, who had prayed and sung hymns at midnight in a Philippian jail, uses the word *rejoice* (eight times in his short letter) to bring his message to a climax (Philippians 4.4-7). Again, like Habakkuk, his conclusion is accompanied by a call to prayer and to thanksgiving based upon a peace which comes from *recognizing who God is.*

It is this lesson which stands out above all others in the study of this *Land Between.*

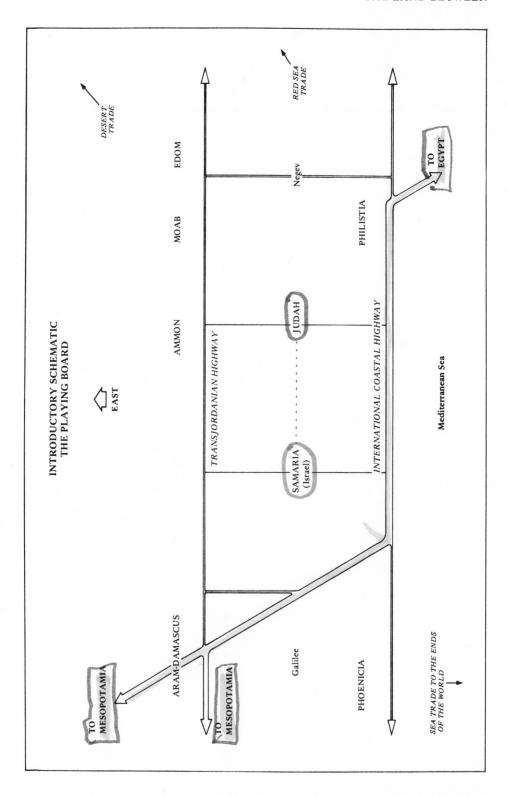

INTRODUCTORY SCHEMATIC
THE PLAYING BOARD

EAST

DESERT TRADE

EDOM

MOAB

AMMON

TRANSJORDANIAN HIGHWAY

JUDAH

SAMARIA
(Israel)

RED SEA TRADE

Negev

PHILISTIA

INTERNATIONAL COASTAL HIGHWAY

TO EGYPT

Mediterranean Sea

TO MESOPOTAMIA

ARAM-DAMASCUS

TO MESOPOTAMIA

Galilee

PHOENICIA

SEA TRADE TO THE ENDS
OF THE WORLD

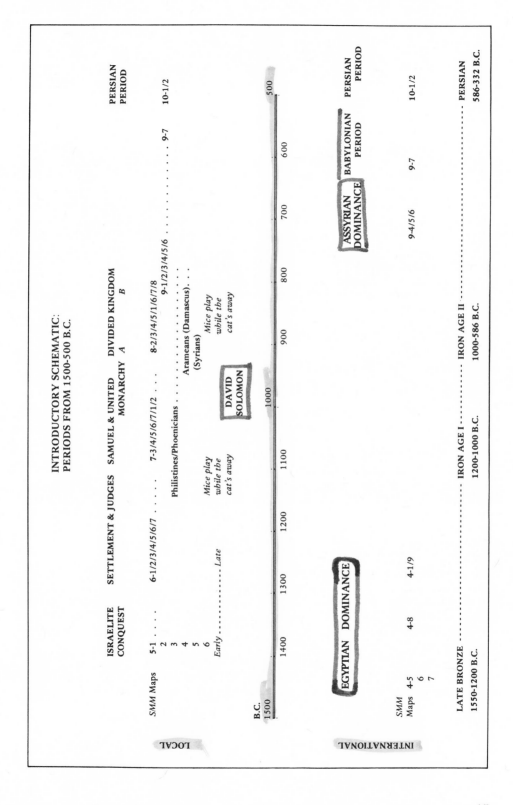

INTRODUCTORY SCHEMATIC: PERIODS FROM 1500-500 B.C.

CHAPTER ONE

THE INTERNATIONAL COASTAL HIGHWAY
AND NORTHERN APPROACHES

INTRODUCTION

The aim of the assignments in Chapter One is to introduce the main international routes which ran through the land in Old Testament times. The five *SMM* maps you will study illustrate the importance of these routes.

At the very outset of this study it should be stressed that there are no remains of a constructed road system in the country prior to Roman times. The lack of such remains in Old Testament times does not mean that trade and communication did not exist in that period. Historical sources and archeological evidence reflect a great deal of commercial and military activity.

In the absence of known constructed roadways, it becomes necessary to link important known centers by *natural routes*. These routes follow lines of least resistance, avoiding areas of difficulty when possible (mountains, swamps, sands, etc.). Security, water supply and sustenance are also important factors to be considered.

In the *SMM*, Sections Three through Eleven, natural routes are called *lines of communication*. In this *Guide*, reference may be made to routes, roads or highways. Remember that these terms actually mean *lines of communication* or *natural routes* linking main centers. (These routes appear on the *SMA: Display Version* but not on the *Student Version* of this same map.)

In this chapter you will study the International Coastal Highway and the northern approaches to the country. These routes form the country's major land bridge between two international power centers not shown on the *SMM* maps. One was Egypt to the southwest. The other was located in Mesopotamia to the north and northeast. The main land bridge linking these two centers has been highlighted on the *Introductory Schematic of the Playing Board* which may be useful to refer to during the marking and discussion of the assignments.

Important historical events have been chosen to illustrate the country's main highways. They are studied on the five *SMM* maps listed below and are taken from the thousand years of history seen on *The Land Between: A Basic Outline of Old Testament History* (Appendix II), can also be a very useful reference as you work through this and subsequent chapters.

    4-5 Egypt's expansion into Canaan in the Eighteenth Dynasty
    4-1 Egypt's operations in Canaan in the Nineteenth Dynasty
    6-1 A preview of regional settlement problems (in the book of Judges)
    7-1 David's census and Solomon's reign
    9-4 Campaigns and provincial organization of Tiglath-pileser III of Assyria

Three of these maps come from the period of Egyptian dominance (two from Egyptian records and one from Judges 1). The fourth map comes from the period of Solomon. It demonstrates his kingdom's dependence upon major highways in a period when international powers around the country were weak. The last map shows one of the important campaigns in the country's history, this time from Assyria (in Mesopotamia). It is useful to put a small check above each map number on the *Introductory Chronology* after the study of each map. This places the map within the larger historical setting.

The moment has come to begin the actual marking of the *SMM* maps. A quick review of the procedure for marking, presented in Appendix I, may be helpful.

S M M   4 − 5

TITLE: EGYPT'S EXPANSION INTO CANAAN IN THE 18TH DYNASTY
(In black caps at top)

DATE: MID-15TH CENTURY B.C. (Underline *LB* in yellow on map title.)

INTRODUCTION
Before you begin marking this map, take a few moments to glance over the names on it. Black names are background names, while those printed in red can be found in the primary sources (written historical texts) for this map. Run your finger over those areas of the map where red names predominate (along the coastlands and in the north). These are the regions which interested some of the most famous of all Egyptian pharaohs. The reason for their interest will become obvious to you as you study the five maps in Chapter One. It is through these regions that international trade and the military might of the ancient world passed during the course of history.

MARKING (Remember that the top of the map is E. You may want to mark an *E* at the top, a *W* at the bottom, an *N* to the left and an *S* to the right.)
Blue write-in with an additional small black arrow:
a. SW corner of the map (lower right), in the small open area above the map number = EGYPT in caps, plus a small black arrow pointing W from the word.

b. NE corner of the map, just E of the city named Laish = MITANNI in caps, plus a small black arrow pointing N from the word.

DISCUSSION
Great kingdoms had flourished in the Near East prior to 1500 B.C. However, this general date serves as a reminder that during this time Egypt was awakening to a new and mighty surge of nationalism and expansion. This awakening changed the course of history in the region. It ushered in the period of the *New Kingdom* in Egypt and ultimately an archeological period called the Late Bronze Age (LB). To emphasize this you may want to underline *LB* in yellow at the top of this map.

One of the greatest names among many in this period was that of Thutmose III (of the   4-5 b
Eighteenth Egyptian Dynasty), who ruled Egypt in the mid-fifteenth century B.C. He campaigned against the kingdom of Mitanni in northern Mesopotamia (to the north, off the map) and all others who stood in his way. To reach Mitanni the Pharaoh's forces had to conquer Canaan, the region shown on Map 4-5.

Pharoah Thutmose III thoroughly documented his campaign. This documentation provides one of the best sources for place-names (cities) along the International Coastal Highway of Canaan and main northern approach routes. The *SCS (Summary of Contents and Sources* at the beginning of each section) for Map 4-5 shows that there are no primary sources for this map from the Bible. This historical information comes from Egyptian inscriptions, which provide a rich background for later Biblical periods. You now are going to prepare a plan of attack for the Egyptian army through Canaan along the best possible route.

MARKING

1. **Yellow HL on names** (HL means to highlight the following boldface names): SW corner = **Gaza**; W center = **Aphek**; N center = **Megiddo**; N on coast = **Acco**; N of the Sea of Galilee = **Hazor**; S of the Sea of Galilee = **Beth-shan**.

2. **Yellow HL on routes**: Main international link (printed in red on the map) from Egypt (off the map) to Mitanni = Coastal Highway from Egypt to **Gaza** and then on N via Ashdod, Joppa, **Aphek**, Socoh, **Megiddo**, Ophel, Chinnereth, **Hazor** and due N off the map. Also HL the connection S of Aphek to Lod and turning W out to the Coastal Highway by Mahoz. (Part of this connection is printed in black.)

3. **Red circle around name** (always including the dot) = **Megiddo**.

DISCUSSION

You have just noted the main *way between* Egypt and Mesopotamia with some of the strategic centers in this *Land Between.* You can regard this route as somewhat of a *Suez Canal* in importance to the great powers of that day. Can you see obvious areas of difficulty along this route (mountains, canyons, swamps, bodies of water, rivers, etc.)? Be aware of these as you mark your maps. (If you have the *SMA* posted on the wall in front of you, this is a good moment to refer to it.)

Almost all of the red names on Map 4-5 are part of the city-list of Thutmose III inscribed in stone at the temple of Karnak (by Luxor) in Egypt. Note the centrality of Megiddo on the map. Here the Pharaoh won an all-important battle in Canaan.

MARKING

1. **Sweeping blue arrows**: Sweeping arrows along highlighted routes indicate the advance of the Egyptian army through Canaan. It is your chance to make the map your own by adding your own touch. Do not be afraid to show your artistic ability. The arrows will be blue since the Egyptians are non-Israelite forces. Practice with the dry end of your pen before completing the assignment below. Make breaks in your arrows as you come to city names. Avoid touching yellow, since blue and yellow make green. The points of these five arrows should show definite direction.

   a. Starting from the SW corner of the map, draw a long arrow (blue) northward to Aphek (along the side of the road you just highlighted). Note: As you draw skip over the names of Gaza and Ashdod and let the arrow point to the name Aphek.

   b. Starting just N of Aphek, draw a long arrow northward along the plain toward Aruna (letting the arrow run just W of the road you earlier highlighted).

   c. Starting just E of Megiddo draw a long sweeping arrow to Hazor, running just E of the road highlighted earlier. It can run through the edge of the lake.

    d. Starting N of Megiddo draw an arrow N to the region of Acco.

    e. Starting SE of Shunem (E of Megiddo) draw an arrow SE to Beth-shan.

2. **Brown write-in**: In the N of the country find the open area (mountainous, but no names) just W of two possible sites of Merom and the city of Shemesh-edom = GALILEE.

DISCUSSION

You have just completed your sketch of one of the country's most famous invasions dating from the mid-fifteenth century B.C. — some 3500 years ago! Sit back and look at your map. Try to familiarize yourself with some of the international priorities in the land (both roads and sites). If you have the time, you may enjoy turning back to the *Key to Regional Maps*, the page which introduces Section One of the *SMM*. It is on the same scale as the map you just marked and has regional names printed on it *(Coastal Plain, Valley of Jezreel, etc.)*. It would be helpful to acquaint yourself with regions through which you have just campaigned with the Egyptians. You can gain a detailed look at these regions by choosing the appropriate color map in Section One of the *SMM* or by referring again to *SMA*.

LEGEND (To copy in the open sea area at the bottom of Map 4-5. Use your colored pens only to indicate a color. Write the explanation in black beside the color.)

Yellow HL on name	=	Main strategic center.
Yellow HL on route	=	Main trunk route from Egypt to Mitanni via Canaan.
Red names on map	=	Egyptian regional priorities in Canaan (city-list of Pharaoh Thutmose III and campaigns of his son, Amenhotep II).

S M M   4 − 1

TITLE: **EGYPT'S OPERATIONS IN CANAAN IN THE 19TH DYNASTY**

DATE: **13TH CENTURY B.C.** (Underline *LB* in yellow in map title)

INTRODUCTION

In the century following the great campaigns of Thutmose III, Egypt became preoccupied in an internal religious dispute. As a result, she did not have an active policy of expansion but was satisfied with the status quo in Canaan where her control was still recognized. (*SMM* 4-8 covers this period known as the *Amarna Age*.)

It was another Egyptian Dynasty (the Nineteenth) which later led Egypt again on to the battlefield and again through the International Highway of Canaan. Maps 4-1 and 4-9 cover these developments in Canaan. (Map 4-9, a detail of the northern part of the country, is studied later in the course.)

MARKING (Map 4-1)

1. **Blue write-in with black arrow**:

    a. In the same position as on Map 4-5 = EGYPT.

    b. In the same position as Mitanni on Map 4-5 = HITTITE EMPIRE (with black arrow pointing N).

4-1 b   2. **Yellow HL on names**: Places mentioned in the campaign of Seti I (1303 B.C.).
a. In the SW = **Raphia** and **Pa-Canaan** (an Egyptian name for Gaza) and **Gaza**.

b. In the N = **Beth-shan, Rehob, Hammath** (the one S of Rehob), **Pehel, Yenoam, Kiriath-anab, Hazor, Kedesh, Beth-anath, Tyre** and **Uzu**.

4-1 c   3. **Orange on dot or on arrow** (pointing to a site off the map): Places mentioned by an Egyptian scribe in the days of Ramses II (early thirteenth century B.C.).
a. Along the southern coast = **Raphia, Pa-Canaan** and **Joppa**.

b. In the N = **Megiddo, Beth-shan, Rehob, Kiriath-anab, Yenoam, Hammath** (N of Yenoam), **Adamim, Hazor, Aduru, Tyre, Uzu, Acco, Achshaph** and **Selaim** (meaning *cliffs* and therefore having no dot. Underline in orange.)

4-1 d   4. **Red underlining**: Underline in red those places in boldface below in a passage from Pharaoh Merneptah's victory statement (about 1220 B.C.).

> *Plundered is Canaan with every evil;*
> *Carried off is **Ashkelon**; seized upon is **Gezer**;*
> *Yenoam is made as that which does not exist;*
> *Israel is laid waste, his seed is not . . .*

5. **Green write-in**: In the center of the map, printed in large capitals = I S R A E L (In the open area between Aphek and Bethel/Luz, at least 4 cm./1½ in. long.) This green represents an Israelite population mentioned by Merneptah above.

6. **Yellow HL on roads**:
a. The same roads which you highlighted on Map 4-5.

b. The shortest road from Megiddo to Tyre via Acco.

c. The shortest road from Megiddo to Beth-shan.

d. The shortest road from Beth-shan to Karnaim (NE of Beth-shan).

e. The shortest road from Beth-shan to Ramoth-gilead (E of Beth-shan via Ham).

DISCUSSION (Remember to read these discussions with the map in hand.)
As you have been highlighting these roads, you have probably noted that Egyptian interests in the Nineteenth Dynasty are similar to those of earlier Egyptian pharaohs: control of the International Coastal Highway and its northern approaches. Merneptah's account is especially vivid as it sweeps across the country.

On this map we have highlighted other northern routes in addition to the main highway via Hazor. Note how both the route to Tyre via Acco and the route to Beth-shan (and then on to the Transjordanian Highway in two ways) avoid areas of difficulty (swamps, sands, canyons, etc.).

Some feel it was in this period of history (thirteenth century B.C.) that Joshua led the Israelites into Canaan via Jericho. Others place Joshua's campaigns more than a century earlier, in the Amarna Age (Map 4-8), between the events of Maps 4-5 and

4-1/9. This is not the time to discuss this question. It should be noted, however, that campaigns of these pharaohs (Thutmose III, Seti I, Ramses II and Merneptah) provide the geopolitical background of the fifteenth and thirteenth centuries B.C. This means that great armies of Egypt were passing through the country in the same period that Joshua entered Canaan. Therefore, the Old Testament books of Joshua and Judges have their setting within this larger extra-Biblical context.

LEGEND

Yellow HL on route = Main routes.
Yellow HL on name = *SCS* 4-9a (Seti I, 1303 B.C.).
Orange on dot = *SCS* 4-9b (Satire by Egyptian scribe, early 13th century B.C.).
Red underlining = *SCS* 4-9c (Merneptah, about 1220 B.C.).

This overview map provides the larger geographical context of events on Map 4-9. Map 4-9 appears in the proper chronological order.

S M M 6 − 1

TITLE: **A PREVIEW OF REGIONAL SETTLEMENT PROBLEMS (IN THE BOOK OF JUDGES)**

DATE: **14TH TO 12TH CENTURY B.C.**

INTRODUCTION

This map shows the important bridge between Egyptian interests along main international routes and Canaanite power centers mentioned in the Bible. No doubt these Canaanite centers had been weakened by Egyptian campaigns seen on Maps 4-5 and 4-1. However, they appear to have maintained a degree of independence and power which allowed them to resist Israelite control. This map furnishes us with an important geopolitical background needed in our later studies in the book of Judges.

MARKING (in the N of the country)

1. **Blue on dot or on arrow,** and **yellow HL on name** (Do not mix colors!) = **Megiddo, Taanach, Ibleam, Beth-shan, Dor** (on the coast), **Aphek** (N of Megiddo), **Rehob, Acco,** (N of Aphek) **Achzib, Sidon, Beth-anath** and **Beth-shemesh** (of Galilee, E of Achzib). Note the position of most of these Canaanite centers along main routes in the north.

2. **Green write-in:** Clearly write in the following tribal names (in small caps) in the appropriate open areas.
   a. E of Acco, W of Rehob = ASHER.

   b. Just W of the dot of Rimmon and the name Chisloth-tabor = ZEBULUN.

   c. Just W of Hazor and Chinnereth = NAPHTALI.

   d. Between En-gannim and Kishion = ISSACHAR.

DISCUSSION

From what you already know about this northern region (in and around Galilee), how secure would you feel being a member of one of the above tribes (Naphtali, Issachar, Zebulun or Asher)? Recall the Egyptian priorities in the region, and note the strong Canaanite centers (marked with blue and yellow). Studies in later chapters show how these tribes joined to meet some of their common regional threats in the period of the Judges.

The threatened position of Galilee explains why deliverance and salvation stand out so vividly in this region, known as *Galilee of the Nations/Gentiles* (Isaiah 9.1-7). This term will mean much more when studied in its actual historical setting on Map 9-4. The point to underscore now is simply that important international highways run around and through the northern region. Local centers and international powers desired to control these routes for obvious political and economic reasons.

MARKING (central part of the country)
1. **Blue on dot and yellow HL on name** (Do not mix colors!) = **Jerusalem/Jebus, Gezer, Aijalon, Shaalbim** and **Har-heres**. (The latter, another name for Beth-shemesh, was omitted in the original printing of the *SMM*. If the name *Har-heres* is missing on this map, please make the following correction. Color the dot of Beth-shemesh blue, highlight (yellow) a small space to the right of the dot and allow to dry. Then write in the red name of *Har-heres* in the yellow space using a fine point red pen.)

2. **Yellow HL on name with a blue box around it**: the five famous Philistine cities = **Gaza, Ashkelon, Ashdod, Ekron** and **Gath**.

3. **Blue write-in**: in the open area W of Ekron and Gath = PHILISTINES.

4. **Green write-in**:
   a. On an angle from just W of Beth-dagon to the dot of Gibbethon = DAN.

   b. In the open area between Bethlehem, Hebron and Kiriath-jearim = JUDAH.
   Draw a green box around JUDAH showing it was one of the strongest tribes.

   c. From the dot of Jericho westward to just below Gibeon = BENJAMIN. (Print name vertically and avoid writing on city names.)

   d. In the center of the map, in a long and narrow open area just W of the names of Shamir, Pirathon and Ataroth-addar = EPHRAIM-MANASSEH. Be careful! The name Timnath-serah on the map will later have orange around the name. Draw a green box around EPHRAIM-MANASSEH showing that they were stronger tribes. Both were sons of Joseph and sometimes called the *House of Joseph*.

5. **Orange circle around name**: in center of the map = **Shechem** and **Timnath-serah**.

6. **Black write-in** (small caps):
   a. Beside the orange circle of Shechem = JOSHUA 24, COVENANT RECON-FIRMED.

   b. Below the orange circle of Timnath-serah = JOSHUA'S INHERITANCE.

DISCUSSION

The existence of Canaanite centers near the International Coastal Highway (Gezer,   6-1 b
Shaalbim, Aijalon and Har-heres), coupled with the arrival of the Sea Peoples (the
Philistines), was a serious obstacle to Israelite settlement in these regions. The territory of Dan posed a particular problem. Certainly the Philistines were aware of the
opportunities for political and economic expansion from their coveted position on the
country's International Coastal Highway. The resulting confrontation later emerges
in the story of Samson.

Before the final discussion, the marking of Map 6-1 must be completed. Most of the
following items do not relate to the main goal of this chapter but are a part of the total
historical dynamic of the map as it fits into later studies.

MARKING (on the eastern side of the map, called Transjordan):
1. **Blue write-in:**
   a. Below the name Rabbath-ammon = AMMON.

   b. In the SE corner, halfway to the top of the map from Kir-hareseth/Kir of Moab =
      MOAB. Between MOAB and Kir-hareseth write in (**in small black caps**) RUTH'S
      HOMELAND.

2. **Green write-in:**
   a. In open area between Heshbon and Aroer = REUBEN.

   b. In open area S of Penuel and W of Abel-keramim = GAD.

   c. In open area between Jabesh-gilead and Ramoth-gilead write as follows (on three
      lines) =

      ½ MANASSEH
      MACHIR
      (GILEAD).

   d. In open area just E of Beer-sheba = SIMEON.

LEGEND

Blue on dot and yellow HL on name	= Unconquered Canaanite cities (Jebus = inhabitants not driven out).
Yellow HL on name and blue box	= Philistine cities.
Green name (like Asher)	= Tribal name (from the text of Map 6-2 on the next page).
Green name + green box	= Strongest tribes (Manasseh + Ephraim = House of Joseph).

DISCUSSION AND READING

The importance of the International Coastal Highway and its northern approaches is
not stated specifically in the Bible; it is taken for granted. The first chapter of the
book of Judges discusses the difficulties which faced particular tribes. These difficulties occurred in regions where strong Canaanite centers jealously guarded strategic   6-1 c
points along main routes. Israelite tribes in these regions had to wait for the development of strong military leadership which unified them against their enemies. Partial
help came to the local scene from men and women called *champions* (judges). However, total independence and enforced unification developed later, culminating in a
series of leaders: Saul, David and Solomon.

Map 6-1 provides the necessary background for understanding the early problems facing the Israelite tribes in the period following Joshua's conquest. With this map in hand, read **Judges 1.27-35.** Another description is found in Joshua 17.11-18 and 16.10, which you may also want to read.

S M M   7 – 1

TITLE: DAVID'S CENSUS AND SOLOMON'S REIGN

DATE: 10TH CENTURY B.C.

INTRODUCTION

So far in your map study you have seen that Egypt dominated the country's main highways during various periods between 1500 and 1200 B.C. You have also noted local Canaanite power centers along this same international route and seen the arrival of the Philistines in the Coastal Plain.

Some four centuries later another great power, Assyria, expanded beyond her borders in Mesopotamia. After securing the northern approaches of the country and the Coastal Highway, she realized her dream, the control of Egypt.

Between the periods of Egyptian and Assyrian dominance, smaller local powers were able to consolidate and extend their economic and political influence. During this time smaller powers struggled to control important trade routes within the land. In other words, *the mice could play while the cat was away.* We shall spend considerable time in later chapters studying this most interesting period of the land's history.

Around 1000 B.C. in the midst of this period of local power struggles a remarkable political, military and spiritual leader unified the Israelite tribes. He then extended his control to highways far beyond the region of predominantly Israelite settlement. His name was David, son of Jesse of the tribe of Judah in the southern Hill Country, a boy from Bethlehem.

MARKING

1. **Yellow HL on name plus a green box around name = Jerusalem** (Include the name Jebus and the dot in this box.)

2. **Yellow HL on name plus a small green circle around each name = Dan** (in the N) and **Beer-sheba** (in the S).

DISCUSSION

After ruling a few years in Hebron, David moved to a new capital, Jerusalem. From 7-1 b here he extended his borders. Two names on Map 7-1 (included in David's census) mark the general limit of Israelite settlement in this period, Dan and Beer-sheba. David's accomplishment paved the way for the reign of his son Solomon.

7-1 c Solomon fortified Jerusalem, its approaches and certain strategic centers along the main International Highway: Gezer, Megiddo and Hazor. These sites reflect important political and economic advantages which made Israel a powerful country in the eastern

Mediterranean. It was Israel's first period of relative greatness when her influence extended over the international routes of the region and beyond. This could only occur in a time when big powers were not strong enough to enforce their rule.

MARKING

1. **Yellow HL on names plus an orange circle around each name** = **Gezer** (between Jerusalem and the Mediterranean Sea), **Megiddo** and **Hazor** (both in the N).

2. **Yellow HL on names** (no circle) = **Upper Beth-horon** and **Lower Beth-horon** (between Jerusalem and Gezer) and **Baalah** (sometimes called *Baalath*).

3. **Yellow HL on roads:**
   a. The same roads as you highlighted on Map 4-5.

   b. The road between Jerusalem and Gezer via Upper Beth-horon and Lower Beth-horon (connecting to the Coastal Highway at Gittaim) and on out to Joppa (Jerusalem's port on the Mediterranean). Also HL the short route descending W of Gibeon (via Baalah) to meet the route to Gezer. Note how Jerusalem's control of Joppa would frustrate other political powers in their free movement along the Coastal Highway. History often illustrates this. It is part of the game of geography, history and economics.

   c. The Transjordanian Highway (printed in red on the eastern side of the map).

   d. The shortest route from Jerusalem to Heshbon on the Transjordanian Highway (via Jericho); also HL the route W from Jericho to Ramah.

DISCUSSION

Israel's priorities in the land under David and Solomon can be seen on the map you have just marked. After establishing his new capital in Jerusalem, David extended his control out to both the Coastal and Transjordanian Highways. Solomon's major building projects included the strategic sites of Hazor, Megiddo and Gezer. Do you remember their importance in Egypt's earlier control of the land?

Gezer is situated at the junction of the Coastal Highway and Jerusalem's main western approach (via Lower and Upper Beth-horon or via Baalah). Solomon was concerned about his capital's main approach from the Coastal Highway. The Bible highlights Gezer's importance by providing us with the explanation of how Gezer came under Solomon's control. It is no surprise, therefore, that it was to the *high place of Gibeon* (along this Jerusalem—Gezer route) that Solomon went to worship and to celebrate the beginning of his rule. From there, more than from anywhere else in the country, one realizes the importance of this natural link between Jerusalem and the International Coastal Highway.

READING

The relevance of what you have just marked will become apparent by noting a few chapters of the Bible. They will also provide an introduction to the next paragraph of marking. Skim over the following chapters, noting the names with which you have already become familiar: **2 Chronicles 1; 1 Kings 9.**

MARKING

Complete the marking of this map by writing in Israelite regional or tribal names, names of non-Israelite nations and other notes. All of the names are mentioned in the Bible during the period of Solomon's reign.

1. **Green write-in** (Israelite names):

    a. S of the map, in the open area between Hebron, Beth-zur and Hushah = JUDAH.

    b. Central part of the map, in the open area between Dothan, Shechem, Bethel and Pirathon = MT. EPHRAIM. (This name is sometimes used in the Bible for the hills of Ephraim and Manasseh, two tribes of the House of Joseph.)

    c. In exactly the same area as on Map 6-1 = NAPHTALI, ISSACHAR, ZEBULUN and BENJAMIN.

    d. In Transjordan (eastern side of the map), in the open area between the two possible sites of Mahanaim = GILEAD.

2. **Blue write-in** (non-Israelite names):

    a. Same locations as on Map 6-1 = AMMON (W of Rabbath-ammon), MOAB (in SE corner of the map just E of the highway) and PHILISTINES (E of Ashdod).

    b. Just W of the Dead Sea and S of *The Stronghold* = EDOM with a black arrow pointing to the SE off the map.

    c. Extreme NE corner of the map above the name Damascus = ARAM. (Damascus was to become the political center of the Arameans, whom some call the Syrians.)

    d. Between the names Damascus and Dan = MAACAH.

    e. By the Sea of Galilee, just E of (Lower) Aphek = GESHER.

3. **Brown write-in**: At the N end of the map, just E of the name Sidon = LEBANON with a black arrow pointing N off the map.

4. **Blue border** (Try a few times with dry end of pen and then draw in free hand. Some students try a light blue pencil line first since that is erasable.):

    a. Tyre (in the N on the Mediterranean coast) represented the limit of Phoenician control. Beginning just S of Tyre (about .5 cm./¼ in. S of Tyre), draw in a short blue line, curving E and then NE, going off the map just beyond the arrow of Sidon. After drawing this with your light blue pen, **shade in** the N side of this line (just along the line) with your light blue **pencil** to show that from that line N belonged to Tyre.

    b. Solomon purchased timber from Hiram, king of Tyre. It was sent from the forests of Lebanon via Tyre to the area of Joppa, where it was transported overland to Jerusalem. Solomon overextended his credit with Hiram and had to cede certain northern coastlands of Asher to Tyre. These regions will now be outlined by a **broken** blue line. Draw such a line from the dot of Libnath (by Mt. Carmel) around the E side of the name Mishal along the edge of the hills, then N (along the hills E of Achzib), curving NE to join your other blue line by the arrow of Sidon. **Shade in** light blue the W side of this line (just along the line) to show that it belonged to Tyre.

5. **Green write-in**: E of Acco and just E of the broken blue border = ASHER.

6. **Black write-in**:
   a. By the city Tyre = HIRAM.

   b. Inside coastal area ceded to Tyre = SOLOMON CEDES TO TYRE.

   c. In NE corner by the name Damascus = REZON BECOMES SOLOMON'S AD-VERSARY — 1 KINGS 11.23-25. Underline **Rezon** in red and then put the red pen away.

   d. E of Jerusalem, in three lines near the city = CAPITAL, TEMPLE, HIGH PLACES FOR FOREIGN GODS.

7. **Green boxes around these names** which paid taxes or tributes to Solomon = ARAM (include the name Damascus in the box), MAACAH, GESHER, AMMON, MOAB and EDOM.

8. **Sweeping green arrows** generally along the side of routes: (These show Solomon's sources of income from taxes and tribute, or those trading with him.)
   a. In the Mediterranean Sea, from Tyre to T. Qasile by Joppa, draw a long green arrow pointing toward T. Qasile. Along this line write in (**in small black caps**) TIMBER AND GOLD FOR SOLOMON'S TEMPLE.

   b. In the N = an arrow from the region ceded to Tyre, pointing toward Megiddo; an arrow from the N pointing toward Hazor; an arrow from the region of Hazor and Chinnereth pointing toward Megiddo; an arrow from the box of Aram (Damascus) running to the box of Gesher and beyond, pointing toward Beth-shan.

   c. In the E = arrows from the boxes of Ammon and Moab, joining together W of Heshbon and pointing toward Jericho.

   d. In the S = an arrow from Gaza running to the word Philistines and beyond, pointing to Gezer.

   e. In the S = an arrow from the box of Edom pointing toward the region of Jerusalem (curving around by the Arad road junction, Maon and Ziph).

   f. In the central part of the country = an arrow from the region of Tirzah, just E of MT. EPHRAIM, pointing toward the region of Jerusalem.

LEGEND

Yellow HL on name & green circle	= Dan to Beer-sheba or limits of Jewish settlement (1 Kings 4.20-28).
Yellow HL on name & orange circle	= Solomon's main fortifications (Cf. 1 Kings 9.15-19 and 2 Chronicles 8.5-6).
Blue write-in & green box (like MOAB)	= Area of sovereignty of the king of Israel.
Green arrow	= Taxes and tribute to Jerusalem and/or trade.

S M M   9 — 4

TITLE: CAMPAIGNS & PROVINCIAL ORGANIZATION OF TIGLATH-PILESER III OF ASSYRIA

DATE: THE 730'S B.C.

INTRODUCTION

After Solomon's death Jerusalem's hold on the country was not strong enough to maintain the unity which David and Solomon had enforced. Internal discord was evident during the reign of David in various revolts. Solomon was confronted with certain *adversaries* in Damascus, in Edom and in Egypt, as we are told in 1 Kings 11. After the death of Solomon it did not take long for these problems to break out into the open again.

8-2 a The inherent tensions between the northern and southern tribes exploded when Solomon's son (Rehoboam) attempted to tighten his control on the north. He needed that control to insure his kingdom's financial security. The Northern Kingdom (called from that point on *Israel*) declared independence and pursued its own political and economic interests. The Southern Kingdom (*Judah*) was left to rebuild its own economic base with far fewer resources.

Following the division of David's and Solomon's kingdom, the region returned to unstable conditions in which local powers struggled for control of strategic regions. Israel inherited the northern approaches to the country and portions of the Transjordanian and International Coastal Highways, vital to her trade and economic growth. These routes had to be protected from surrounding nations which were also consolidating and expanding. Political and trade agreements important during Solomon's reign would still be necessary. However, war on the local scene was inevitable since each nation coveted key military and economic positions on this small *playing board.*

Such was the background of Israel's relations with such nations as Aram-Damascus (Syria), Phoenicia, Moab and Ammon, all names which appear often in later studies, and other surrounding powers. This situation lasted for some 200 years with few interludes of peace or cooperation among the participants. For this reason we earlier called this period a time when *the mice could play while the cat was away.* The *cat*, however, was returning in the form of the revitalized and expanding Assyria, already on the move. The prophets recognized what was happening and pointed to the danger looming on the horizon. Among other things these men could be considered as some
9-4 of the foremost political analysts of their day. Finally, in 734 B.C. Assyria steamrollered through the land on her way to head off Egypt southwest of Gaza. This time she came in the person of Tiglath-pileser III, the head of a terribly efficient and cruel Assyrian army. He would reinstate a policy of expansionism which would ultimately make Assyria into the greatest empire the world had yet seen. From regions to the north (already under Assyrian control) her forces entered the country via Phoenicia and swept down the Coastal Highway, conquering Gezer and Gaza before halting at the natural frontier between the land and Egypt, the *Brook of Egypt* (modern Wadi el-Arish in northern Sinai). This action was carried out to prevent Egypt from interfering in Assyria's subsequent operations in the country.

MARKING

1. **Write-in** (Divided Kingdom names) and **boxes** (Divided Kingdom capitals):
   a. **Green**: In the open area from Upper Beth-horon to the S (running between Manahath and Beth-zur) = JUDAH (large caps); green box around **Jerusalem**.

   b. **Orange**: In the open area in the center of the map, E of Tirzah and S to above Arumah = ISRAEL (large caps); orange box around **Samaria**. (Orange will be the color for Israel in contrast to green for Judah during the period of the Divided Monarchy. This applies only on Maps 8-1 through 9-5.)

2. **Blue write-in**:
   a. Southern coastland, in open area between Ashdod and Gath = PHILISTINES.

   b. In the N along the coastland (beginning just E of Tyre) = PHOENICIANS.

   c. In the NE corner of the map, just under the name Damascus = ARAM-DAMASCUS (Syria). Add a black arrow pointing NE from ARAM-DAMASCUS (Syria).

3. **Yellow HL on routes**:
   a. The coastal route (beginning in the N of the country) from the region of Tyre to Acco, to Jokneam and then SW (on gray road) to meet the Coastal Highway (printed in red), continuing S to Aphek and the region of Gezer; from Gittaim (by Gezer) HL both roads through Philistia to Egypt (via Ashdod and Gaza, and via Ekron, Gath and Philistia).

4. **Sweeping blue arrows** (Do you remember suggestions about drawing these types of arrows on your Map 4-5? You may want to review them.):
   a. One long arrow from Tyre and pointing toward the region of Gezer near Ono or Lod. (This arrow can run along the road you have just highlighted. In the N it can run just E of the road, crossing to the W side of the road by Jokneam and remaining on the W side of the road as it runs S.).

   b. Another arrow from the region of Gezer (by Gibbethon) running just E of the Coastal Highway (skipping over names) and pointing in the direction of Egypt, just SW of Gaza.

5. **Red on dot: Gezer** (assault known from Assyrian palace relief) and **Gaza** (conquered).

6. **Black write-in**: In the N part of the map, just S of Tyre, on or under the blue line of your long arrow = I-734 B.C.

7. **Brown write-in**: In the SW corner of the map, in the open area just E of the map number = BROOK OF EGYPT with a black arrow pointing W from this name.

DISCUSSION

It is clear that in his first lightning attack on the country (734 B.C.), Tiglath-pileser III had as his main objective the control of the Coastal Highway. In fact, the king of Gaza was forced to flee to Egypt, leaving this vital region in the hand of Assyria.

In the decades which followed, Egypt would attempt to reassert her influence in the area through various offers of aid to Israel and to Judah, at times even resorting to armed intervention along the southern coastland. This ultimately led to the destruction of Samaria (Israel's capital) by Assyrian forces and to a serious threat on Jerusalem (Judah's capital).

During these decades Isaiah taunted those who thought that Egypt would come to the rescue: *And Egypt? The help they offer is hot air and worthless! I'd call her the Big-mouth-do-nothing!* (Isaiah 30.7). Better yet is Assyria's gibe to the men of Jerusalem: *Look! You put your trust on a crutch - that broken reed - on Egypt which pushes against and pierces the hand of the man who leans upon it! This is what the pharaoh, king of Egypt, is to all who trust him!* (Isaiah 36.6). Other references to Egypt in this period are found in Isaiah 19, 30, 31 and 36.

Despite Tiglath-pileser III's impressive coastal campaign of 734 B.C., other regions of the country had yet to be subdued (Galilee, Gilead in Transjordan and even Damascus, capital of Syria). Concerning these campaigns, the Bible and Assyrian records provide some very helpful and sobering statements.

MARKING
1. **Brown write-in on yellow HL** (First color in a background of yellow and let dry. Then write in the appropriate name in brown.):
   a. In Transjordan, in the open area between the two possible sites of Mahanaim, but N of the large river canyon = GILEAD (in large caps).

   b. In the N, in the open area just W of the name Chinnereth = LAND OF NAPHTALI (in two lines just below Chinnereth). Do you remember the same tribal name on Map 6-1?

   c. In the N, in the open area between LAND OF NAPHTALI (which you just wrote) and Gath-hepher = GALILEE OF THE NATIONS (again in two lines).

2. **Brown write-in** (with no yellow background): In the open area between the Jordan River and the end of GILEAD (just S of Succoth) = BEYOND THE JORDAN.

3. **Yellow HL** = the boldface names in the following text from the Bible. This is one of the most famous *headlines* in the Old Testament. You can better appreciate the shock it must have caused now that you understand its setting. Think of how the inhabitants of Gath-hepher (Jonah's village) felt. After all, it was Jonah who had delivered Nineveh (Assyria's capital) from destruction a few years before! (These names are found in the N of the country.)

   *In the days of Pekah, king of Israel, Tiglath-pileser, king of Assyria came and seized **Ijon, Abel-beth-maachah, Janoah, Kedesh, Hazor**, Gilead and Galilee, all the land of Naphtali, and he deported the inhabitants to Assyria.* (2 Kings 15.29).

4. **Red on dot (or arrow) or red underlining**: To emphasize the destruction left in the wake of the events described in 2 Kings 15.29, color the dot of the towns you just highlighted. (Finds at Hazor indicate such a destruction.) Then underline (in red) the names of the regions listed in that verse: **GILEAD, GALILEE OF THE NATIONS** and all the **LAND OF NAPHTALI.**

DISCUSSION

In this exercise you have no doubt noticed that one city, Janoah, was somewhat *off the beaten track*. For that reason one Israeli scholar is trying to identify the name Janoah with a site closer to Abel-beth-maachah. Thus the name sequence in 2 Kings 15.29 could be traced in a direct line (from north to south) along the main highway into Galilee via Hazor. (Another scholar feels that Janoah should be located farther north, on the way from Abel-beth-maachah to Tyre.) By observing such detail you are already involved in the game of historical geography, using general observations in a specific discussion. Keep your eyes open for more information of this type as you proceed in the course.

MARKING

1. **Yellow HL on route:** From just N of Abel-beth-maachah (the region of Ijon which is just off the map) HL the main northern approach route via Abel-beth-maachah, Hazor, Chinnereth (not mentioned in 2 Kings 15.29) to Megiddo (via Ophrah) and on to the Coastal Highway.

2. **Red on dot:** In addition to 2 Kings 15.29, Assyrian records (lists of towns and captives) add a few names to our map. They are no doubt from the same campaign summarized in the Bible. These lists sometimes even give the number of captives taken from a town, a sad echo of what we have read in 1 Kings, . . . *and he deported the inhabitants to Assyria.* **Color the dot (red)** of the following names (no highlighting): **Hannathon, Kanah** (where Jesus would minister over 700 years later), **Jotbah, (A)Rumah, Yiron** and **Merom** (only the one next to Yiron).

3. **Yellow HL on route:** The cluster of four towns (by Kanah) indicates that the Assyrians used this important side route from the land of Naphtali to Megiddo, via (A)Rumah and Hannathon. **HL in yellow** this route (with both ends connecting to the route you earlier highlighted).

4. **Sweeping blue arrows** along the side of the routes:
   a. From Abel-beth-maachah to Hazor.

   b. From Hazor around to the region of Gath-hepher.

   c. A branch from the previous arrow drawn (starting by the Sea of Galilee), running S by Lo-debar to the region of Succoth in the land *Beyond the Jordan.*

   d. A branch from the previous arrow drawn (starting S of the Sea of Galilee), running E of Lo-debar to the region of Gilead.

   e. An arrow from Hannathon, branching into two: one to Megiddo (where finds indicate a destruction although it is not mentioned in any known text), and the other to Dor (on the coast) via Jokneam. (Part of the way there is no route printed on the map.) Be careful not to mix this arrow with that of Tiglath-pileser III's earlier campaign. Make a break in this new arrow when you come to the other one W of Jokneam.

5. **Black write-in** (small caps): On (or below) the blue arrow N of Hazor = II-733 B.C.

DISCUSSION AND READING

Sit back and look over the work you have just done. Do you see why Tiglath-pileser III could not allow these northern regions to continue unconquered? Compare this map with 4-5 and 4-1. Note the same basic priority in reverse by the pharaohs of Egypt who came from the south in his campaign some seven centuries earlier. It is not difficult to sympathize with the inhabitants of these regions in this *Land Between*.

4-5
4-1

Now look at the position of the tribes of Naphtali and Zebulun again on Map 6-1 and compare it with Map 9-4. Their territories no doubt look even less attractive now, despite the economic value of the routes running through them which made Solomon rich as seen on Map 7-1. Indeed, one had to be strong enough to hold these routes if their value were to be realized. The Assyrian invasion vividly illustrates that point. The impact of that catastrophe is even remembered in the genealogical lists of Reuben, Gad and half of Manasseh, since it affected their life along the Transjordanian routes (1 Chronicles 5.6, 25-26).

6-1

7-1 e

The best way to gain a feeling for these regions at this point in our study is to turn again to **Isaiah 9.1-7** (with Map 9-4 in hand). You may want to note certain similarities between the period we are studying and the days of Roman control in this same land, when *Jesus began to preach* (Matthew 4.12-25). Those beginnings were in this very land of Zebulun and Naphtali, at the New Testament sites of Nazareth and Capernaum, or, as John tells us in his account, at the village called *Cana (Kanah) in Galilee* (Map 12-7).

9-4

12-8

MARKING (The final phase of Tiglath-pileser III's campaigns.)

1. **Red on arrows**: NE corner of the map, on the arrows pointing to Damascus and to Ashtaroth (both off the map).

2. **Sweeping blue arrows**:
   a. From the extreme NE corner of the map, one arrow to the name Damascus, capital of Aram (Syria). (The city is off the map, but the blue arrow indicates that it was finally taken by Tiglath-pileser III in this campaign.)

   b. Beginning at the same place (NE corner of the map), draw an arrow branching off to the S along the very top (E) side of the map (below the title), running S by Ashtaroth to the region of Ramoth-gilead.

3. **Black write-in** (small caps): on blue arrow E of Damascus = III-732 B.C.

DISCUSSION

It appears that the Assyrian leader finalized his hold on the country by securing a tight control on the Transjordanian Highway. The key to that route (as well as the route to Hazor) was Damascus, capital of Aram (Syria). An Assyrian relief shows captives being led from Ashtaroth, a key site along the Transjordanian Highway.

9-4

Israel (the Northern Kingdom) had once controlled many of the northern regions which we have been studying. After the campaign of Tiglath-pileser III, the political, military and economic strength of Aram (Syria), Israel's northern neighbor, was destroyed. Assyrian control over the north was insured and enforced through the creation of administrative districts which would remain constant for many centuries.

These included the districts of Megiddo (taking over the importance of Hazor), Damascus, which consisted of much of former Aram (Syria), Karnaim and Gilead (both along the Transjordanian Highway). Dor was also a district but would later be included in the Assyrian district of Samaria after the fall of the Northern Kingdom.

With these Assyrian administrative districts controlling the highways of the north, Israel's economic base was all but gone. She was simply an Assyrian vassal. On Map 9-5 (studied later in the course), we shall see that Israel's response to Egyptian overtures brought a swift and cruel Assyrian response — and with it the end of the Northern Kingdom's political life.

We are left with the task of drawing the approximate limits of Israel and Judah in the period following the campaigns of Tiglath-pileser III and prior to Israel's fall. Use the dry end of your pen or your colored pencil on your first try to mark borders. Also make a break when you come to names and dots.

MARKING

1. **Solid green line** (frontiers of Judah):
   a. Begin at the N end of the Dead Sea (at the mouth of the River Jordan), proceeding N along the river about .5 cm./¼ in.

   b. Swing NW to the first *l* of Gilgal.

   c. W to the middle of Michmash (keeping just S of the road and the town's dot).

   d. W to the dot of Lower Beth-horon (via the *e* of Geba, and *m* of Ramah, the *z* of Mizpah and the *n* of both Upper and Lower Beth-horon).

   e. Swing S, leaving Aijalon and Zanoah below (W) of your line, and then SW (via the first *o* of Socoh and the *o* of Moresheth-gath).

   f. Swing further SW leaving Lachish above (E) of your line, but T. Nagila and Ziklag below (W) of your line.

   g. Your line should pass off the map about 3 cm./1¼ in. E of the map number in the SW corner of the map.

   h. **Shade in** the Judah side of the frontier in light green pencil (but only along the line itself).

2. **Orange broken line** (limit of Israel's semi-independent control):
   a. Begin from Judah's border on the River Jordan and continue (in orange) N up the river passing Adam and reaching Zaphon.

   b. NW along the foot of the mountains to about 1.5 cm./½ in. before Jezreel.

   c. Swing SW to touch Ibleam, and then NW again to the *aa* of Taanach.

   d. Swing SW, just above the main Coastal Highway (do not cross it or touch it) until you can swing in (between Neballat and Hadid) to touch the frontier of Judah near Lower Beth-horon.

DISCUSSION AND READING

You may become slightly discouraged in such a study of aggressive military might and the apparent helplessness of the individual caught in such conditions. Isaiah, however, expresses a far-reaching view, looking beyond present difficulties to the reality of the One who actually is in total control. This is reflected in **Isaiah 40.21-24**. One verse, especially, puts *the rulers of the world* — including the mighty Assyria — in proper perspective:

> *They are only just planted, only just sown, their stem has only just taken root,*
> *And He puffs on them and they dry up; the storm carries them off like chaff.*

LEGEND

Broken orange line	= Israel after campaigns of Tiglath-pileser III.
Red dot (no HL)	= Names from Assyrian records.
Red dot or underlining + yellow HL	= Names from 2 Kings 15.29.
Name in box	= Capital city

REVIEW AND CONCLUDING ASSIGNMENT

REVIEW

You have come to the end of Chapter One in the *SMM* assignments and have worked on five maps spread over a thousand years of history. These maps have had one major geographical theme: the country's main Coastal Highway and its northern approaches. The history studied has illustrated that theme.

You first saw Egypt's priorities in the land along the main Coastal Highway, branching off from the key point of Megiddo (Maps 4-5 and 4-1). Then you noted local Canaanite power centers mentioned in Judges 1 and located along these main routes (Map 6-1). These centers, together with the trade routes they controlled, finally came under the rule of David and Solomon. This contributed greatly to a strong, united and affluent Israel, governed from Jerusalem (Map 7-1). Finally, in the aftermath of local wars the mighty power of Assyria swept into the country along these same routes. It brought with it a harsh and cruel oppression in the regions of Galilee and Gilead (Map 9-4).

CONCLUDING ASSIGNMENT

Your last assignment in Chapter One consists of a personal exploration through the land with special emphasis upon regional features along the highways you have studied.

This can be done best by using *SMA: Student Version*. The object of the assignment is to discover regional features and areas of difficulty on the maps which define the natural routes you have studied in this chapter. Since the map before you has no routes printed on it, you must compare it with those you have just marked and define the road on the full color map. Areas of difficulty must be avoided, and yet the route must arrive at key centers.

1. **Gaza to Aphek**: Find Gaza in the southwest corner of SMA. How would you propose to travel from Gaza to Aphek (right center of the map)? The shaded areas

along the coastline are coastal sand dunes. The clear light gray areas represent the built-up areas around modern-day cities (Gaza, Joppa/Tel-Aviv, etc.). Compare your projected route with Map 4-5 and Map 9-4.

2. **Aphek to Megiddo**: Note the river which originates by Aphek, just northeast of Joppa. It is called the Yarqon River. To the north of this river is the Sharon Plain, a region of some swamps and thick oak forests in antiquity. Given this difficulty how would you plot the natural route from Aphek to Megiddo? Can you find the pass to Megiddo? Compare your projected route with Maps 4-5 and 7-1.

3. **Megiddo to Hazor**: Find what you feel to be the line of least resistance through this very complex region of the Jezreel Valley and Galilee. How would you proceed north of Hazor to the region of Dan? Compare your results with Maps 4-5 and 9-4.

4. **Megiddo to Beth-shan**: As you project this route, avoid the obvious difficulties. By comparing this map with Map 4-1, find the main routes east and northeast of Beth-shan connecting to the Transjordanian Highway farther east (off the map).

5. **Megiddo to Acco and Tyre**: Project your route northwest of Megiddo to Tyre via Acco. Avoid obvious areas of difficulty and compare your projection with Maps 4-1 and 9-4.

This chapter introduced you to some of the major historical events taking place in the land during Old Testament times. This brief introduction serves as a framework for all subsequent assignments. For that reason it would be wise to take a few minutes to skim over the discussions in this chapter again. Note the basic ebb and flow of history during the centuries while keeping the *Introductory Schematic of the Playing Board* and *The Land Between* schematic in Appendix II in view.

RELEVANCE

The highways you have been working on are always a part of the country's history, even if they are not specifically mentioned in a particular narrative. Much can be learned if you recall the influence of these routes in subsequent assignments. The Philistines expanded along them. Saul and others desperately fought to halt this advance, providing us with one of the most exciting chapters in Israel's history. As a direct result of her proximity to these routes, Israel (the Northern Kingdom) became affluent but ultimately fell captive to Assyria. The prophets knew this connection and used it in their preaching. They also looked beyond present difficulties to a brighter future.

> *In that day there will be a highway from Egypt to Assyria, linking Assyria*
> *with Egypt and Egypt with Assyria [via Israel]. Egypt, with Assyria, will serve*
> *[the Lord]. In that day, Israel will be the third party, together with Egypt and*
> *Assyria, a blessing in the midst of the earth whom the Lord Sabaoth blesses*
> *saying,*
>
> 'Blessed be my people   —   Egypt,
> the work of my hands   —   Assyria,
> and my own possession —   Israel.'   (Isaiah 19.23-25)

Subsequently, Babylonians, Persians, Macedonians and Greeks (under Alexander the Great), Seleucids and Ptolemies all marched along these highways. Maccabean and first century zealots attempted to break the hold of Greek or Roman forces on these routes. Temporary relief was gained, but disaster followed in the periods before and after the days of the New Testament.

In our day these same routes have been used by Turks, British, Egyptians, Syrians, Jordanians and Israelis (in 1917, 1948, 1956, 1967 and 1973). In the late 1970's President Sadat of Egypt gained important territorial concessions from Israel, which brought Egyptian political, military and economic influence closer to that region through which Thutmose III and other pharaohs had marched some 3500 years earlier.

12-4   It is interesting to note that it was along this same route (via Philistia) that Joseph and Mary made their way back to the country from the land of Egypt. With them was their young son, Joshua (the Hebrew form of the Greek *Jesus*). Thus as a child the *Prince of Peace* passed through regions in which Egypt, Assyria and Israel had fought bitterly.

This small family of the tribe of Judah also passed sites which were ravished by war later in that very century. Their way led them to Nazareth, that small, insignificant village which overlooks much of what we have come to understand as *Galilee of the Nations*. Here He would grow to manhood, filled with the impressions of Galilee and the north, regions so different from Jerusalem and Judea. What these perspectives mean to our understanding of His words will have to wait for later studies.

CHAPTER TWO

GALILEE AND SURROUNDING REGIONS

INTRODUCTION

The aim of the assignments in Chapter Two is to explore more thoroughly the geographical features and the main routes of the north. Particular emphasis is placed on Galilee, the Jezreel Valley and surrounding regions.

This study builds upon the routes introduced in Chapter One. The same procedure used there should be followed in completing the assignments in this chapter. To maintain an historical and geographical point of reference during the study, consult the *Introductory Chronology* or the chart *The Land Between* (Appendix II) before beginning each assignment. Remember to write in the title and date at the top of each map.

The *SMA* is a basic reference for each *SMM* assignment. Keep this full color map in view for handy reference, perhaps on the wall in front of your desk. Make a habit of glancing often at this map while completing each assignment. In this way many of the geographical features will become familiar. Take special note of areas of difficulty (swamps, sands, hills, canyons, etc.) which dictate the path of most natural routes.

In this chapter the history of the country illustrates the regional detail of the north. The *SCS* reference for each map may be helpful for a quick overview of the topics covered on the map. Remember, however, that the study of the region's history is not the main objective of these assignments.

The twelve *SMM* maps studied in this chapter are listed below. An asterisk indicates that the map was marked in Chapter One of the *Guide*. These may be discussed here in relationship to the more detailed regional work of this chapter.

4-7	Campaign of Thutmose III
4-9	Egyptian operations in Canaan in the Nineteenth Dynasty
5-6	Joshua's campaign in northern Canaan: Merom and Hazor
6-5	Northern confrontation: Deborah and Barak
6-6	Eastern confrontation: Gideon and Jephthah (Ehud = 6-7)
7-4	Saul's beginning and end (partial marking)
*7-1	David's census and Solomon's reign
8-2	Division of the kingdom and Shishak's campaign in Israel
8-5	Israel's relations with Aram-Damascus (Syria) and Sidon; internal apostasy under Ahab and Jezebel
8-1	Elijah's ministry
8-7	Elisha's, J(eh)oram's, Jehu's and Israel's relations with Aram (Syria) and Assyria
*9-4	Campaigns and provincial organization of Tiglath-pileser III of Assyria

S M M   4 − 7

TITLE: **CAMPAIGN OF THUTMOSE III** (Detail on Map 4-5)

DATE: **MID-15TH CENTURY B.C.** (Underline *LB* in yellow in the title of this map.)

INTRODUCTION

4-5 b   The geographical and historical context of this map can be seen best on Map 4-5, which was studied in Chapter One. By glancing at that map you will recall that Pharaoh Thutmose III provided us with one of the most complete lists of place-names along the Coastal Highway and in the north of the country. Megiddo played a central role in the Egyptian drive through the country.

At the close of Chapter One you *explored* the geographical setting of the country's main international route. This was done on your full color *SMA*. As you moved north of the Sharon Plain, it became clear that you had to cross a range of hills before reaching Megiddo. The strategic importance of the site is its geographical setting at the
4-7   mouth of one of the great passes from the Coastal Plain (Sharon) to the famous Jezreel Valley. Now you are going to write in some of the general geographical regions surrounding Megiddo on Map 4-7. These are standard terms for these geographical features, although they are not mentioned as such in Egyptian texts.

MARKING (On Map 4-7)

1. **Brown write-in** (geographical information) in large caps: There are two words in each name. Write the second under the first so that the entire name will not become too long.
   a. In the N of the map, on the large mountain near the sea, in the large open area W of the name Geba-shemen and S of the name Libnath = MT. CARMEL.

   b. In the coastland (center of the map) in the open area SW of the name Socoh, between the red road and the sea = SHARON PLAIN. (Note: Keep off the red road and off the area around Yaham.)

   c. In the open area between Megiddo and Ophel = JEZREEL VALLEY. (Note: Keep off of the region around Taanach.) Some call this valley *The Great Plain.*

2. **Yellow HL on names = Megiddo** and **Yaham**. Note: Be careful to only HL the names themselves since the area adjacent to the name will be used for other markings.)

DISCUSSION

As you look at the area between the three geographical regions just written in, note the three distinct passes through the hills from the Sharon Plain to the Jezreel Valley. Each pass takes the path of least resistance, following natural routes. Each ends up at a different location on the Jezreel Valley.

Egyptian sources tell us that the Pharaoh had successfully completed his coastal campaign and had taken time out to call together his top advisors for a council meeting at Yaham. A glance at the map shows why a decision had to be made here. The three options open to the Egyptians were 1) the southern route (swinging around to Taanach), 2) the northern route (via Zephath and the region of Jokneam), or 3) the narrow but more direct route to Megiddo via Aruna. Canaanite forces attempted to stop the mighty Egyptian army of Thutmose III along these passes.

MARKING

1. **Blue box around name** = Yaham.

2. **Yellow HL on routes**: the Coastal Highway and the three passes.
   a. The route from the S to Aphek, and from Aphek to Socoh and Yaham.

   b. From Yaham to Gath and then directly E on the shorter route around to Taanach.

   c. From Gath along the shortest route to Megiddo.

   d. From Gath via Zephath and on to Jokneam.

3. **One sweeping blue arrow** = from the region of Aphek pointing to the box of Yaham (running just to the W of the highlighted route). This shows the Egyptian advance to a key position at Yaham, before the three passes.

4. **Orange box around dot** (only around the dot) of Taanach and Jokneam.

5. **Black write-in** (small caps) in the open area just W of Yaham = WAR COUNCIL TO DECIDE ATTACK ROUTE. Avoid spreading this out. Write it in three lines.

DISCUSSION

The Canaanites of Megiddo did not think that the Egyptian chariots would venture through the narrow pass of Megiddo via Aruna. They placed their camps at the two other possible approaches to the valley: at Taanach and in the region of Jokneam (represented by the orange squares on your map).

The map is now set up for the Pharaoh's council of war at Yaham. His scouts no doubt brought him information concerning the various routes and the Canaanite camps. His advisors warned him against any attempt to send his forces through the Aruna-Megiddo pass, since each chariot could be picked off individually before they reorganized themselves near Megiddo.

Thutmose III overruled his council's advice and gave orders to proceed single file through the Aruna-Megiddo pass. As it turned out, his forces did have time to regroup on the plain, before the Canaanites could rush their men and equipment back to Megiddo. The Egyptians won the battle on the plain below Megiddo. However, they were so taken up with the spoil of war that the city itself had time to man its defenses and to close its gates. Subsequently, the Egyptian army had to lay siege to the city. Opposing camps on the low hills just west of the city provided the setting for the final scene in this episode of Megiddo's history.

MARKING

    1. **Red circle around name** (and dot, as usual) = Megiddo.

    2. **One sweeping blue arrow** = from the box of Yaham via the name of Aruna (skip over the name itself) and pointing toward the red circle of Megiddo.

    3. **Orange arrows** from each Canaanite camp (from Taanach and from the region of Jokneam) toward the red circle of Megiddo (drawn on the E side of the road).

    4. **Black write-in** (small caps) in the open area just S of the Aruna-Megiddo route = ROUTE OF PHARAOH THUTMOSE III with a small black arrow from the write-in pointing toward the Aruna-Megiddo pass.

DISCUSSION (with Map 4-7 and *SMA* before you)

The importance of these three passes (which we can call the *Carmel Passes*) cannot be overestimated. They carried almost all of the commerce and military might of the ancient world which passed through the land between the Nile and Mesopotamian river valleys.

The centrality of Megiddo, located at this economic, military and cultural crossroads, can best be seen by turning from Map 4-7 back to Map 4-5 for a moment. Indeed, Thutmose III was not far from the truth when he stated that *taking Megiddo is as good as capturing a thousand cities*.

The site of Megiddo not only overlooks the scene of the battle between Thutmose III and the Canaanites. From the summit of the ancient fortified city one can survey the Jezreel Valley, that famous interchange on the International Highway. In this small *Land Between* no other region compares with it.

The valley itself is seen clearly on Map 4-7, and better yet in full color on Map 1-7 or on the northern sheet of *SMA*. The mound on which the site of Megiddo is located has lent its name to the Valley of Jezreel. The valley of the *Hill of Megiddo* (in Hebrew *Har Megiddo*) has come to us through a Greek form in Revelation 16.16. There it states that the kings of the world would mobilize their forces *at a place which is called Armageddon* (Hill of Megiddo).

LEGEND

Orange box   = Canaanite camp.

S M M   4 – 9

TITLE: **EGYPTIAN OPERATIONS IN CANAAN IN THE 19TH DYNASTY** (Detail of Map 4-1)

DATE: **ABOUT 1300 B.C.** (Underline *LB* in yellow in the title of this map.)

INTRODUCTION

Thus far your study in Chapter Two has introduced three entrances from the west into the famed Jezreel Valley. The strategic value of these western entrances (via the

Carmel Passes) was illustrated vividly in the campaign of Pharaoh Thutmose III against the defenders of Megiddo.

The present study (Map 4-9) introduces the southeastern approach to the Jezreel Valley from Beth-shan. Beth-shan links the Jezreel Valley with routes coming from the Transjordanian Highway farther east (seen on Map 4-1, an overview of the events of the period).

The Megiddo—Beth-shan route now can be seen in detail on Map 4-9. It descends SE from the Jezreel Valley to Beth-shan via Shunem and what we shall come to know as the Harod Valley. This small valley is situated between Mt. Gilboa and the Hill of Moreh. This new geographical information now will be filled in on Map 4-9 in preparation for the arrival of another Egyptian pharaoh, Seti I.

MARKING
1. **Yellow HL on route**: Begin in the SW corner of the map with the route by Yaham.
   a. From Yaham to Megiddo via Aruna.

   b. From Megiddo to Beth-shan via Ophel and passing near Shunem.

   c. From Beth-shan NE (as on Map 4-1) dividing into two routes which continue off the map to the E (one due E from the fork in the road, and the other proceeding N from the fork and then NE through the name Kiriath-anab).

2. **Yellow HL on name** = Beth-shan.

3. **Brown write-in**: Before writing in the following geographical names, locate them on Map 1-6 or Map 1-7 where they appear in light gray.
   a. MEDITERRANEAN SEA (and its Old Testament name, GREAT SEA, just below it) and SEA OF CHINNERETH (the Old Testament name for the Sea of Galilee).

   b. JEZREEL VALLEY (for Valley of Jezreel), MT. CARMEL and MT. GILBOA.

   c. HILL OF MOREH (in small caps) located NW of Mt. Gilboa.

   d. MT. TABOR (in small caps) located NE of the Hill of Moreh.

   e. HAROD VALLEY (in small caps) just N of Mt. Gilboa. (Stay away from Beth-shan.)

DISCUSSION
Compare the detail of Map 4-9 with the overview of Map 4-1 and *SMA*. Obviously the control of the region of Beth-shan was vital to Egypt's interests in this land and beyond. It was in this region that forces from Pehel and Hammath mobilized against the Egyptians and other Canaanites.

4-9 a
4-1 b

The capture of Beth-shan by the kings of Pehel and Hammath could not be tolerated. Egypt's political and economic interests were threatened. It was the task of the army of Pharaoh Seti I to *liberate* Beth-shan and to bring relief to the besieged city of Rehob.

As in the case of Thutmose III a century and a half before, Egyptian military might marched along the Coastal Highway. The objective once again was to solidify Egyptian control over the northern approaches to the country. These same approaches served Egypt well as a springboard for conquests farther north. The Stele of Seti I found at Beth-shan provides detail about his campaign in this *Land Between*.

MARKING

1. **Yellow HL on names** in the region of Beth-shan = **Pehel**, **Rehob** and **Hammath**.

2. **Red circle around names** = Beth-shan and Rehob.

3. **Sweeping orange arrows** (showing attack on Beth-shan and Rehob):
   a. From Pehel one arrow branching into two, toward Beth-shan and Rehob.

   b. From the dot of Hammath sweeping slightly E and then back to Rehob.

4. **Black write-in** (small caps) in the open area just E of Rehob = BETH-SHAN TAKEN AND REHOB BESIEGED.

5. **Sweeping blue arrows** just W and N of the highlighted route:
   a. From Yaham to Aruna.

   b. From Aruna to Megiddo.

   c. From Megiddo to Beth-shan.

6. **Black write-in** (small caps) in the open area just E of the Hill of Moreh and just N of the highlighted route = CAMPAIGN OF PHARAOH SETI I TO REESTABLISH EGYPTIAN CONTROL.

7. **Yellow HL on names** of cities where Seti I campaigned in the north = the same names as are highlighted in this region on Map 4-1.

8. **Orange on dots only** (optional since this is already seen on Map 4-1): Cities in the north mentioned in an Egyptian scribal satire reflecting centers in the land during the days of Ramses II (early thirteenth century B.C.) = the same dots which appear in orange in this region on Map 4-1.

4-1 c
4-9 b

9. **Brown write-in** (small caps): A plateau due N of Beth-shan (about 3 cm./1¼ in.) N of the dot of Beth-shan) = MT. YARMUTA. It was in this area that Seti I campaigned according to the Beth-shan Stele.

DISCUSSION

Thus far your study may appear to have little connection with the Biblical stories. They will come shortly. In the meantime, you have come to appreciate the position of Megiddo and of Beth-shan. Important connections between the Coastal Highway (on the Sharon Plain) and the Transjordanian Highway ran through the Jezreel Valley and through these centers. They are essential elements for political and economic superiority in the north of the country.

Later in this chapter you will discover that Gideon met the Midianite threat in this   6-6 b
region (*SMM* 6-6). Attempts to unify the Israelite tribes were thwarted by Philistine
expansionism into the Jezreel, Harod and Beth-shan Valleys. Saul, Israel's first king,   7-4 h
lost his life in an attempt to break the Philistine hold on the region (*SMM* 7-4).

During the Divided Kingdom and the Maccabean/Hasmonean period the same route
plagued and stunted Jewish nationalism and expansion (*SMM* Sections Eight, Nine and
Eleven). Rome finally put her foot down at Beth-shan (or Scythopolis as it was called
then). The frustration would continue into the first century A.D. as a backdrop for
New Testament times (*SMM* Section Twelve).

What you have learned from this map is not merely another chapter in the land's
history or another episode from the life of an Egyptian pharaoh. You have seen that
this highway, as other main routes of the north, tolerates no compromise. There is no
room for division of control. International and local struggles revolve around the
question of who controls these northern routes.

For this reason the north is not unified easily. Once unified, internal strength and
extreme vigilance must be maintained, with full knowledge of international and local
political developments. It is precisely this situation in which the modern State of
Israel finds herself today.

LEGEND (The second item below is optional on Map 4-9 since it is covered already on
           Map 4-1.)
Yellow HL on name   = Campaign of Seti I, 1303 B.C. (*SCS* a).
Orange on dot   = Satirical scribe, early 13th century B.C. (*SCS* b).

S M M   5 — 6

TITLE: **JOSHUA'S CAMPAIGN IN NORTHERN CANAAN**

DATE: **EARLY 14TH CENTURY B.C.** (or MID-13TH CENTURY B.C. as many
            prefer)

INTRODUCTION

Opening to Map 5-6 you probably already recognize some sites and features on the
map. You should, for instance, be able to find the Jezreel Valley and the Aruna-
Megiddo Pass. The route to Beth-shan via the Harod Valley is also now a known
feature. Can you point out the Jezreel Valley, Mt. Gilboa, the Harod Valley, the Hill
of Moreh, Mt. Tabor and Mt. Carmel? You will write in these names when you begin
marking below. If you have difficulty locating them, consult Map 4-9 and Map 1-7.

As you may have already guessed, this study concentrates on the routes to the north
of the Jezreel Valley through Galilee to Hazor. That is one side of the Jezreel Valley
not yet discussed in previous maps. At the end of Chapter One some of the geographical obstacles which the Megiddo-Hazor route avoids were seen as you explored this
region on *SMA*. In this study we are to look at Galilee in more detail and to recognize
Hazor's unique position along the major entrance to the country from the north.

MARKING

1. **Brown write-in:**
   a. From Map 4-9 transfer MEDITERRANEAN SEA/GREAT SEA, SEA OF CHIN-NERETH, MT. CARMEL, JEZREEL VALLEY, MT. GILBOA, HILL OF MOREH, MT. TABOR and HAROD VALLEY.

   b. The valley in which the route runs, due E of Acco = BET-HACCEREM VALLEY. Note the location of this valley on Map 1-7, where it is printed in light gray. Position it on Map 5-6 in about the same location.

   c. Due E of the Bet-haccerem Valley and just W of the name Chinnereth on Map 5-6 is a blue stream bed. Write in N. AMMUD along this stream bed, W of the city name Chinnereth. Compare Map 1-7 if you have difficulty. *N.* means *Nahal*, or *stream bed* in Hebrew.

2. **Yellow HL on name = Hazor.**

3. **Yellow HL on route:**
   a. The international route (printed in red) from Megiddo to Hazor (via Mt. Tabor and the plain near the Sea of Chinnereth) and then due N via Hazor off the map toward Ijon.

   b. The route which runs N of Megiddo to Hannathon (via Shimron) and then turns due E to join the highway you just highlighted.

   c. The route from Acco (on the coast) running SE to Hannathon.

   d. The route from Megiddo to Acco via Achshaph.

DISCUSSION

The routes you have just highlighted (together with what you already know about the route to Beth-shan) comprise the main communication links of Galilee. Lower Galilee (with some ridges above 500 m./1500 ft.) lies between the Bet-haccerem Valley and the Jezreel Valley. It extends to the Sea of Chinnereth dropping to some 200 m./600 ft. below the level of the Mediterranean Sea.

Upper Galilee is mainly Hill Country, rising at times above 1000 m./3000 ft. While Map 5-6 shows a number of routes in Upper Galilee, they are much more difficult to traverse than those in Lower Galilee.

MARKING: Brown write-in:

1. In the open area N of the Bet-haccerem Valley and just E of Yattir and Hekhalim = UPPER GALILEE (large caps).

2. In the open area S of the Bet-haccerem Valley and N of the region of Mt. Tabor = LOWER GALILEE (large caps).

3. In the region of low hills between Shimron and Achshaph (in the middle of the triangle of highlighted roads) = SHEPHELAH (LOWLAND) in two lines.

4. In the very NE corner of the map, with part of the name in white area off the map = MT. HERMON. Note: Leave room for the next brown write-in.

5. In the open area between Mt. Hermon and the city name Ijon = LAND OF MIZPAH (in two lines with a small brown arrow pointing N from the name).

DISCUSSION

Ridges in Lower Galilee hamper north-south travel in the region and can best be seen on Map 1-7. Names of some of the hills and intervening valleys are printed on Map 1-7   1-7 in light gray. Today the city of Nazareth and modern routes to it dominate the ridge just north of the Jezreel Valley. The reason for this is that after New Testament times Nazareth developed into a Christian pilgrim center. Today we call this ridge the *Nazareth Ridge*.

Turning back to Map 5-6 find the *Nazareth Ridge* (without the city of Nazareth on it). Note that natural lines of communication avoid this ridge, preferring the surrounding valleys and passes. On Map 5-6 you can see the centrality of Megiddo. Natural routes extend out from Megiddo to the north and northeast (highlighted routes). These connect Megiddo (and other sites) to the Acco-Sea of Chinnereth route (highlighted) through three natural passes. Anyone who controls these three passes also controls these main roads of Lower Galilee.

The routes we have been discussing join near the center of the map at a possible site of Madon (perhaps called Shemesh-edom in Thutmose III's city-list). From there the road   4-5 b descends from about 200 m./600 ft. above sea level to about 200 m./600 ft. below sea level. By the sea it comes onto a plain and passes near the Old Testament city of Chinnereth (better known by its New Testament Greek form as Gennesaret). In   12-8 making this descent the route avoids the mountains and forests of Upper Galilee and the difficult canyon of the Nahal Ammud. From Chinnereth the route ascends above sea level again to the plain surrounding one of the greatest cities of the north, Hazor. Before we begin our discussion of Joshua's campaign in the north, it would be very helpful for you to review this discussion with *SMA* in hand and Map 5-6 at your side. (Madon and Shemesh-edom are represented on *SMA* by the tribal name Adamah.)

Prior to the northern campaign, the Israelites had won impressive battles in the South-   5-5 c ern Hill Country (studied in a later chapter). A summary of these campaigns (Joshua 10.40-42) makes it clear why northern leaders led by Jabin, king of Hazor, felt the   5-6 need to mobilize. Hazor's place of leadership in this northern defense league is under-scored in Joshua 11.10 where the city's past record (also established by archeological discoveries) is mentioned: *Up to that time Hazor itself led in the affairs of all those*   2-3 *[northern] administrative centers.*   2-4

MARKING

1. In the following excerpt from Joshua 11.1-5 certain names appear in boldface. Find these names on Map 5-6 and draw **a blue circle** around each name.

*When word [of Israelite victories in the south] reached Jabin, king of **Hazor**,*
*he contacted Jobab, the king of **Madon** [some prefer the name Merom from*
*the Greek and therefore also circle the northern **Merom**], the king of **Shimron**,*
*the king of **Achshaph** and the [other] northern kings in the Hill Country [Upper*
Galilee], in the plains south of Chinneroth [Sea of Chinnereth], in the Shephelah
*[lowlands of Galilee] and in the western regions around **Dor** . . . [here follows*
an impressive list]. These kings rallied to the call and mobilized their joint
forces at the waters of Merom for the express purpose of waging war on Israel.

2. **Yellow HL on route:**
    a. Shortest route from Hazor to Tyre (on the coast) and then N toward Sidon.

    b. Two short routes running off the route you just highlighted — first, the route into the blue-circled Merom; second, the route NE of Kedesh.

3. **Yellow HL on name = Merom** (in blue circle) and **Sidon.**

4. **Sweeping blue arrows:**
    a. From the blue circle of Dor to the Shimron area in a more or less direct line.

    b. Two arrows joining to form one = from Achshaph and from Shimron, joining just E of Hannathon and pointing toward Madon.

    c. Two arrows joining to form one = from Madon and from the plain S of the Sea of Chinnereth, joining just S of the city of Chinnereth and pointing toward Hazor. Note: Leave enough room around Hazor for another circle later.

    d. An arrow from Hazor to the blue-circled Merom via the name Kedesh.

    e. An arrow sweeping toward blue-circled Merom from NE (from Abel-beth-maachah).

    f. An arrow sweeping toward blue-circled Merom from NW (from region of Yattir).

5. **Blue write-in:** W of Merom and S of Abel (leaving enough room around Merom's blue circle for another circle) = CANAANITE MOBILIZATION (written in two lines).

DISCUSSION AND READING

Such was the situation which faced Joshua and the Israelites as they moved their forces north to meet the Canaanite threat. How they arrived on the scene is not known. We are told, however, that *all of a sudden Joshua, together with all the fighting forces [of Israel], appeared at the Waters of Merom and swooped down upon them [the Canaanites] . . . and then returned . . . seized Hazor . . . and burned Hazor with fire.* Read now **Joshua 11.6-13.**

MARKING

1. **Red circle** around blue circle at Merom and Hazor with a number *1* by Merom and a number *2* by Hazor.

2. **Sweeping green arrow** from Merom to Hazor via the region of Kedesh.

3. **Flight (blue) and chase (green) arrows** (Practice these *flight and chase* arrows before marking. They are described in Appendix I.): From Merom to the name Sidon = three such arrows; from the region of Kedesh to the name Ijon = two such arrows.

4. **Orange on dot** (representing kings of the cities defeated by Joshua in the north as on Map 5-1 and in Joshua 12.19-23) = **Hazor, Merom** (only the northern one), **Kedesh, Madon, Shimron, Achshaph, Jokneam, Megiddo, Taanach** and **Dor** (arrow).

DISCUSSION

In this study you have seen that Hazor's strategic position is due to constriction created by surrounding regions (mountains, swamps, etc.). These are best seen on *SMA*. Geographical features and international routes north and northeast of *SMA* dramatically underscore the city's unique position on what could be termed the *Northern Gateway to Galilee*. Archeological evidences and the testimony of history (on maps you will study later in this chapter) combine to make Hazor one of the truly great sites in the country.

LEGEND

Blue circle around name = Canaanite city in northern league with Hazor (cf. Joshua 11.10).

Orange dot   = Northern cities listed as defeated in Joshua 12.19-23 (See also Map 5-1 = Kings of Canaan).

S M M   6 – 5

TITLE: NORTHERN CONFRONTATION: DEBORAH AND BARAK

DATE: 13TH OR 12TH CENTURY B.C.

INTRODUCTION

The background to the study of Map 6-5 is found on Map 6-1. On that map regional settlement problems during the period of the Judges were discussed. Judges 1.27-33 listed a number of unconquered Canaanite centers in the north which frustrated the Israelite tribes. These sites are highlighted on Map 6-1 and their dots colored in blue. They will be transferred to Map 6-5 in the marking instructions below. Geographical and tribal names will be written in. Tribal cities and border sites will be color coded.

6-1 *o*

MARKING

1. **Brown write-in**: By comparing Map 6-5 with Map 5-6, locate and write in the names of the following geographical features = GREAT SEA/MEDITERRANEAN SEA, MT. CARMEL, JEZREEL VALLEY, MT. GILBOA, HAROD VALLEY, HILL OF MOREH, BET-HACCEREM VALLEY, N. AMMUD, UPPER GALILEE and LOWER GALILEE.

2. **Underlining in blue** (but no blue on the name):
   On Map 6-1 find the unconquered Canaanite sites (with a blue dot). On Map 6-5 locate the corresponding site and underline its name in blue. There are eleven names to find and to underline in blue on Map 6-5.

3. **Yellow on dot** (do not mix with blue): Sites allotted to the tribe of Asher (also listed above Map 6-2), beginning in the N of the map = **Kanah** (not the same Kanah as marked on Map 9-4), **Usu/Hosah, Hammon, Achzib, Abdon/Ebron, Beth-emek,**

Acco, Rehob, Kabul/Cabul, Neiel, Mishal, Aphek (not the Aphek on Map 4-5), **Hali,
Beten, Achshaph** and **Helkath**. In **green**, write in the tribal name of ASHER in the
open area between Mishal, Hali and Aphek. Add a **yellow box** around this name.
Yellow dots in this part of the map represent cities or border sites in the territory
allotted to the tribe of Asher.

4. **Green on dot** (not too dark): Sites allotted to the tribe of Zebulun (also listed
   above Map 6-2) beginning just SE of Helkath = **Dabbesheth, Maralah/Mareal,
   Bethlehem** (of Galilee, not Bethlehem of Judah), **Shimron, Sarid, Japhia, Daberath,
   Gath-hepher** (Jonah's village), **Rimmon** and **Hannathon**. Also underline the name
   Valley of Iphtahel in green. In **green**, write in the tribal name ZEBULUN in the
   open space between Rimmon, Hannathon and Japhia. Add a **green box** around this
   name. The green dots in this part of the map represent cities or border sites in the
   territory allotted to the tribe of Zebulun.

5. **Yellow on dot**: Sites allotted to the tribe of Issachar (also listed above Map 6-2)
   beginning in the Jezreel Valley and moving E = **Jezreel, Shunem, Chesulloth/
   Chisloth-tabor, Kishion, Hapharaim, Remeth/Jarmuth, Anaharath, Beth-shemesh**
   (the one just NE of Anaharath), **En-haddah** and **En-gannim**. In **green**, write in the
   tribal name of ISSACHAR in the open space between Anaharath, Beth-shemesh and
   Remeth. Add a **yellow box** around this name. The yellow sites in this part of the
   map represent cities or border sites in the territory allotted to the tribe of Issachar.

6. **Orange on dot** (not too dark): Sites allotted to the tribe of Naphtali (also listed
   above Map 6-2) beginning just N of Mt. Tabor.
   a. In Lower Galilee = **Aznoth-tabor, Heleph, Adami-nekeb, Jabneel, Oak in Zaanan-
      nim, Lakkum, Hammath, Rakkath/ Karthan, Chinnereth, Adamah, Hukkok** (near
      the tribe of Asher) and **Ramah** (N center in the Bet-haccerem Valley).

   b. In Upper Galilee = **Hazor, Kedesh, Yiron, Beth-anath** and **Beth-shemesh** (of
      Upper Galilee). In **green**, write in the tribal name NAPHTALI in the open space
      between N. Ammud and Ramah. Add an **orange box** around this name. The
      orange dots in this part of the map represent cities in the border description of
      the territory belonging to the tribe of Naphtali.

7. **Yellow HL on routes** = the routes connecting Megiddo, Acco and Hazor (the four
   routes highlighted on Map 5-6), but not routes N of Hazor.

DISCUSSION

The problems facing the northern tribes were complex. Not only were they separated
from the stronger tribes of Manasseh/Ephraim and Judah in the Central Hill Country,
they also were plagued by a number of unconquered Canaanite centers (underlined in
blue on Map 6-5 and designated by a blue dot on Map 6-1). Most of these Canaanite
cities were located at strategic road centers, keys to the political and economic control
of the north. Although Hazor was not in this general list, it represented the main
Canaanite contender in the Canaanite-Israelite struggle in the north.

6-1 c

The routes connecting Hazor with the Jezreel Valley were the most important in
Lower Galilee. The tribal allotment of Zebulun was in the center of these natural
routes. This may account for the detailed description and the city-list given in the
book of Joshua for this small but strategically located tribe.

6-2 b iii

To the northeast of Zebulun the main International Highway passed through the
territory allotted to the tribe of Naphtali. It is no coincidence that both the Old   6-2 b vi
Testament prophet (Isaiah 9.1-2) and the New Testament Gospel writer (Matthew
4.12-17) brought out the importance of these two tribes during periods of foreign
domination in the north. (A glance at Map 12-4 shows that New Testament Nazareth
was in the region of Zebulun and that New Testament Capernaum was in Naphtali.
This connection shows that Matthew's regional reference is very specific and quite
intentional.)

Returning to Map 6-5, we are now prepared for the story of deliverance recorded in   6-5 a
Judges 4 and 5. It was a battle between the Israelite forces of the north (led by
Deborah and Barak) and the Canaanite forces of the same region (led by Hazor's
general Sisera, under the king of Hazor, Jabin). The place of the mobilization of these
forces was on either side of the Jezreel Valley. The battle took place on the plain
below Mt. Tabor, a part of the Jezreel Valley we might call the *Plain of Tabor*.

Hazor appears at the head of the Canaanites from the region of Galilee (called *Haro-
sheth-ha-goiim* in Judges 4.2, 13, no doubt the same as *Goiim in Gilgal/Galilee* in
Joshua 12.23). The oppression of the Israelite tribes by the Canaanites must have
caused serious economic problems for these tribes. Judges 5.6-8 mentions the difficulties facing the Israelites of the north, who tended to keep off main roads controlled
by Canaanite power centers: *They avoided highways, and those who [dared] take
trips kept to the back roads.*

Barak came from Kedesh, a city in Naphtali not far from the Oak in Zaanannim, near
the southern tip of the Sea of Galilee/Chinnereth (not the Kedesh near Hazor). He
was summoned to a meeting with Deborah, who was concerned about the situation in
the north. Deborah was *judging Israel* from a much more secure position *between
Ramah and Bethel in the Hill Country of Ephraim* (right center of Map 6-1). An
agreement was made whereby northern Israelite forces were gathered under Deborah
and Barak at the prominent site of Mt. Tabor. This mount was central to the tribes
of Zebulun, Naphtali and Issachar and overlooked the strategic Plain of Tabor, through
which one of the main highways of the north passed (Map 6-5). It should be no
surprise that the two most prominent tribes in this confrontation were Zebulun and
Naphtali. They had the most to gain in any Israelite victory in the region and the
most to lose in a defeat.

Jabin, king of Canaan, who reigned in Hazor, sent his armed forces to the Jezreel
Valley under the leadership of Sisera. They mobilized at the most natural place, in the
region of Megiddo and Taanach. The battle which followed was fought on the Plain of
Tabor, to which the Canaanite forces had been drawn. The west side of this plain is
rather flat and poorly drained by the *Nahal Kishon*. This system drains most of the
Jezreel Valley. During the confrontation, it appears that a storm soaked the region
with water, making the Kishon a *surging nahal/stream* (Judges 5.21). This placed the
Canaanite chariots at a definite disadvantage. The Israelite foot soldiers were quick to
make the best of the situation.

In the face of disaster, Sisera fled by foot to the east of Mt. Tabor, toward the tent of
a Kenite named Heber, who had a wife called Jael. The Kenites had joined the Israelites
during the wilderness wanderings. Heber had moved his tents and herds much farther

north than other Kenites, perhaps to take advantage of the deteriorating situation in the area. Details on how this story ends are given in your reading. First, however, it is necessary to put the final touches on Map 6-5.

MARKING

1. **Brown write-in**: NE by Megiddo, by the lake and swamps, just S of Sarid = NAHAL KISHON (in small caps on an angle in the swamps and E).

2. **Blue around name and black write-in** = Hazor (blue circle) with JABIN, KING OF HAZOR in small black caps above the blue circle (two lines).

3. **Yellow HL on name** = **Hazor, Megiddo, Taanach, Oak in Zaanannim** and **Kedesh** (of Naphtali).

4. **A green, round circle with yellow HL inside** around **Mt. Tabor**.

5. **Blue write-in**: In the open area between Megiddo and Taanach (E of Megiddo and W of Taanach in three lines) = CANAANITE MOBILIZATION UNDER SISERA.

6. **Red confrontation mark**: SW of Mt. Tabor between the *th* of Dabereth and the *th* of Chesulloth = ✳ .

7. **Long sweeping blue arrow** = from the region of Megiddo pointing to the red confrontation mark. This arrow runs along the highlighted route and can cross it.

8. **Two curved, short green arrows** = from the green circle of Mt. Tabor around both sides of the name Daberath pointing to the red confrontation mark.

9. **Flight (blue) and chase (green) arrows** = from the battlefield pointing W to the direction of Nahal Kishon (two arrows).

10. **Short blue flight arrows and black write-in** = six short blue arrows from the battlefield to the Oak in Zaanannim via the *o* of Kishion and the first *b* of Anaharath. By one of these arrows (in small black caps) = SISERA'S FLIGHT.

READING

With Map 6-5 in hand, read over **Judges 4 and 5**. Note the geographical information and the vivid description in Deborah and Barak's song in chapter five. If one keeps in mind the difficulties of living in the north, the note of triumph and joy in the song can be appreciated. Simple people were victors over the mighty.

> . . . *they recount the defense of the Lord, a defense of country folk in Israel* . . .

> *From the heavens the stars waged war; from their courses they waged war on Sisera.*

> *Nahal Kishon whisked them away — that surging nahal — Nahal Kishon!*
> *March on, O my soul, with might!*   (Judges 5.11, 20-21)

LEGEND
Blue underlining = Unconquered Canaanite centers (Map 6-1).
Orange dot   = Naphtali.
Green dot   = Zebulun.
Yellow dot   = Issachar or Asher.

S M M   6 – 6

TITLE: EASTERN CONFRONTATION: GIDEON AND JEPHTHAH (EHUD = 6-7)

DATE: 12TH CENTURY B.C.

INTRODUCTION

Another threat to the Israelite tribes came from the east in the form of herdsmen from Midian. Normally flocks were allowed to graze in the fields in the early summer (after the harvest) to eat the stubble. However, these invaders ravished the land each spring before and during the grain harvest. This had happened for seven years creating a very serious situation.

The Beth-shan and Harod Valleys offered these desert invaders a convenient approach into the heart of the country. This approach took them directly to the fertile regions around the great Jezreel Valley. Without the produce of these regions the agricultural and economic base of the northern tribes was threatened.

MARKING

1. **Brown write-in** (after locating by comparing Map 6-6 and Map 6-5) = MT. GILBOA and JEZREEL VALLEY. (The latter name can be written just W of the city Jezreel.)

2. **Israelite tribal information**: By comparing Map 6-6 with Map 6-5 copy the markings for the Israelite tribes onto Map 6-6. The name Zebulun will have to be shortened to ZEB. and written in the very bottom left corner of the map. NAPH. (Naphtali) can be written at the extreme left hand side of the map, between Lakkum and Jabneel. Box each name in the appropriate color.

3. **Yellow HL** = **Hill of Moreh** and **Mt. Tabor** (HL the name and the actual top of each hill by the name).

4. **Blue write-in**: In a half circle, beginning W of Kishion and running E and SE of the Hill of Moreh = MIDIANITES.

5. **Yellow HL on name** = **En Harod** (Hebrew for *Spring of Harod*, not an actual city), **Ophrah, Abel-meholah, Succoth, Penuel** and **Jogbehah**.

6. **Green write-in**: Just above En Harod = GIDEON (in small caps).

READING

Read **Judges 6 and 7**. (Chapter 8 is optional after the marking below.)

MARKING

1. **Red confrontation mark:** Just W of En-dor = ✻ .

2. **Sweeping green arrow** = from En Harod to En-dor, running just W of the name of Hill of Moreh.

3. **Yellow HL on route** = from the word Midianites down the route SE to Beth-shan, S and SE to Abel-meholah, S to Succoth, E to Mahanaim (near Penuel), SE to Rabbath-ammon and SE off the map.

4. **Brown write-in:**
   a. The Jordan River crossings by Abel-meholah and by Adam = FORDS OF THE JORDAN (at each crossing with a small brown arrow pointing to the crossing).

   b. In the hills just E of Zaphon/Zarethan = TABBATH (in small caps).

   c. Large caps, half way between the two sites for Mahanaim = GILEAD (with four of the letters N of Nahal Jabbok).

   d. Just E of Penuel, to the S of the large canyon = NAHAL JABBOK (small caps in two lines with small brown arrow pointing to the large river canyon).

5. **Flight (blue) and chase (green) arrows** = six such arrows spread out along the length of the highlighted route from the Hill of Moreh to the SE corner of the map. **Black write-in** in SE corner = KARKOR (small caps with small black arrow to SE).

6. **Green write-in:**
   a. In the lower left center of the map, in the open area between the names Bezek and Ibleam = MANASSEH (in large caps).

   b. In the lower right corner, in the open area just E of Shiloh = EPHRAIM.

7. **Sweeping green arrow** = from the names of Manasseh and Ephraim two lines turning SE by Tirzah, running together and SE down the valley to the fords of the Jordan, with a point toward Adam.

DISCUSSION

6-6 b   Map 6-6 is linked to Map 6-5 by a region common to both maps, the area from Mt. Tabor and the Hill of Moreh to the Beth-shan Valley. On Map 4-1 and Map 4-9 the Beth-shan Valley was seen to be vitally important to Egyptian national interests because of the region's connections to the Transjordanian Highway. Map 6-6 demonstrates that this same region has important links with the Jordan Valley south of Beth-shan.

        The fords of the Jordan serve as important strategic points in the Jordan Valley. Today the Jordan River serves as a cease-fire line between Israel and Jordan. The modern bridge at Damiya (Adam) still carries traffic and trade between the east and west banks of the Jordan. At times, political or military tension closes the bridge, effectively stopping communication by land. This is what Gideon called for in his appeal to Ephraim in Judges 7.24-25.

The psalmist and the prophet used the great victories portrayed on Map 6-5 and Map 6-6 as object lessons to Israel and to surrounding nations (Psalm 83 and Isaiah 9.4). One can hear the echoes of triumph in Psalm 83.9-10. Note the play on the word *Adam* (which in Hebrew means both the name of the city and *earth*).

> *Make them like Midian — like Sisera, like Jabin in Nahal Kishon;*
> *They were wiped out at En-dor; they became dung at Adam [or for the earth].*

The only marking left to do on Map 6-6 relates to the judge Jephthah. While some of the events are covered on this map, others can be seen on Map 6-1. The story is briefly introduced below. It also appears in Chapters Three and Four where its relationship to Ephraim, Benjamin and Judah is discussed.

MARKING

1. **Brown write-in**: NE side of the map, beneath the word Judges = LAND OF TOB with a small brown arrow pointing E from the name.

2. **Blue write-in**: SE corner of the map, beneath Rabbath-ammon = AMMON (large caps).

3. **Yellow HL on name and orange circle around name = Mizpeh-gilead.** (Circle both the double name and the dot.)

4. **Sweeping orange arrows:**
   a. Along the route printed in red on the map and coming from the Land of Tob = a long arrow pointing toward the orange circle.

   b. From the orange circle = an arrow to the SE pointing toward Jazer.

5. **Orange underlining of name = Aroer, Abel-keramim** and **Zaphon** (the Zaphon which is listed as Zaphon/Zarethan next to the Jordan River).

6. **Black write-in** (small caps):
   a. Along the arrow from the Land of Tob = JEPHTHAH (Map 6-1 = LARGER CONTEXT).

   b. Above the orange circle = JEPHTHAH MOBILIZES AGAINST AMMON (in four lines).

DISCUSSION AND READING

Jephthah's campaign was important for Israelite security in Transjordan (Beyond-the-Jordan). However, it is also true that the Jordan Valley served as a barrier to east-west communication and allowed linguistic distinctions to develop between the Israelite tribes on either side. As time passed, a variation developed in the spoken Hebrew accent between eastern and western tribes. With this in mind read **Judges 12.1-6**, an account of events subsequent to Jephthah's victory over the Ammonites. Note the importance of the *fords of the Jordan*. Keep Map 6-6 in view as you read. (Judges 11 is also interesting to skim, especially if Jephthah's argument is read in light of events seen on Maps 5-3 and 6-6.)

6-6 c

S M M   7 − 4

TITLE: SAUL'S BEGINNING AND END

DATE: LATE 11TH CENTURY B.C.

INTRODUCTION

While deliverance came from a variety of tribal heroes during the period of the Judges, internal decay had set in. Within Israelite society there was a growing acceptance of the *ways of the world*. Samuel, who could be considered one of the last judges, preached spiritual renewal of the inner man which resulted in obedience to God. From this would come the security for which the individual and the nation longed. In his own words,

> *If you are coming back to the Lord with all your heart, then throw*
> *away the strange gods from your midst — as well as the Ashtaroth —*
> *and fix your heart firmly on the Lord, worshiping Him alone; and He*
> *will deliver you from Philistine domination.*   (1 Samuel 7.3)

The nation, however, wanted a more visible assurance of deliverance in the form of a national leader, a king. (At Shechem an earlier attempt to establish this type of rule by Abimelech, son of Gideon had not succeeded.) In spite of misgivings, Samuel honored the people's request. Saul, of the tribe of Benjamin, was anointed as the first

7-4 a b   king of Israel (*SCS* 7-4 a, b). Before he was accepted by all, he would have to prove himself.

7-4 c   The first crisis recorded in Saul's administration was a renewed Ammonite attack on Israelites in Transjordan. This time the city of Jabesh-gilead (in the hills southeast of Beth-shan) was under siege. Both the lives of the Israelites in Transjordan and the security of the northern tribes were at stake. The newly appointed leader mustered his forces and headed north, keeping to the Hill Country for reasons of security. Skim over **1 Samuel 11** to discover the outcome of this campaign.

MARKING

1. **Yellow HL on name = Jabesh-gilead** (NE part of the map), **Bezek** (W of Jabesh-gilead), **Gilgal** (N of the Dead Sea) and **Shechem** (center).

2. **Brown write-in:**
   a. Along the river, between Adam and the Dead Sea = JORDAN RIVER.

   b. By comparing Map 7-4 with Map 6-5, locate and write in = MT. CARMEL and MT. GILBOA. (Stay away from the site of Jezreel.)

   c. Along the coast between Migdal and Hepher = SHARON PLAIN.

   d. Between the two names of Mahanaim = GILEAD (large caps).

3. **Blue write-in:** In Transjordan, just E of Rabbath-ammon = AMMON.

4. **Sweeping blue arrow** = Draw an arrow from Ammon directly along the top of the map, and then swinging down to point at Jabesh-gilead. (Do not touch it.)

5. **Red circle around name** = Jabesh-gilead.

6. **Yellow HL on route:** Among the red names in the right center of the map, find Ramah. This was Samuel's home town. (Keep this area of the map clean since it will be marked in Chapter Four.) Just S of Ramah is Gibeah. This was Saul's home and headquarters. Beginning from Gibeah, HL the most direct route to Bezek, where Saul mobilized his troops against the Ammonites at Jabesh-gilead.

7. **Green box around name:** Saul's camp = **Bezek**.

8. **Sweeping green arrows:**
   a. Beginning by Shiloh (center of map) and pointing to the green box around Bezek via Shechem and the highlighted route. This shows Saul's advance to Bezek.

   b. From Bezek moving E out of the hills and across the Jordan River at Abel-meholah, ascending E into the hills and pointing toward Jabesh-gilead.

9. **Blue flight arrows** = three short arrows from Jabesh-gilead in the direction of Ammon (but only as far as Nahal Jabbok, the deep canyon half way to Ammon). These show the flight of the Ammonites after Saul's victory at Jabesh-gilead.

DISCUSSION

Following their victory at Jabesh-gilead, the Israelites went to Gilgal where *they*   7-4 c
declared Saul to be king before the Lord . . . and Samuel sacrificed peace offerings before the Lord; there Saul and all the people of Israel joyously celebrated. Maps relating to Saul's reign will be studied in later chapters. Saul's accomplishments are summarized in 1 Samuel 14.47-48. After he *assumed the task of ruling Israel, he waged war on all his enemies in every direction . . . thus delivering Israel from those who had been looting them.*

Saul's success did not satisfy the needs of his threatened spirit. He appears to have had difficulty applying the message which Samuel had been preaching. Finally, Samuel found it necessary to reject Saul's leadership and secretly to anoint a young, new king, David, son of Jesse of the tribe of Judah. With the rise of David, Saul's spirit became even more restless and suspicious. David and Saul are the subject of Map 7-5.

The Philistine policy of expansionism runs like a thread throughout the book of 1 Samuel (the main Biblical record for events portrayed on this map). Checking Philis-   7-4 d
tine penetration into the Hill Country was Saul's major concern as the first king of Israel. Toward the end of his reign, Philistine control in the Jezreel, Harod and Beth-shan Valleys appears to have threatened the livelihood of the northern tribes. It also divided these tribes from the rest of the Israelites in the Hill Country farther south.

The Philistines were in control of Aphek (in the Sharon Plain) and the main route to Beth-shan (via Megiddo and Shunem). The worst had happened, similar to the invasion of the Midianite herdsmen from the East and the Ammonite threat earlier in Saul's reign. Our task is to prepare carefully Map 7-4 for Saul's last battle on the slopes of Mt. Gilboa, just above En Harod, the spring SE of the city of Jezreel. At this same spring Gideon earlier had chosen his three hundred men.

MARKING

1. **Yellow HL on name** = **Aphek** (on the Sharon Plain), **Shunem** and **Jezreel** (just NW of Mt. Gilboa) and **Beth-shan**.

2. **Blue on dot**: The unconquered Canaanite centers from Map 6-1 = **Megiddo, Taanach, Ibleam** and **Beth-shan**. No doubt they had come to terms with the Philistines.

3. **Blue boxes around name**: Philistine camps = **Aphek, Beth-shan** and **Shunem**.

4. **Green border** (first with green pencil and then with green pen): This line is very subjective and is meant to show graphically the limits of Israelite control at the end of Saul's reign =

   a. A **solid green line** along the NE slope of Mt. Carmel, running just W of Jokneam and the dot of ha-Zorea, turning NE via the hyphen of ha-Zorea toward the small lake in the Jezreel Valley (N of Megiddo).

   b. Continue SE with a **broken green line** toward Ibleam, ending just E of the name Ibleam.

   c. Continue with a **solid green line**, turning W via the *th* of Dothan and on toward Socoh; just before Socoh turn S and SW, passing between Ebenezer and Aphek. (Never cross the main Coastal Highway.) Continue S between Gezer and Beth-shemesh, curving around E of Shaaraim and Azekah, and continuing SW via the final *th* of Moresheth-gath to pass off the map due S between Lachish and the map number.

   d. Shade in the E side of this *border* with a green pencil (about 3 mm./1/8 in. deep) showing Israelite settlement to the E, but leaving the Aphek-Megiddo route outside Israelite control.

5. **Yellow HL on route** = the route from Aphek to Beth-shan via Megiddo and Shunem.

6. **Blue write-in**: In the open area W of Gittaim and Ekron (SW part of map) = PHILISTINES.

7. **Sweeping blue arrows**:

   a. Two short lines both sides of the word Philistines, joining to form one arrow pointing to Aphek.

   b. From Aphek to Megiddo (running just W of the highlighted route).

   c. From Megiddo to Shunem.

   d. From Shunem to Beth-shan.

8. **Green write-in and arrow**: Just S of the word Philistines = DAVID'S MEN with a short green arrow from these words to the word Philistines.

9. **Green box around name**: Saul's camp was at a spring near here = **Jezreel**.

10. **Red confrontation mark**: Between Shunem and Jezreel = ✱ .

11. **Flight (green!) and chase (blue!) arrow** from the battlefield toward Mt. Gilboa.

12. **Green write-in**: Israelite tribal names. (Compare Map 6-6.)
    a. In open area just W of Bezek = MANASSEH.

    b. In open area between the names of Beth-shan and Hazor = ISSACHAR.

    c. In hills due N of Shunem (on N edge of map) = ZEB.

    d. On red road NE of En-dor (on N edge of map) = NAPH.

    e. In SW part of the map, in open area SE of Kiriath-jearim = JUDAH.

DISCUSSION AND READING

The scene is now set for one of the most vivid descriptions in the Old Testament. The   7-4 h
map before you makes it obvious why Saul was forced into action. The Philistines had
consolidated their control on the Coastal Highway and had expanded to the Jezreel
Valley and Beth-shan. This drove a wedge between tribes in the center of the country
and the northern tribes. If you remember the struggles portrayed on Maps 6-5 and 6-6
during the period of the Judges, it is easier to understand Saul's desperate move to
break the tightening Philistine grip on this region.

Saul mobilized his troops this time at Jezreel, a few miles from Bezek and a stone's
throw from En Harod. From Jezreel one gains total visual coverage of the Harod
Valley, the Hill of Moreh and much of the Jezreel Valley. Behind (to the SE) Mt.
Gilboa rises to almost 500 meters/1600 feet.

With this background, read **1 Samuel 28, 29 and 31**. You may want to glance at **1
Chronicles 10** also. Try to put yourself in the place of Saul. How do you suppose he
felt as he led his troops north again, this time to meet the Philistines? Why might he
have chosen Jezreel as his headquarters? Why did he make his desperate, last minute .
attempt to consult Samuel through the witch of En-dor? Why do you suppose the
men of Jabesh-gilead risked their lives to give Saul and his son Jonathan a proper
funeral? Do you see how David was spared from fighting Saul?

Before putting this map aside (to be finished in a later chapter), read **1 Samuel 14.47-
48 and 2 Samuel 1.17-27.**

S   M   M   7 – 1

This map was marked in Chapter One. Its significance in terms of the International
Coastal Highway was discussed and may be reviewed. The additional background gained
so far in Chapter Two underscores the extent of David's and Solomon's achievements in
the north. The Canaanite centers which had plagued earlier Israelite settlement and
development came under the control of Jerusalem. We are not told how this happened,
but the result is the same. Great building projects by Solomon at Megiddo and Hazor   7-1 c
demonstrate Israel's strong control of the north from Jerusalem. (Archeological evidence
shows that these projects were not nearly as extensive as Egyptian and Canaanite efforts.)

David's and Solomon's kingdoms extended far beyond the limits of Map 7-1. In fact, the
only limit of Israelite control shown on Map 7-1 is in the region of Phoenicia. Map 6-5

shows that the allotment of the tribe of Asher had extended to the Mediterranean Sea. Solomon, however, decided to turn part of this region over to Phoenicia in order to pay off his accumulated bills with Hiram, king of Tyre. Tyre appears to have come out on the poor side of the *deal*.

Israel's united and powerful position in the eastern Mediterranean would not last for long. With the death of Solomon the remaining ties enforced by David were broken. Surrounding nations were waiting on the sidelines, anxious and ready to throw off Israelite dominance. This would give them their chance again to exert their influence over those parts of the *playing board* nearest them. Each country's national interests would be promoted. Again *the mice could play!*

S M M   8 – 2

TITLE: **DIVISION OF THE KINGDOM AND SHISHAK'S CAMPAIGN IN ISRAEL (NORTHERN KINGDOM)**

DATE: **LATE 10TH CENTURY B.C.**

INTRODUCTION

The degree of stability and economic prosperity enjoyed under Solomon's rule was attained at the expense of the northern tribes and by means of Jerusalem's control over important routes which passed through these tribal territories. Egypt had also paid a heavy price for Solomon's glory. Due to its relatively weak position, it had no other choice than to relinquish principal trade routes to Israel. True, the Pharaoh's forces had penetrated the Coastal Plain and had destroyed Gezer, but he then gave it to Solomon, who rebuilt and fortified it.

8-2 a   With the death of Solomon the facade of stability in Israel crumbled. The land returned to the unstable conditions which had characterized it prior to the reigns of Saul and David. The north threw off the enforced control from Jerusalem. One of the leaders of the northern revolt was **Jeroboam**, son of Nebat from the village of Zeredah in Ephraim. Earlier, during the reign of Solomon, the king had noted that Jeroboam *was an ambitious fellow* and that the young man showed definite promise. Solomon therefore had him *take charge of all the forced labor [mandatory work on governmental building projects and roads] for the House of Joseph.* In such an important position in the north of the country (where the strong and independent minded House of Joseph resented Judah's rule over them) Jeroboam must have quickly gained experience, power and influence. The nationalistic spirit of the north and Jeroboam's growing threat to Jerusalem's control inevitably led to political intrigue. Finally, we read that *Solomon tried to have Jeroboam assassinated, but Jeroboam escaped, seeking political asylum in Egypt with Shishak, where he stayed until Solomon's death.* What is known about this period of internal scheming and unrest appears in 1 Kings 11.26-40. Much of the background which helps one to read *between the lines* is covered in Chapter Three.

Jeroboam and Pharaoh Shishak no doubt agreed on a number of issues. Although there is no record of a unified plan by the two, it is not difficult to imagine. Shishak certainly would not have discouraged Jeroboam in his quest for northern independence. The logic of *divide and conquer* no doubt was basic in Shishak's strategy.

After Solomon's death the flames of the separatist movement in the north could easily be kindled. This would quickly lead to division in Israel. Egypt would then attack, breaking Jerusalem's hold on the country. Two kingdoms (Israel in the north led by Jeroboam, and Judah in the south led by **Rehoboam,** Solomon's son) were far easier to take on than the unified administration (be it enforced) which had characterized Solomon's rule. This meant, of course, that Egypt would have to turn on its *friend* Jeroboam once he successfully had completed the revolution. However, such intrigue is not unusual in the politics of the region.

Once the land was weakened, Egypt would be in a much stronger position to extend   8-2 c
her influence again over the country or at least to reap some of the benefits of coastal and southern trade. In this process continued conflict between the Northern and Southern Kingdoms (Israel and Judah) was advantageous to Egypt since it would drain the energy of both sides. It is not strange, therefore, to read in 1 Kings 14.30 that *military conflicts [emerging from territorial and economic issues] were always break-ing out between Rehoboam and Jeroboam.* The details of these wars and skirmishes are studied in Chapters Three and Four.

In the marking below, the color green is reserved for Judah (the Southern Kingdom), and the color orange is used for Israel (the Northern Kingdom). A glance at Map 8-2 before marking reveals the location of the red names. It is in these areas that the action will take place. It will be drawn from both Biblical and Egyptian sources.

MARKING

1. **Yellow HL on name and green box around name**: Judah's capital = **Jerusalem.**

2. **Yellow HL on name and orange box around name**: Israel's first administrative centers built by Jeroboam on either side of the Jordan Valley = **Shechem** (center) and **Penuel** (Transjordan). Put a small orange number *1* above each orange box.

3. **Yellow HL on name and orange underlining**: Religious centers on the northern and southern frontiers of Jeroboam's kingdom = **Bethel** (center) and **Dan** (north).

4. **Green write-in**: The name of the Southern Kingdom in the open area between Kiriath-jearim and Manahath = JUDAH (large caps).

5. **Green border**: The extent of Judah's control after the division of Solomon's kingdom between Rehoboam (Solomon's son) and Jeroboam (leader of the north). Draw the border in green pencil first and then in green pen. = From the mouth of the Jordan River at the Dead Sea draw the border N up the river and then curve W via the *h* of Jericho; continue W and then NW to pass just N of the dot of Geba and via the *m* of Ramah and the *M* of Mizpah; continue W via the last *r* of し ·
Beth-horon and the second *b* of Rabbah (leaving the dots of Upper and Lower Beth-horon S of the border); curve around Gezer (just W of the dot and the name) and turn S to pass just E of Timnah and SW off the map (leaving Ekron and Gath to the W of the border). With a green pencil shade in the S edge of the border (Judah's side) with Jerusalem as its capital.

6. **Orange write-in**: The name of the Northern Kingdom in the open area between Shechem and Kh. el-Makhruq (S center) = ISRAEL (large caps).

7. **Blue write-in**: Surrounding nations.
   a. SW corner, just above the map number = EGYPT with a black arrow pointing SW from the name. (Before marking read the next item.)

   b. SW corner, just W of Ekron and Gath = PHILISTINES.

   c. NW corner following along the coastland S of Tyre = PHOENICIANS.

   d. In the NE corner of the map = ARAM-DAMASCUS (SYRIA). (This term refers to the Arameans in the regions around Damascus. *Aram* comes from Hebrew. Some translators prefer the term *Syrians* following Greek manuscripts of the Old Testament. *Aram* is used in all further marking.)

   e. SE corner just below Rabbath-ammon = AMMON.

   f. SE corner just E of Beth-diblathaim = MOAB with a small black arrow pointing SW from the name.

8. **Orange border**: The extent of Israel's control (Northern Kingdom) after its revolt against Jerusalem (first in pencil and then in pen).
   a. Border with Philistia = Beginning at the green border near Gezer, draw Israel's border NW (between Gittaim and Gibbethon) out to T. Qudadi on the coast. Shade in the E edge of this border with an orange pencil.

   b. Border with Phoenicia = Beginning on the N of the map draw Israel's border running S (beginning just E of the arrow of Sidon). Complete the border along the same line as the broken blue line on Map 7-1 (but in solid orange). With an orange pencil shade in the E edge of this border.

   c. Border with Aram-Damascus (Syria) = Starting with Mt. Hermon in the N (seen on the map which introduces Section One of the *SMM*), draw the border of Israel to the Sea of Galilee by curving to the E of Dan (about 1 cm./3/8 in.) and then S to the Sea of Galilee along the edge of the Golan Heights. The swamps and the Jordan River coming out of them should be just W of this border. Shade in the W side of this border with an orange pencil.

   On the SE side of the Sea of Galilee, begin the border again, connecting it to Nahal Yarmuk (the large river canyon E of the S tip of the sea). Follow the river NE and then curve around to the E and SE off the map. With an orange pencil shade in the S side of this border.

   d. Border with Ammon = Draw the border coming on the map from the E about 1 cm./3/8 in. N of the name Rabbath-ammon. Extend it W and S around the blue name of Ammon which has been written in (about 1.5 cm./3/4 in. inside the map) and then back to the E and off the map (between the dot of Rabbath-ammon and the dot of Bezer). With an orange pencil shade in Israel's side of this border (outside of Ammon).

9. **Yellow HL on route** =
   a. The Jerusalem-Shechem connection via Bethel.

   b. The Shechem-Penuel connection via Adam and Succoth.

READING AND DISCUSSION

Read **1 Kings 11.41-12.33**. This passage is basic to subsequent developments in the period of the Divided Monarchy (*SMM* Sections 8 and 9). The events mentioned in this passage reflect the markings thus far completed on Map 8-2. Some of the more important matters, especially those relevant to subsequent assignments, are discussed here.

Jeroboam needed a religious revolution in the north in order to offset the dominance   8-2 b
of Jerusalem. He therefore erected apostate shrines at both ends of his kingdom, at Bethel and Dan. Both sites had rich historical and religious roots. Dan, the gateway of the north, had always been noted for misguided religious fervor, as we shall see in   6-4 a
our study of Map 6-4 in Chapter Four. The shrine at Bethel (in the Hill Country of Ephraim north of Jerusalem) was especially significant if Jeroboam was to protect the southern flank of his kingdom. Jeroboam's explicit policy promoting religious apostasy in the north is remembered throughout the rest of Old Testament history as *the sin of Jeroboam.*

When Israel became independent from Jerusalem she gained control of major routes on the coast, in the north and in Transjordan (Map 8-2). The advantage of the two administrative centers (Shechem in the Hill Country and Penuel in Transjordan) is obvious. However, these routes were not only avenues of trade and commerce but also entrances for invasion. The defense of these territories and the exploitation of these routes would be the major concern of the kings of Israel for about 200 years. With this in mind, take a close look at the position of Israel in relationship to Philistia, Phoenicia, Aram-Damascus (Syria), Ammon and Moab. These nations, together with Judah and Edom (south of Moab), are *the mice who would play while the cat was away.* Their actions and reactions make the *playing board* spring to life during this most exciting period of Biblical history.

Our main concern on this map, however, is a much more immediate threat, that of   8-2 c
Shishak, pharaoh of Egypt. The Bible mentions his attack on the country. Note it now by reading **2 Chronicles 12.1-12.**

Shishak recorded his campaign on the walls of the Temple of Karnak (near Luxor) in Upper Egypt (only a hundred and thirty meters from the famous inscription of Thutmose III, which had been erected about 500 years earlier to commemorate victories in Canaan). Although partially destroyed, this list of names mentions sites along important routes in and around Israel and Judah. Shishak's objectives in this campaign should become obvious as you mark the cities in his list.

In the midst of these developments it appears that Jeroboam had second thoughts about the location of his capital. Shechem was much too vulnerable (as Chapter Three will make clear). A location which offered better security was that of Tirzah. This beautiful area was far less accessible from the Coastal Highway. Just when this move took place is not known. In 1 Kings 14.17 we are told that Jeroboam's wife left   8-2 b
Shiloh (where she had been consulting the prophet Ahijah) and returned to her home in Tirzah. Therefore, the move of Jeroboam to Tirzah must have taken place prior to 1 Kings 14.

MARKING

1. **Yellow HL on name and orange box around it:** Israel's second capital = **Tirzah** (center). Put a small orange number *2* just above the orange box.

2. **Red on dot:** Names on Shishak's inscription. (Scholars do not agree on the reconstruction of a few of the damaged names, nor on the order of the names in the various lines of the inscription. The names are listed here in order of geographical proximity for convenience.)

    a. The main entrance into the land from Egypt = **Gaza** (red on the arrow).

    b. Approaches to Jerusalem from the Coastal Highway. (Do you remember Solomon's defense of this region on Map 7-1?) = **Gezer, Rabbah/Rubute, Aijalon, Upper and Lower Beth-horon, Kiriath-jearim, Gibeon** and **Zemaraim.** (Jerusalem is not included in this list which reflects the fact that Rehoboam was able to negotiate with Egypt as recorded in 2 Chronicles 12.1-12.)

    c. The Shechem-Penuel connection = **Tirzah, Adam, Succoth, Mahanaim** (by Penuel), and **Penuel.** (Although Shechem is not listed here, it is likely that it was one of the names in the damaged portion of the inscription.)

    d. The Succoth-Megiddo-Coastal Highway connection = **Succoth, Zaphon** (the one on the Jordan River), **Rehob, Beth-shan, Shunem, Megiddo** (a fragment of a stele of Shishak was found here), **Taanach, Aruna, Borim, Gath** (by Borim), **Yaham** and **Socoh.**

3. **Yellow HL on routes =**
    a. From Gaza (off the map) to Ramah (N of Jerusalem) via Ashdod, Gittaim, Gezer and Gibeon and on to Ramah. Compare the same routes on Map 7-1. Note the fortification of Solomon in the region between Gezer and Jerusalem. Shishak's invasion appears to be exactly what Solomon had feared when he took Pharaoh's daughter as his wife and received Gezer (1 Kings 9.16-17).

    b. The Jordan Valley-Jezreel Valley-Coastal Highway connection =
    1) The route from Succoth to Beth-shan (via Rehob).

    2) The route from Beth-shan to Megiddo via Shunem.

    3) The route from Megiddo to Gittaim via Aruna, Socoh and Aphek.

4. **Sweeping blue arrows:** Shishak's possible campaign route =
    a. From the region of Gaza to Gezer (via Ashdod).

    b. From the region of Gezer to Gibeon.

    c. From the region of Tirzah to Succoth via Adam.

    d. From Zaphon to Aruna along the highlighted route.

DISCUSSION

8-2 c Although the exact order of Shishak's campaign is not known, the impact of the campaign on the Northern Kingdom is clear by the list of cities in the inscription.

Egypt achieved her objective by weakening Jeroboam's kingdom in three important regions:

    1. In the administrative centers of Tirzah and Penuel and probably Shechem;

    2. The strategic routes in the Jezreel and Beth-shan Valleys;

    3. Along the all important Coastal Highway, the key to north-south trade as well as the gateway from Socoh to Shechem.

It would take the Northern Kingdom some time to recover from this attack. Internal political rivalries would further weaken the new nation. Ultimately a new dynasty would arise at Tirzah, one which would grow strong enough to change the history of the north. Expansion by the Northern Kingdom in all directions would lead to conflicts in the regions of Transjordan, Bethel-Ramah and around Gezer. However, the most difficult area to control would be in the north, especially the routes leading from Aram-Damascus (Syria) to the Jezreel Valley via Hazor and via Beth-shan. These routes will dominate our study on the following map.

Before leaving Map 8-2, again carefully note frontiers with neighboring nations. From what you already know about the routes of the north, attempt to anticipate potential trouble spots along major routes. If you were a king in Israel, where would your priorities be in terms of expansion and control for trade and commerce? In other words, how would you rebuild in the wake of Shishak's campaign?

S M M   8 – 5

TITLE: ISRAEL'S RELATIONS WITH ARAM-DAMASCUS (SYRIA) AND SIDON

DATE: 9TH CENTURY B.C.

INTRODUCTION

Up to this point in our study of the north we have become acquainted with various features in and around the Jezreel Valley and the region of Hazor. Map 8-5 expands our horizons to important connections between these regions and the Transjordanian Highway. Israel (the Northern Kingdom) coveted these routes as she expanded.

Farther north another nation in the region was gaining strength and beginning to threaten Israel's northern frontier. That nation was Aram (Syria). The king of Damascus was at the head of this Aramean coalition. Diplomatic contacts between Israel and Aram turned into serious military confrontation by the mid-ninth century B.C. In the latter half of this century, Damascus was able to break through Israel's defenses and to take control of both the Transjordanian and Coastal Highways. The events of Maps 8-5 and 8-7 evolved within this ninth century setting.

MARKING
    1. **Brown write-in:**
        a. W center of the map (just above the binding) on the mountain in the open area just SE of Libnath = MT. CARMEL.

    b. E center of the map, just S of the large river canyon which runs from the E edge of the map to the Jordan River just S of the Sea of Galilee = NAHAL YARMUK (in two lines about halfway between the Jordan River and the E edge of the map). Add a small brown arrow pointing N to the river canyon.

2. **Orange border**: Israel's northern borders as seen on Map 8-2. (Sketch with a pencil, draw with a pen and then shade the proper edge with an orange pencil.)
    a. Border with Phoenicia (with space to write in 5b below).

    b. Border with Aram (from Mt. Hermon to the Sea of Galilee and the border up the Yarmuk River).

3. **Orange write-in**: In the open area between Tirzah and Kh. el-Makhruq = ISRAEL (large caps).

4. **Yellow HL on name and an orange box around it**:
    a. Israel's second capital = **Tirzah** with a small orange number *2* just above the box.

    b. Israel's third and final capital = **Samaria** with a small orange number *3* just above the box.

5. **Blue write-in**:
    a. In the NE corner between Damascus and the title = ARAM (in large caps).

    b. In the NW part of the map, in the open area just E and SE of the name Sidon = PHOENICIANS (written in large caps on the same angle as the coast). Leave space S of Tyre to write in more information later.

6. **Yellow on name and blue box around it** = **Sidon** (NW corner) and **Damascus** (NE corner).

7. **Yellow HL on routes**:
    a. The route printed in red coming along the coast from Sidon (N off the map) to Acco and then on to Megiddo.

    b. The route printed in red from Aram (NE corner) to Megiddo (via Dan, Abel-beth-maachah, Hazor and Chinnereth) and the route N of Abel-beth-maachah and Ijon (N off the map).

    c. The route from Ramoth-gilead (E edge of the map) to Megiddo via Lo-debar, Beth-shan and Shunem. (This route connects Beth-shan and the Jezreel Valley with the Transjordanian Highway via the region S of Nahal Yarmuk. This region is called Lower Gilead. (Do not write this name on the map.)

    d. The route coming onto the E side of the map (N of Nahal Yarmuk) and passing through (Upper) Aphek and near Lo-debar to Beth-shan. This route connects Beth-shan and the Jezreel Valley with the Transjordanian Highway via the region just N of Nahal Yarmuk. This region is called Lower Golan. (Do not write this name on the map.)

    e. The route connecting Beth-shan with Samaria via Jezreel, Ibleam and Geba.

    f. The route connecting Megiddo with Samaria via Aruna, Gath and Socoh.

DISCUSSION

In the decades between Jeroboam's takeover of the north and the expansion of the
House of Omri from Samaria, political turmoil characterized the Northern Kingdom.   8-4 d
The House of **Baasha** came to power in Tirzah at this time.

In the midst of this turmoil territorial disputes between Israel and Judah (in the region   8-5 a
of Bethel and Ramah north of Jerusalem) forced Judah to seek help from the king of
Damascus. This help to Judah came in the form of an invasion of Israel by Damascus
via Dan and Chinnereth.

READING
1 Kings 15.16-22.

MARKING

1. **Yellow HL on name and red on dot** (or arrow) = **Dan, Ijon, Abel-beth-maachah** and
   Chinnereth.

2. **Brown write-in on dry yellow background with red underlining:** by comparing Map
   8-5 with Map 6-5 find *N. Ammud* W of Chinnereth. Just SW of *N. Ammud* =
   LAND OF NAPHTALI (in two lines on a background which has been highlighted in
   yellow).

3. **Red underlining on name** = **Hazor** with SOLOMONIC CITY DESTROYED (small
   caps) written in black just beneath Hazor (in two lines).

4. **Brown write-in:**
   a. In the NE part of the map just SW of the word Aram = UPPER GOLAN (in two
      lines). Between Lower and Upper Aphek = LOWER GOLAN.

   b. On the mountain (part of which is seen on the N edge of the map), NE of Dan
      and W of the name Damascus = MT. HERMON (small caps).

   c. In the N of the map, W of the name Kedesh = UPPER GALILEE (in two lines).

   d. In the SE part of the map in the open area SE of the name Jabesh-gilead =
      GILEAD.

5. **Sweeping blue arrows:** Campaign of the king of Damascus against the northern
   approach to Israel =
   a. From the word Aram to Ijon (S of Mt. Hermon and the highlighted route and
      then NW of Dan to Ijon).

   b. From Abel-beth-maachah to Hazor.

   c. From Hazor to Chinnereth.

DISCUSSION

The invasion of the king of Damascus into Northern Israel during the early ninth cen-   8-5 a
tury B.C. illustrates the importance of the northern approaches to the land via Dan,
Hazor and Chinnereth. The valley running northeast from Abel-beth-maachah is an
important approach not seen on Map 8-5. The city of Ijon controls that part of the

valley which adjoins Abel-beth-maachah. Since Ijon is the first name mentioned in both accounts of the invasion (1 Kings 15.20 and 2 Chronicles 16.4), the Aramean forces probably came from that direction. Another possible route from Damascus is via Upper Golan, passing just south of Mt. Hermon before descending to the region of Dan.

Both of these routes (from the north and from the northeast) lead to the strategic area around Dan. This region could be called the *Gateway to Galilee*. Even after the tribe of Dan had gone into captivity (three centuries after the invasion described above), **9-7 a b** Jeremiah spoke of conquerers (Babylonians) entering the land through this gateway.

> *A voice is making an announcement from Dan . . . Take it seriously.*
> *Warn the nations [along the country's main highways] . . . The shock*
> *troops are coming from a distant country . . . Why aren't we doing*
> *anything? Get mobilized! Come into the fortified cities . . . You can*
> *hear from Dan the snorting of their horses. The sound of their stallions*
> *neighing shakes the whole land.*   (Jeremiah 4.15-16; 8.14-16)

The region of Dan slopes gently to the south, into a major area of difficulty, the swamps of the Huleh Basin. These swamps can be seen on Map 8-5, but even better on Map 1-8 and on *SMA*. They lie just above sea level. The basin is outlined on the east by slopes rising to Upper Golan (about 750 meters/2400 feet above sea level). On the west the hills of Upper Galilee rise even more abruptly. Mt. Hermon (2700 meters/ 9000 feet) dominates the entire region.

Water from these surrounding regions flows into the Huleh Basin and is augmented by underground springs which line its edge (shown by the solid blue dots seen clearly on Map 1-8 and *SMA*). The swamps formed by this abundance of water form a major obstacle to travel in the region. South of the swamps the drainage from the basin has been blocked by a higher region of volcanic lava. This basaltic dam is called the *Rosh Pinna Sill* (Map 1-8). In the geological past the Jordan River has cut a path through the higher ground at least twice. The all-important site of Hazor controls this very strategic area.

It is not difficult to understand the strategic importance of the regions of Ijon and Dan and the Golan Heights (Upper Golan to the north by Mt. Hermon and Lower Golan, the region just north of Nahal Yarmuk). The strip of land between the swamps of the Huleh Basin and the hills of Upper Galilee provides a narrow passageway from the region of Dan and Abel-beth-maachah to Hazor. In addition to controlling this northern approach, Hazor also commands the natural eastern approach. Descending from the Upper Golan this approach crosses the Jordan River just south of the Huleh Basin and then ascends a gentle slope to Hazor. From Hazor the highway crosses the Rosh Pinna Sill before descending to the shores of the Sea of Galilee (about 200 meters/660 feet below sea level) and the site of Chinnereth.

While Hazor is not mentioned in the list of cities conquered by the king of Damascus in the early ninth century B.C., archeological evidence indicates that the Solomonic city was destroyed about this time. It would be the task of a later king of Israel (Ahab of the House of Omri) to rebuild and to expand Hazor's fortifications to meet the growing threat of the Arameans unified under Damascus.

Omri, Ahab's father, reigned six years from Tirzah. His development policy appears to   8-5 b
have included a number of important actions.   There was first the move of Israel's
capital to the far more advantageous position of Samaria with its convenient link to
the important International Coastal Highway. This move improved Israel's commercial
connections with cities of Phoenicia.   Phoenicia (especially Tyre) was becoming the
major maritime power on the Mediterranean Sea. The Sidonians were part of this
movement.

Ahab, Omri's son, carried his father's policies to their logical conclusion, as the famous
sixteenth chapter of 1 Kings recounts.

READING
1 Kings 16. 23-33.

MARKING
1. **Sweeping blue arrow with blue write-in** on and below the arrow: In the territory of
   Phoenicia = An arrow from the region of Tyre to the region of Acco with CUL-
   TURAL/RELIGIOUS INVASION written in blue on the arrow, and POLITICAL/
   ECONOMIC OVERTONES written in blue beneath the arrow (all in small caps).

2. **Blue arrow** = Just E of the highway from the region S of Acco to the region just E
   of Jokneam (crossing the border of Israel). Just above this arrow write JEZEBEL
   (blue). Below it write MARRIES (black) and AHAB (orange).

DISCUSSION
Foremost in Israel's strategy was no doubt the goal of controlling part of the Trans-   8-5 c
jordanian Highway and the trade routes which connected it to Phoenicia. However,
the commercial and political alignment of Israel and Sidon (in Phoenicia) was a threat
to Aramean interests. This may have helped the king of Damascus to consolidate the
Arameans under his leadership. In any event, a stronger Damascus ultimately led to
Aramean expansion in Transjordan.   This expansion was reflected in a growing
Aramean military presence along the same Transjordanian Highway coveted by Israel.

The economic and political interests of Aram, Phoenicia and Israel and the resulting
military conflicts between Aram and Israel created one of the most illustrative periods
of history ever seen on this part of the country's *playing board*. Once the goals of the
players are defined, the *game* becomes clear and the decisions of the various leaders are
understood (but not necessarily condoned). It is in this context that Elijah ministered,   8-5 d
attempting to preserve and to restore the worship of the one true God, the Lord. (His   8-1 b
ministry is studied on Map 8-1.)

One of the first events of this period was the siege of Israel's capital, Samaria, by the   8-5 e
king of Damascus (1 Kings 20.1-20). This time (about 856 B.C.) the king of Damascus
was able to penetrate into the heart of Israel. In the thirty years since the campaign
from Dan to Chinnereth the Aramean military machine had grown stronger. This
trend soon forced Israel to take serious action in order to protect her northern frontiers.

MARKING
1. **Blue arrow:** Syrian advance = From Dothan to Samaria (W of the route) with
   SYRIAN SIEGE written in blue beneath the arrow.

2. **Flight (blue) and chase (orange) arrow** = From Geba (by Samaria) to Beth-haggan.

DISCUSSION

8-5 f   Shortly thereafter (about 855) Israel overcame Aram at another important gateway to the country, on the Beth-shan—Lower Golan (Aphek) route. This route comes from the Transjordanian Highway and passes just north of Nahal Yarmuk via Lower Golan and (Upper and Lower) Aphek. The region is flat and fertile except for steep slopes which descend to the Yarmuk and Jordan River valleys. It can best be seen in the northeastern part of Map 1-9. If Aram were to penetrate the Jordan Valley south of the Yarmuk River, nothing would stop her from continuing south to the Beth-shan Valley. As was seen on Map 4-9 this valley is an important road center. It would serve as a staging area for an attack up the Harod Valley to Jezreel and beyond. In short, Aramean control of this region would break Israel's economic hold on the north.

It was in this context that Israel met the Aramean challenge. The battle probably took place on the flat land (the plain) just southeast of the Sea of Galilee, perhaps near the outlet of the Yarmuk River from the hills of Transjordan. Defeated on the battlefield, the Aramean forces retreated to Aphek. The name Aphek is preserved at the site of (Upper) Aphek. However, substantial remains of the period have been found at the site of En Gev or (Lower) Aphek. It has been suggested that the name Aphek applied to both of these sites. The one on the shore (En Gev) is called *(Lower) Aphek*. while the one dominating the area from the heights is designated *(Upper) Aphek*. (Lower) Aphek has been chosen as the probable site of the Aramean retreat and the Israelite siege. In the subsequent negotiations substantial economic concessions were made by the king of Damascus similar to those earlier given to the Aramean merchants in Samaria. These concessions allowed Israel to expand her trade into the heart of Aramean Territory, to Damascus itself. This development should not be surprising since economic factors were the cause of the conflict in the first place.

MARKING

1. **Sweeping blue arrow**: Aramean advance = From the word Aram to (Upper) Aphek.

2. **Sweeping orange arrow**: Israel's advance = From Beth-shan to the NE (to a point about 1 cm./3/8 in. N of Lo-debar). Note the next point before marking.

3. **Red confrontation mark**: On the highlighted route about 1.5 cm./5/8 in. N of Lo-debar = ✳ .

4. **Yellow HL on name and red on dot** = Aphek in (Lower) Aphek/En Gev.

5. **Flight (blue) and chase (orange) arrow** = From the red confrontation mark to (Lower) Aphek.

READING

1 Kings 20.22-34.

DISCUSSION

8-5 g   It appears that the serious Assyrian threat from the north drew local nations into a common front for a few years in the mid-ninth century (853 B.C.). The Bible alludes to this in 1 Kings 22.1: *For three years there was a lull with no hostilities between Aram (Syria) and Israel.* Israel and Aram joined forces with others to meet Shalmaneser III of Assyria farther north. However, once this threat was reduced (but not eliminated), local powers again resorted to force to settle disputes and territorial claims.

During the last half of the ninth century B.C., Judah and Israel cooperated in a number of campaigns in northern and southern Transjordan. Damascus was becoming stronger in the north, while in the south the Moabite independence movement was claiming important territories. It was in both of their national interests to keep these regions free from Aramean domination and to discourage Moabite nationalism.

One of the early examples of such a cooperative military venture took place late in   8-5 h
853 B.C. at a key point on the Transjordanian Highway, due east of Beth-shan. The region is called Lower Gilead (see Map 1-9), and the site is Ramoth-gilead, just off the eastern edge of Map 8-5. In the strategic region of Ramoth-gilead, the Transjordanian Highway (off the map) connects with the important route from Beth-shan. From Ramoth-gilead this route makes its way west, descending along the ridges to Lo-debar and across the Jordan Valley to Beth-shan. Like the Aphek route via Lower Golan, the route from Ramoth-gilead protects the strategic center of Beth-shan. The issue this time, however, was Israel's claim that the region of Ramoth-gilead actually belonged to her, probably under an agreement negotiated after the Battle of Aphek. In the rush to meet the Assyrian threat the Aramean withdrawal was apparently not completed. Israelite command of this position would allow her to reassert her control in this part of Transjordan, thwart Aram's expansionist policy, and thereby protect Israelite tribes in the north and in Transjordan (Map 6-1). The campaign had important economic and political overtones and demanded a unified effort on the part of Israel and Judah.

Jehoshaphat, the king of Judah, came to Samaria to confer with Ahab, king of Israel, concerning these matters. Ahab's famous statement in 1 Kings 22.3 reflects his concerns: *Do you realize that Ramoth-gilead should be under our control, and yet we are doing nothing about taking it from the king of Aram?* The full account of this impressive meeting in Samaria and the amusing yet tragic dialogues make very interesting reading in 1 Kings 22.2-28.

The campaign which resulted from this conference cost Ahab his life. The attempt to check Aramean southern expansion in Transjordan failed, and the region and its routes were open to Aramean infiltration. This only encouraged Moabite nationalism farther south. Israel's and Judah's positions in Transjordan were dangerously weakened.

MARKING

1. **Sweeping green arrow and write-in**: Jehoshaphat's trip to confer with Ahab = From the region of Shiloh (S edge of the map) via Shechem to the region of Samaria. Beneath this arrow write JEHOSHAPHAT (green) CONFERS WITH (black) AHAB (orange) in three lines.

2. **Sweeping orange arrow**: Israel's forces advance to Ramoth-gilead = From the region of Lo-debar to the name Ramoth-gilead (S of the highlighted route) with AHAB written in orange along this arrow (on the northern side).

3. **Sweeping green arrow**: Judah's forces advance to Ramoth-gilead = A green arrow parallel to the orange arrow from Lo-debar to Ramoth-gilead, but running just S of it with JEHOSHAPHAT written in green along this arrow (on the northern side of it).

4. **Sweeping blue arrow**: Aramean forces advance to Ramoth-gilead = From the word Aram along the E edge of the map (the actual route is farther E) to a point just off the map, due E of the *R* of **Ramoth-gilead**.

5. **Red confrontation mark**: Just off the map to the E of the arrow of Ramoth-gilead = ✳ .

6. **Flight arrows:**
   a. Three or more flight arrows in orange from Ramoth-gilead toward Lo-debar (running along just N of the highlighted route and pointing W).

   b. Three or more flight arrows in green from Ramoth-gilead toward Lo-debar (running along just S of the sweeping green arrow and pointing W).

7. **Yellow HL on name = Ramoth-gilead.**

READING
1 Kings 22.29-40.

DISCUSSION
The events which are brought together on this map come from the early and mid-ninth century (890-850 B.C.). The routes reflected in these events constitute the main approaches to the country from the north and northeast. Each of these gateways (via Dan and Hazor, via Aphek in Lower Golan and via Ramoth-gilead and Lo-debar in Lower Gilead) was important for Israel's political and economic security.

Aram's policy in the region was to unify her own control in the Golan and in Gilead as a prelude to her southern expansion along the Transjordanian Highway. Anything which weakened Israel, either on her frontiers or internally, aided Aram in accomplishing her goal.

In order to strengthen your control of this important part of the *playing board*, open your *SMA* and compare it with Map 8-5. Carefully work out how these routes pass through various geographical features and areas of difficulty. It may be of interest to you that today the country of Jordan controls the area of Gilead (south of the Nahal Yarmuk and east of the Jordan River). Modern Syria controls the northeast corner of the map (and much more territory to the north and northeast off the map). The northern half of Upper Galilee and the valley north of Ijon belong to Lebanon.

Since 1948 the regions of the Jezreel Valley, the Beth-shan Valley, Lower and part of Upper Galilee and the Huleh Basin (with the region of Hazor and Dan) have been a part of modern-day Israel. Anyone who has kept abreast with the events of the latter half of the twentieth century can apply the lessons of the past to the contemporary scene.

LEGEND
This is the first map you have marked on which the number of campaigns calls for a method of identification. It is helpful to **write in certain *SCS* subjects** (such as *a*, *e*, *f* and *h*) in **small black letters, each in a small circle**. Position each letter where it is visually linked to the event portrayed on the map.

S M M   8 − 1

TITLE: ELIJAH'S MINISTRY

DATE: MID-9TH CENTURY BC

INTRODUCTION
The House of Omri received special note in our study of Map 8-5 because of the events during the reign of Omri's son, Ahab. The interrelationships of politics, economics and religion introduced on Map 8-5 form the basis of our current study. Preparatory marking of Map 8-1, therefore, sets the scene for the life and times of Elijah the prophet.

MARKING
1. **Orange border**: Israel's northern border =
   a. Border with Phoenicia (as on Map 8-2).

   b. Border with Aram (as on Map 8-2).

   c. Border with Ammon (as on Map 8-2).

   d. Border with Moab: Draw the border along the largest river canyon E of the Dead Sea (Nahal Arnon), starting by the Dead Sea and moving E (below Aroer) and continuing E to the edge of the map. Shade in the N side of the border with an orange pencil.

2. **Blue border**: Limit of Philistine control.
   From T. Mikhal on the coast SE to the dot of Gittaim (running just E of the name T. Qasila), continuing S just under the name Gezer and between the names Timnah and Azekah, bending SW via the *n* of T. El-Areini, the *H* of T. el-Hesi, just left of Kh. Huj, to the dot of Yurza and off the map between the coast and the map number (8-1). Shade in the W side of this border with a blue pencil.

3. **Green border**: Northern limit of Judah's control.
   From the mouth of the Jordan River (N end of the Dead Sea) bending NW (just S of Jericho) and W of the *G* of Geba, NW via the *h* of Ramah and between the dots of Zemaraim and Mizpah, W via the *n* of both Beth-horons and SW via the *b* of Rubute to the blue border between Gittaim and Gezer. Shade in the S side of the border with a green pencil.

4. **Blue write-in**:
   a. W of Ekron = PHILISTINES.

   b. NW corner of map, E of Achzib = PHOENICIANS (on a slight angle).

   c. NE corner of the map, S of the name Damascus = ARAM.

   d. E edge of the map, in open area between Rabbath-ammon and the orange border = AMMON.

e. SE corner, E of Kir-haresheth = MOAB; underline the name in **orange** to show Israelite control over Moab during most of this period.

5. **Green write-in**: right center of map in open area just W of Kiriath-jearim and Beth-zur = JUDAH.

6. **Orange write-in**: left center of map in open area NW of the name Samaria = ISRAEL.

7. **Boxes around names** of capital cities:
   a. Green box = Jerusalem.

   b. Orange box = Samaria.

   c. Blue box = Damascus.

8. **Brown write-in**:
   a. In Transjordan between the two names of Mahanaim, N and S of the large river canyon (Nahal Jabbok) = GILEAD.

   b. By comparing this map with Map 8-5 = NAHAL YARMUK (small caps with an arrow pointing N to the river canyon).

   c. In the SE corner of the map in the open area between Kir-hareshet and the orange border = NAHAL ARNON (small caps with small arrow pointing N to the river canyon which served as the N limit of Moabite settlement for most of this period).

DISCUSSION

8-1 b c

Elijah, a ninth century prophet in Israel, is one of the most colorful and important figures of the Old Testament. His name means *the Lord is God*. Elijah witnessed many of the events which have been discussed on Map 8-5. His ministry is recorded in the latter part of the book of 1 Kings and the opening chapters of the book of 2 Kings (noted in the *SCS* of Map 8-1).

8-5 c

During this period Israel's stability and economic growth were based largely upon the ability to exploit her unique geographical position between Transjordanian trade routes and Mediterranean markets, i.e., a position between sea and desert. Israel's alliance with Judah, her control of key regions along the Transjordanian Highway (Gilead, Moab and the Medeba Plateau) and her ability to check Aramean expansionism were basic to her foreign and economic policies. Ahab's alignment with the maritime Phoenician city of Sidon meant that Israel's exports could reach Mediterranean markets which were being exploited by Phoenician fleets. A Phoenician-Israelite cultural and trade alliance was in the interests of both countries. Such an agreement appears to have been sealed by Ahab's marriage to Jezebel, the Sidonian princess. This insured Israel's trade benefits and paved the way for one of the most affluent periods in the country's history. The writer of 1 Kings characterizes this period when he speaks of *all that he [Ahab] accomplished [during his reign], including the house which he built with ivory [decorations] and all the cities which he had [re]built.* (1 Kings 22.39)

In spite of the economic advantages, the Phoenician-Israelite alliance resulted in serious repercussions for Israel:
   1. Israel's exploitation of the east (Gilead and Moab) was met by a hostile Aramean reaction, both in Transjordan and in Israel itself. Israelite forces were called upon to protect her interests and to expand her control in these areas.

   2. Jezebel, the Sidonian princess, brought with her a strong religious/cultural influence. This led the Northern Kingdom and its king even further away from a dependence on and a worship of the God of Israel.

> *What Ahab, son of Omri, did in God's sight was worse than all those*
> *who had preceded him. In fact, he did not even think twice about*
> *continuing in the bad precedents set by Jeroboam, son of Nebat*
> *[over a half century before]. Marrying Jezebel, daughter of*
> *Ethbaal, king of the Sidonians [Phoenicians], he went even further —*
> *he worshipped Baal and bowed the knee before him [the*
> *Phoenician fertility god of the storm and rain]. He put up an*
> *altar to Baal, a Temple of Baal which he constructed in Samaria.*
> *Ahab also produced the Asherah [the mother goddess, perhaps*
> *symbolized by a sacred post]. Thus Ahab went from bad to worse*
> *reaping the anger of the Lord, the God of Israel, more than any*
> *of the kings who had preceded him.* (1 Kings 16.30-33)

With official blessing the cult of Baal and Asherah quickly grew until we hear of *the 450 prophets of Baal and the 400 prophets of Asherah who eat at Jezebel's table.* (1 Kings 18.19)

   3. In this period of apostasy Israel's economic growth and material affluency caused internal decay, characterized by greed, intrigue and a lack of concern for others. Elijah's words to Ahab in the context of one of the incidents preserved for us from this period sum up prevailing attitudes: *Do you murder only to make it your own?* (1 Kings 21.19). Centuries before, Moses had issued a serious warning in regard to the economic, religious and political implications of such a lifestyle in this *Land Between.*

> *Be careful in case you say to yourself, 'My power and the might of my*
> *own hand have made me successful! Remember the Lord your God, since*
> *it is He who gives you strength to succeed in order to carry out His*
> *covenant which He swore to your fathers . . . But in the event that you*
> *totally forget the Lord your God and pursue other gods, worshiping them*
> *and bowing the knee to them, I warn you right now, you will be wiped*
> *out. Like the nations which the Lord is destroying before you, in the*
> *same way will you be destroyed for not taking seriously the voice of*
> *the Lord your God.* (Deuteronomy 8.17-20)

MARKING AND READING

Read the passages below and **highlight in yellow** the names in the text which appear on Map 8-1. The exact location of some names or features in the passages are not known and, therefore, do not appear on the map. The *Brook Cherith* may be located in the mountains east of the Jordan River across from Jericho. Between the Jordan River and the name *Nebo* write in small black caps *ELIJAH TAKEN UP.* While reading, it may be helpful to number the order of the incidents on the map in some form. The contest between Elijah and the prophets of Baal can be shown by **circling in red** the entire region of Mt. Carmel. Mt. Carmel's position (between Israel and Phoenicia) was the ideal location for such a contest. Note the sarcasm in Elijah's mockery of the worship of the Phoenician Baal (the storm god who each year was supposed to bring rain and new life to the earth) during this severe drought.

Passages to read: 1 Kings 17-19, 21, 22.51-53; 2 Kings 1.2-2.14. These texts portray special events in the life of Elijah. The greater context of his ministry (including military operations in the north and in Transjordan) under Ahab and his sons, Ahaziah and Jehoram, is noted in the *SCS* of Maps 8-5 and 8-6.

DISCUSSION

8-5 i
Elijah's ministry began and ended *across the Jordan,* probably in the region east of Jericho and the River Jordan. Here the dramatic exodus of Elijah occurred. Centuries before, the children of Israel had received their instructions from Moses in this same region, after he had led their exodus from Egypt. Here they celebrated their first Passover in the land of Canaan. Before entering the land, however, Moses charged them to renew their covenant with the Lord their God.

Given this impressive historical and theological setting, it is not surprising that in New Testament times John the Baptist (the new Elijah) chose this region for a major part of his ministry, preaching a message of repentance to Israel. It was in this context that Jesus of Nazareth came to John to be baptized and to begin His ministry.

The echo of Elijah's message is heard throughout the Old and the New Testaments. The lives of Moses, Elijah and Jesus are intertwined in the closing verses of Malachi's prophecy (4.4-5) and in the Gospel of Matthew (11.2-19). The strong link between these three figures is vividly illustrated in Jesus' transfiguration (most likely on Mt. Hermon, almost 200 kilometers to the north, up the Jordan Valley). There, *two men, Moses and Elijah, suddenly were seen having a discussion with Him [Jesus]; these [three], appearing in glory, spoke of His exodus which was going to be completed in Jerusalem.* (Luke 9.30-31)

8-5 d
The reaction which Elijah's message received in the Northern Kingdom in the days of Ahab served as an illustration for Jesus when he spoke in Nazareth at the beginning of his Galilean ministry. From a hill above the city one sees the Mediterranean Sea (in the direction of Phoenicia), Mt. Carmel, the Jezreel Valley, the Transjordanian highlands and the hills of Samaria. On a clear day Mt. Hermon can be seen to the northeast, a vivid reminder of Damascus and the routes linking it to the Jezreel Valley. All of these played a part in Elijah's ministry. It should, therefore, not be surprising that Jesus drew lessons from Elijah's ministry as he began his own.

> *Take to heart what I am telling you. No prophet is recognized in the region from which he comes. Think about Elijah, for example. There were certainly many Israelite widows in those days [of God's judgment] when the drought lasted three and a half years and food was almost impossible to find throughout the entire country — but Elijah was sent to none of them. He **was** sent to a widow, however — to a woman from Zarephath in the region of Sidon [the homeland of Jezebel!].*   (Luke 4.24-26)

S M M   8 – 7

TITLE: **ELISHA'S, J(EH)ORAM'S, JEHU'S AND ISRAEL'S RELATIONS WITH ARAM (SYRIA) AND ASSYRIA**

DATE: **MID-9TH CENTURY B.C.**

INTRODUCTION (Geographical review)

Open Map 8-5 and review the main routes which enter the Jezreel Valley from the north and east:

1. From the regions of Dan, Hazor and Lower Galilee.

2. From Aphek in Lower Golan (the region just north of Nahal Yarmuk) via Lo-debar in the Jordan Valley to Beth-shan and Shunem.

3. From Ramoth-gilead on the Transjordanian Highway via Lower Gilead (the region south of Nahal Yarmuk) to Lo-debar, Beth-shan and Shunem.

These three entrances are illustrated by events which occurred in the first eighty years of Israel's history (Northern Kingdom). The *SMM* maps studied so far in this chapter have helped you to understand various strategic regions and sites along these routes. Much of the importance of these three routes lies in the fact that they connect the Jezreel Valley (and therefore the Coastal Highway) to the Transjordanian Highway and the northern approaches of the country. The red road in the southeast part of Map 8-5 is one branch of the Transjordanian Highway. Although it runs off Map 8-5 by Ramoth-gilead, its importance, together with Damascus which absorbs it, should never be forgotten.

Damascus longed for control of the Transjordanian Highway and the connecting routes to the Coastal Highway. Israel (the Northern Kingdom) coveted the same routes and strived to control the Transjordanian Highway from the region of Nahal Yarmuk in the north to Moab in the south (seen on Map 7-1). Map 8-7 again illustrates Israel's priorities in Transjordan. Some background marking will prepare for later military maneuvers on Map 8-7.

MARKING (Map 8-7)

1. **Brown write-in:**

   a. NW part of map = MT. CARMEL (as on Map 8-5).

   b. SE of Sea of Galilee = NAHAL YARMUK (as on Map 8-5).

   c. In Transjordan = NAHAL JABBOK (as on Map 6-6).

2. **Green border of Judah, write-in and box:**

   a. From the mouth of the Jordan River (north end of Dead Sea), bending NW and passing just S of Jericho, ascending W and NW along the wadi (canyon with blue broken line in it) which runs just N of the dot of Geba, passing just N of the name Ramah and S of the dot of Zemaraim, descending W via the last two letters of the two Beth-hor**ons**, slightly SW to the edge of the map near the tiny blue lake; shade in the S side of this border.

b. In the open area E of Kiriath-jearim = JUDAH.

c. Box around Judah's capital = **Jerusalem.**

3. **Blue border of Phoenicia and write-in:**
   a. NW corner of map = same border as on Map 8-5; shade in the W side of border.

   b. In the open area W of Mishal = PHOENICIANS.

4. **Blue border of Moab and write-in:**
   a. From the NE corner of the Dead Sea (not Sea of Galilee) running slightly NE around (just N of) the names Heshbon and Bezer to the E edge of the map; shade in the S side of the border.

   b. In the SE corner of the map, written from E to W = MOAB.

5. **Orange border of Israel with Aram and write-in:**
   a. N of the Sea of Galilee, just E of the name Dan (as on Map 8-5).

   b. From the S end of the Sea of Galilee and E up Nahal Yarmuk (as on Map 8-5).

   c. Shade in the appropriate side of both borders (as on Map 8-5).

   d. In the open area between Tirzah (center and Adam (on the Jordan River) = ISRAEL.

   e. Small box around Israel's capital = **Samaria.**

6. **Orange border of Israel with Ammon:**
   Beginning on Nahal Jabbok on the E edge of the map and running W to the river just W of the (red) Transjordanian Highway and there turning sharply S, running S and then bending SE to join the border with Moab near the name Bezer; shade in the N and W side of the border.

7. **Blue write-in:**
   a. Just NW of Rabbath-ammon = AMMON.

   b. In the NE edge of the map, just W of the word *Kingdom* in the title = ARAM.

DISCUSSION (A historical summary of events on Map 8-7)

Israel's power and influence in the mid-ninth century B.C. culminated under Ahab. His reign, however, was not without internal problems and in-fighting with local regional powers. During the same period the Assyrian Empire in Mesopotamia was gaining strength and again extending its control over the strategic region west of the Euphrates River (about 300 kilometers/185 miles north of the region of Dan). These developments had serious implications for the nations around Israel. Local powers, including Israel, were wise enough to stop their feuding briefly and organize a unified front against this rising Assyrian threat. They met Shalmaneser III, king of Assyria, in battle near Qarqar on the Orontes River in the territory of Hamath in 853 B.C. and stopped him from advancing southward. Once the Assyrian threat was temporarily halted, the league of smaller nations dissolved, and the local skirmishes resumed.

8-5 g

At the end of Ahab's reign rebellion broke out in Transjordan. Moab was able to   8-6 c
extend her control north of the Nahal Arnon, her previous natural border. (Compare
Maps 8-1 and 8-7.) Ammon may also have taken advantage of the situation. Aram,
who had suffered a setback at the Battle of Aphek (Map 8-5), appears to have maintained her control of Ramoth-gilead on the Transjordanian Highway.   From this
position she may have encouraged *liberation movements* in Moab. We shall see that at
one point Aramean forces again entered the country and besieged Samaria, the capital
of Israel!

In 841 B.C. a coup in Damascus brought the new dynasty of Hazael to power, and a
coup in Israel brought the new dynasty of **Jehu** to power. In Jehu's coup, Jehoram   8-7 d
(king of Israel and Ahab's son), Jezebel (queen mother and princess of Phoenicia), the
royal family and administrative officers of Israel were all murdered, together with
Ahaziah (king of Judah) and his royal family. Consequently, Israel's alliances with
Phoenicia and Judah were seriously damaged if not destroyed altogether. In the midst
of these local headlines Assyria was on the move once again under Shalmaneser III.
In 841 B.C. he broke through northern defenses and campaigned briefly in Aram,
Golan, Galilee and Phoenicia.

It is clear that between 853 and 841 B.C. Israel witnessed a tremendous upheaval with
disastrous effects on her political and economic life. Recovery would not begin until a
half century later.   In the meantime (841 to 806 B.C.) Damascus (now ruled by   9-1 d
Hazael) took the opportunity to seize the Transjordanian Highway from Israel. Damascus also appears to have had a free hand along the strategic entrances to Galilee
and the Jezreel Valley. We even find Aramean troops campaigning along the Coastal
Highway as far as the edge of Philistia. What a change from the times of Ahab a few
decades earlier when Israel controlled the north and much of Transjordan! During
these decades Elisha ministered, witnessing the wrath of Hazael, king of Damascus, and
hoping that the once affluent but apostate Northern Kingdom would learn from this
tragic experience.

In His sermon at Nazareth (described in the final paragraphs of the *SMM* 8-1 discussion),
Jesus drew upon this period of Aramean/Syrian oppression for another illustration.

> *There were many Israelite lepers in the time of Elisha the prophet, but none*
> *of them was cleansed — only Naaman, the Syrian [the commander of the*
> *Aramean/Syrian armed forces]!*   (Luke 4.27)

ELISHA'S CALL AND MINISTRY

DISCUSSION, READING AND MARKING
Elijah (Elisha's mentor) had seen the effect of success and affluency upon the apostate
Northern Kingdom in the days of Ahab. His ministry had culminated in the great
contest on Mt. Carmel (Map 8-1). However, even this appears to have had little impact
on official policy and public opinion in Israel. Fleeing south to Judah and beyond to
the Wilderness, Elijah discovered God's strength in weakness in that *calm, quiet voice.*
In this important crisis in his life he received new marching orders, instructions which
would initiate one of the most difficult periods in Israel's history. Read these orders in
1 Kings 19.11-21.

8-7 a Passages which relate events in the life of Elisha the prophet are given in the *SCS* for
this map (8-7a). They are intertwined with the history of the Northern Kingdom
during the period. While these passages may be too long to read now, they do present
perspectives of the prophet and his times. Names of cities which occur in Elisha's life
are listed here and should be highlighted on Map 8-7:

1. **Abel-meholah**, Elisha's home town (1 Kings 19.16).

2. **Bethel, Gilgal** and **Jericho**, towns associated with the end of Elijah's ministry and
the beginning of Elisha's ministry (2 Kings 2). East of Gilgal and Jericho, across
the Jordan River, Elijah was taken up and Elisha formally began his work. In the
open area just east of the Jordan River from Jericho write (in black) ELIJAH
TAKEN UP.

3. **Samaria**, capital of Israel, and Mt. Carmel, where Elisha sometimes lived (2 Kings
2.25; 4.25).

4. **Shunem** and **Dothan**, places visited by Elisha (2 Kings 4.8-10; 6.11-14).

8-7 c 5. **Damascus**, where Elisha anointed a new king of Syria (2 Kings 8.13).

6. **Ramoth-gilead**, where Elisha's servant anointed a new king of Israel.

As a disciple of Elijah, Elisha witnessed the weakening of Israel's control on Transjor-
8-5 h dan. First there was the victory of Aram (led by Ben-hadad) at Ramoth-gilead. In
8-6 c that battle Ahab was killed. Then came the revolt in Moab (under Mesha) when this
former vassal of Israel extended her control north along the Transjordanian Highway.

ARAM'S (SYRIA'S) INCURSION AND SIEGE OF SAMARIA

DISCUSSION, READING AND MARKING
8-7 b Early in Elisha's own ministry (about 843 B.C.) the Aramean threat (under Ben-hadad)
reached the very gates of Samaria. This long and difficult siege brought out the worst
in the city's previously indulged population. The king (Joram, or also called Jehoram)
held Elisha directly responsible for the situation, perhaps partially because of the
healing of Naaman, the commander of the Aramean army (2 Kings 5).

In order to see the serious implications of Ben-hadad's siege on Samaria, some marking
is necessary.
1. **Yellow HL on route:**
   a) The route from Beth-shan to Samaria via Jezreel and Dothan.

   b) The route from Samaria to Beth-shan via Shechem, Tirzah and Rehob.

2. **Red circle around name = Samaria** including its orange box.

3. **Sweeping blue arrow and blue write-in** = From the area of Ibleam (between Jezreel
and Dothan) to the red circle, running the arrow just below the HL route. Write in =
ARAMEAN SIEGE along the arrow.

4. **Blue flight arrows** = A few from Samaria to the region of Tirzah via Shechem
showing the Aramean retreat after deliverance as described in 2 Kings 7.

It was at this point in his ministry (c. 840 B.C.) that Elisha went on a special (and secret ?) mission to Damascus. His assignment altered the course of events from bad to worse for Israel. Read about this mission in **2 Kings 8.7-15.** Elisha lived to see the fulfillment of his own bitter prophecy in later decades as the following passages relate. (Maps 8-1 and 6-1 show the regions and tribes mentioned.)

> *During that period [the reign of Jehu] the Lord began to trim off parts of Israel. Hazael [king of Damascus] attacked Israel's borders from every angle east of the Jordan: throughout the land of Gilead [comprising the territory of] Gad, Reuben and Manasseh even from Aroer on the edge of Nahal Arnon [in the south] to Gilead and [beyond Nahal Yarmuk] to Bashan [in the north].*   (2 Kings 10.32-33)

> *[Because of Jehu] the Lord became very displeased with Israel and kept handing them over to Hazael, king of Aram, and to Ben-hadad, the son of Hazael [a later Ben-hadad]. However, Jehoahaz [son of Jehu] sought after the Lord, and the Lord took note of him, for He had seen the pressure on Israel, pressure being put on them by the king of Aram.*   (2 Kings 13.3-4)

JEHU'S REVOLT AND THE FALL OF THE HOUSE OF OMRI

DISCUSSION, READING AND MARKING
In the light of Aramean expansion and the rebellion in Moab it should be no surprise   8-7 d that in 841 B.C. forces from Israel and Judah again united, as in the days of Ahab and Jehoshaphat (Map 8-5). Joram (Jehoram) of Israel was, after all, the cousin of Ahaziah of Judah through the intermarriage of the families of Ahab and Jehoshaphat.

This time Hazael, the new king of Damascus, was threatening the north from the strategic crossroads at Ramoth-gilead. It was Jehu's task to hold back the Aramean forces while his king, Joram, was recuperating in Jezreel from injuries sustained in his campaign. At this moment (841 B.C.) Elisha the prophet again played an important role. Some of the details of this exciting but terrible juncture in Israel's history were discussed in the historical summary above. It is now time to read the details in **2 Kings 8.25-10.36.** (A condensed version in 2 Chronicles 22.1-9 adds some interesting comments.) The following marking may be done before or after reading the account.

1. **Yellow HL on route** = From Ramoth-gilead (just off the map) W to the Jordan Valley and Beth-shan.

2. **Red confrontation mark:** Just off the E edge of the map in the direction of the arrow for Ramoth-gilead = ✳ .

3. **Sweeping orange arrow** = From the Jordan Valley (E of Beth-shan) to the red confrontation mark of Ramoth-gilead, running just S of the HL route.

4. **Write-in along orange arrow** = AHAZIAH (green) and J(EH)ORAM (orange).

5. **Blue circle and sweeping blue arrow:** Circle = **Aram**; arrow = From the circle S and just off the E edge of the map to the red confrontation mark.

6. **Sweeping red arrow and write-in** showing Jehu's mad drive = From Ramoth-gilead along the N side of the HL route to Jezreel via Beth-shan with JEHU written in somewhere along the arrow.

7. **Red on dot = Jezreel.**

THE CAMPAIGN OF SHALMANESER III OF ASSYRIA

DISCUSSION AND MARKING

8-7 e The king of Damascus had reason to rejoice at developments in Israel, his southern enemy. The powerful Assyrian army had been staging attack after attack on his northern border. Finally in 841 B.C. the change of governments in Damascus and Samaria appears to have given the Assyrians the opportunity they needed. In that year Shalmaneser III, king of Assyria, speaks of the following campaign:

> *In the eighteenth year of my rule [841 B.C.] I crossed the Euphrates for*
> *the sixteenth time. Hazael of Damascus put his trust upon his numerous army*
> *and called upon his troops in great number, making the mountain Senir [the*
> *Hermon range] . . . his fortress. I fought with him and inflicted a defeat*
> *upon him, killing with the sword 16,000 of his experienced soldiers. I*
> *took away from him 1,121 chariots, 470 riding horses as well as his camp.*
> *He disappeared to save his life. I followed him and besieged him in*
> *Damascus, his royal residence. I cut down his gardens. I marched as far*
> *as the mountains of Hauran [northeast of Map 8-7], destroying, tearing*
> *down and burning innumerable towns, carrying booty away from them*
> *which was beyond counting. I marched as far as the mountain of*
> *Ba'lira'si which is by the sea [Mt. Carmel] and erected there a stela with*
> *my image as king. At that time I received the tribute of the inhabitants of*
> *Tyre, Sidon and Jehu, son of Omri. [The use of 'Omri' is a common mistake*
> *in Assyrian inscriptions.]*   (Black Obelisk)

It appears that despite the damage done in the area, Damascus survived this campaign. However, archeological evidence shows that Hazor was destroyed at this time. In 838 B.C. Damascus was again besieged but held its own again. Finally in 806 B.C. Damascus fell to the Assyrians.

In spite of a lull of some decades in the early eighth century, the fact was nevertheless clear: the northern approaches to the country had again become *international territory*. Internal Assyrian politics or campaigns elsewhere allowed another period of expansion and prosperity in Israel (under Jeroboam II), but the end was in sight. In the eighth century other prophets would deal with the political realities of their day both at home and abroad, as Elijah and Elisha had done in the ninth century. Few people or leaders would listen, but this would not change the realities which they proclaimed.

In order to show this first Assyrian campaign in the north, marking must be done on the very northern edge of the map.

1. **Red circle around name = Damascus.**

2. **Blue write-in with circle around it:** In very NE corner of the map = ASSYRIA.

3. **Sweeping blue arrow** = From the blue circle of Assyria to the red circle of Damascus; then from the red circle due W to the name Hazor; then SW and W along the red and black routes and sweeping N toward Sidon and Tyre via Mishal; another blue arrow should branch off and point directly to Mt. Carmel (not following any route printed on the map).

4. **Blue write-in**: On the blue arrow above Chinnereth = SHALMANESER III.

LEGEND
Yellow HL names = places in the ministry of Elisha.

S M M   9 — 4

TITLE: CAMPAIGNS & PROVINCIAL ORGANIZATION OF TIGLATH-PILESER III
           OF ASSYRIA

DATE: THE 730'S B.C.

DISCUSSION (Historical background and summary, also studied later on Map 9-1.) Few details are known of the difficult years of oppression by Hazael, king of Damascus. Jehu now reigned in Israel (841-814 B.C.). This new House of Jehu would last for almost a century, longer than any other.

Hazael's son, Ben-hadad III (as he is sometimes called), continued the oppressive   9-1 d
policy of his father. Jehu's son, **Jehoahaz** (814-798), had to contend with Aramean control of major northern routes. Israel was at the lowest ebb in the 125 years since Jeroboam had led the breakaway movement from Jerusalem. The prophet Amos would later look back with scorn on this period when Damascus *threshed Gilead with iron threshing sledges.* 2 Kings 13.7 tells us that during this time *the forces of Jehoahaz dwindled to barely fifty horsemen, ten chariots and ten infantry squads [or 10,000 infantrymen]. This was because the king of Aram had brought havoc upon them, working them down until they became like dust under foot [or at threshing].* It was probably tempting for veterans to recall the *good old days* of Ahab (House of Omri!) when Israel ruled the north and controlled much of Transjordan.

About 806 B.C. an event took place which could be considered as both *good news and*   9-1 e
bad news. Assyria (this time under Adad-nirari III) captured Damascus, that long sought after prize which was the key to the Transjordanian Highway and the northern approaches to the country. This immediately took the pressure off Israel and allowed her to enter a period of reconstruction. 2 Kings 13.5 states it clearly: *But then the Lord provided Israel with a deliverer, and they were freed from Aramean control. Again, as in the past, the people of Israel were able to settle down [in their land].*

The economic and military rebuilding of the nation culminated in the reign of **Jeroboam II** (as he is known by historians to distinguish him from the first king of the Northern Kingdom, Jeroboam, son of Nebat). In the days of Jeroboam II (793-753 B.C.) Assyria was preoccupied with internal problems and campaigns elsewhere. This (together with a weakened Damascus) allowed the greatest expansion in the history of the Northern Kingdom. The writer of 2 Kings underscores this positive turn of events.

For the Lord understood the bad times through which Israel had passed —
and they had been bitter years indeed; not bound and yet not free, and
[worst of all] Israel had been totally helpless [to remedy the situation].
                                        (2 Kings 14.26-27)

9-1 j   From 753 B.C. (the death of Jeroboam II) until 740 B.C. five rulers struggled to take
control of the governmental reins of Israel!   Finally a strong-willed leader named
Pekah took over the entire country.   Soon he joined forces with Damascus, now ruled
by Rezin.   This time both countries understood the principle that *united we stand,*
9-4   *divided we fall.*   A quickly expanding Assyria was on the move again under the famous
Tiglath-pileser III.   He efficiently exercised a policy of conquering lands, deporting
their populations and setting up a new Assyrian administration.   He could not be
ignored by nations standing in his way.   Already Damascus and Samaria had been
forced to pay tribute to keep this Assyrian leader at bay.

Tiglath-pileser III saw the Damascus-Samaria alliance as a direct threat to Assyrian
control in the region.   He knew of the attempt being made to force Jerusalem into this
alliance (as related in Chapter One).   You will remember that Map 9-4 shows one of
the most famous moments in Old Testament history, the terrible events of 734-732
B.C.   During those years Tiglath-pileser III took control of 1) the Coastal Highway, 2)
Galilee and Gilead, and 3) Damascus and strategic centers on the Transjordanian
Highway.   Details of these campaigns can be reviewed in Chapter One (*SMM* 9-4).

All of the routes studied thus far in Chapters One and Two had high priority in the
minds of these calculating Assyrian invaders.   Although we would like to possess more
information on conquered cities and deportation figures, there is sufficient to make us
tremble.

Later Assyrian kings and conquerors would pass this way, some to besiege and to
conquer Samaria itself.   However, none would leave more of an impact than Tiglath-
pileser III.   It was he who turned the world upside down and left no room for speculation as to who would ultimately control the region which we have studied so carefully
in this chapter.

Isaiah, the prophet of this period in Judah, reflects the attitude of the times.   The
secure, affluent and complacent days of Jeroboam II were still fresh in the memory of
the inhabitants of the north.   The campaigns seen on Map 9-4 must have caused some
bitter questions for that superficially religious population who had been indulged only
a few decades earlier.

He will roam around, miserable and hungry. His hunger will turn into rage,
and he will curse his king and his God as he looks up. But then, looking
around the country again, he will only find trouble and distress, an anxious
gloom, and [a world] driven to despair.   (Isaiah 8.21-22)

Those who wish to read the startling promise attached to these somber words can find
the continuation of Isaiah's prophecy in Isaiah 9.1-7.

REVIEW AND CONCLUDING ASSIGNMENT

We have come to the end of Chapter Two in the *SMM* assignments. While preparing each map, or after its completion, you were advised to relate the geographical and historical study to the *SMA*. In the following review, the use of this map is again advisable. Make every attempt to see the region as a whole as well as the individual parts which make up that whole. The *Introductory Schematic of the Playing Board* and *The Land Between* schematic and other helps in Appendix II are helpful references for this review.

This chapter opened by noting strategic priorities of the Eighteenth and Nineteenth Egyptian Dynasties in and around the Jezreel Valley. The regions and routes around Megiddo and Beth-shan and connections to the Coastal Highway were especially significant (Maps 4-7 and 4-9).

In the same period, the importance of Hazor and routes connecting it with the Jezreel Valley were illustrated by Joshua's campaign in the north and by the battle of Deborah and Barak against the Canaanites in the area (Maps 5-6 and 6-5). Events in the lives of Gideon and Saul underscored the importance of the link between the Jezreel Valley and Transjordan via Beth-shan. Thus international powers (Egypt) and local populations (Canaanites, Midianites, Philistines and Israelites) all placed a high priority on these strategic entrances and exits to the Jezreel Valley, links from south to north and from east to west.

There were great military and economic advantages for a local power (such as Judah under David and Solomon) to control these vital links (Map 7-1). Once this monopoly was broken by internal discord and outside interference (Map 8-2), the security of the region became the major job of the Northern Kingdom. With the consolidation and expansion of the Arameans under the king of Damascus, the routes radiating northeast and east from the Jezreel Valley became the battlefield between Israel and Aram (Maps 8-5 and 8-7).

Pressures from the north by Assyria finally culminated in the full-scale campaigns of Tiglath-pileser III. These events rocked the region and meant that the north would never again be the same. Assyria was on the move toward its ultimate goal, control of Egypt.

As you look at the *SMA* take time to identify all of the entrances to the Jezreel Valley studied in this chapter. Try to find the following lines of communication through natural passes as they avoid areas of difficulty:
1. From the Coastal Plain via the three *Carmel Passes* (Jokneam, Megiddo and Dothan).

2. From the Plain of Acco (the port of Galilee to the west) via the Kishon Pass (between Mt. Carmel and Lower Galilee) or via Hannathon and the Shimron Pass.

3. From the gateways of Dan and Hazor, skirting just west of the Sea of Galilee and ascending to a natural crossroads just west of Adamah, and entering the valley via either the Plain of Tabor or the Shimron Pass.

4. From the Transjordanian Highway to Beth-shan (via Aphek in Lower Golan or via Lower Gilead and Lo-debar) and from there into the valley via the Harod Valley.

There are various ways of counting these entrances. However, their number is not significant. What is important is that the routes leading into the valley come from nations and regions far beyond this small *Land Between*.

There is perhaps no better way to summarize the centrality of the Jezreel Valley than by quoting from George Adam Smith's classic work, *The Historical Geography of the Holy Land*. In his treatment of the valley (which he calls *Esdraelon*, the Greek form of *Jezreel*) he makes the following statement:

> With our eyes on these five entrances [into the Jezreel Valley] and remembering that they are not merely glens into neighbouring provinces, but passes to the sea and to the desert — gates on the great road between the empires of the Euphrates and Nile, between the continents of Asia and Africa — we are ready for the arrival of those armies of all nations whose almost ceaseless contests have rendered this plain the classic battleground of Scripture. Was ever an arena so simple, so regulated for the spectacle of war? Esdraelon [Jezreel] is a vast theatre, with its clearly-defined stage, with its proper exits and entrances.[1]

The only additional comments on this coveted region and its approaches come from the Scriptures themselves. Psalm 89 appears to have been written in a period when the oppressor's hand was heavy on the land. The psalmist prefaces his complaint with an overture of praise for the One who rules over all. He then recites evidence for this fact: the covenant and promises made to David and the fact of David's successful campaigns. After all, did not David conquer and control the strong Canaanite cities and routes of the north as Mt. Hermon (above the gateway of Galilee) and Mt. Tabor (on the edge of the Jezreel Valley) could well testify? Where, then, was the Lord of All now, when the country's defenses were in ruins and the International Highway overrun with foreigners?

> To You belong the heavens as well as the earth,
> You alone established the entire inhabited sphere.
> The north and the south were Your creations,
> **Tabor** and **Hermon** joyously praise Your name . . .
> At that time You spoke to the faithful in a vision, and said,
>> 'I have given support to a brave hero,
>> I have raised up one chosen from among the people,
>> I have found David, My servant,
>> With My holy oil have I anointed him . . .
>> I will crush his foes before him,
>> I will strike down those who hate him.
>> My faithfulness and my constant care will be with him,
>> Through My name his success will be assured . . .'
> Yet You have breached all his defenses,
> You have left his fortifications in ruins.
> All who pass by plunder him,
> And he has become the laughingstock of his neighbors . . .
>
> Where then, O Lord, is that constant care
> You promised to David in Your faithfulness?
>> (Psalm 89.11-12, 19-21, 23-24, 40-41 and 49)

---

[1]George Adam Smith, *The Historical Geography of the Holy Land*, 25th ed. rev. (London: Hodder and Stoughton, 1931), p. 390.

In a later difficult period Jeremiah refers to certain mountains in the Jezreel Valley to re-mind Egypt that the armies of Babylon marching along these northern routes would ultimately reach the Nile.

> *As I live, says the King,*
> *The Lord Sabaoth is His name,*
> *As sure as **Tabor** [stands out] among the mountains*
> *And **Carmel** [sticks out] in the sea, shall one come.*
> *Pack up your bags for the trip into exile,*
> *O Daughter of Egypt, you sitting [duck]!*   (Jeremiah 46.18-19)

The New Testament speaks little of the strategic importance of the Jezreel Valley. It is taken for granted.   However, one reference in Revelation 16.12-16 makes up for silence elsewhere:

> *The sixth angel emptied his bowl on the great river, the Euphrates. Its*
> *water was dried up so that a way could be prepared for the kings of the*
> *East. Then, out of the mouth of the dragon, out of the mouth of the*
> *beast, and out of the mouth of the false prophet I saw three unclean*
> *spirits [emerging] like frogs. Actually they are demonic spirits,*
> *making miracles, which go out to the kings of the whole world to*
> *mobilize them for war on the great day of God the Almighty.*
> *(Watch out! I am coming like a thief . . .) And they mobilized*
> *at the place called in Hebrew '**Armageddon**' [the Hill of Megiddo].*

The entire discussion as to the interpretation of this passage pales before the fact that the Jezreel Valley was understood as one of the great crossroads of the ancient world, a place where local and international powers met in this *Land Between*.

SAMARIA AND SURROUNDING REGIONS

CHAPTER THREE

INTRODUCTION

The assignments in this chapter concentrate on an area commonly known as *Samaria*. This name is actually the Greek form of the Hebrew *Shomeron*. Originally it designated a new capital city built in the ninth century B.C. by Omri, king of Israel. When the Northern Kingdom fell to Assyria (722 B.C.), the conquerors converted the region around the former capital into an Assyrian province and applied the name of the city to the region. This name continued to be used throughout later periods. It is not totally correct to use the name for the region prior to the period of Assyrian administrative control. However, Samaria remains as a generic regional term, and as such it is used on *SMA* and on maps in Section One of the *SMM*.

The following *SMM* maps are studied in this chapter. An asterisk indicates that the map is completely marked in other chapters of the *Guide* and is only discussed in this chapter.

4-2 Political centers from the Execration Texts
*4-3 The Patriarchs: Abraham and Isaac
*4-4 The Patriarchs: Jacob and Joseph
4-8 The Amarna Age: kings of Canaan and interrelations
5-1 Kings of Transjordan and Canaan
*5-3 Campaigns in Transjordan and entry into Canaan
*5-4 Entry into Canaan and initial campaign: Jericho and Ai (Detail of 5-3)
*6-1 A preview of regional settlement problems (in the book of Judges)
6-2 Tribal territories and city-lists in Canaan
*6-5 Northern confrontation: Deborah and Barak
*6-6 Eastern confrontation: Gideon and Jephthah (Ehud = 6-7)
6-7 Internal confrontation: Abimelech and the Benjaminite civil war (and Ehud)
7-3 Samuel's ministry
*7-4 Saul's beginning and end (partial marking)
*7-7 David's reign
*7-1 David's census and Solomon's reign
*8-2 Division of the kingdom and Shishak's campaign in Israel
8-4 Judah-Israel border disputes; Ethiopian threat to Judah (partial marking)
*8-5 Israel's relations with Aram-Damascus (Syria), Sidon; internal apostasy under Ahab and Jezebel
*8-1 Elijah's ministry
*8-7 Elisha's, Jehoram's, Jehu's and Israel's relations with Aram (Syria) and Assyria
*8-8 Approaches to Samaria and regional settlement reflected in the Samaria Ostraca
*9-4 Campaigns and provincial organization of Tiglath-pileser III of Assyria
9-5 Fall of Samaria; Assyrian expansion under Shalmaneser V and Sargon II

GEOGRAPHICAL PREVIEW OF SAMARIA AND SURROUNDING REGIONS

Your first assignment in this chapter is a geographical preview. The main objective of this preview is to introduce important regional features and natural routes in and around Samaria. This will help you to relate new information studied in this chapter to what you have learned in previous chapters. Remember, your first priority is to learn the *playing board* as defined by regional features.

In the following exercise you will explore the *SMA*, comparing it with the regional maps in Section One of the *SMM* and with other selected *SMM* maps. Locate and fix in your mind important regional features (mountains, valleys, nahal or wadi systems, swamps, sands, etc.) and natural routes. Time spent now in careful regional study provides an important basis for map study later in this chapter. It is very helpful to have someone read this section out loud (geographical preview) so that you may be free to concentrate on the *SMA* and other maps. Use any or all of the maps listed for each regional subject. At the end of each discussion try to glance through all the maps relevant to that region for a quick review noting the regional features and natural routes discussed.

With this in mind you are ready to begin the geographical preview of Samaria. Open your full color *SMA* so that Samaria and regions surrounding it are before you. Note that on the west and north, the hills and valleys of Samaria are surrounded by regions which carry international routes studied in Chapters One and Two. To the east the Jordan (Rift) Valley defines Samaria. To the south deeply eroded canyons in the Hill Country tend to cut off Samaria from Judah (Judea).

MARKING (all on *SMM* 8-8)

1. **Yellow HL on name** = **Aphek** (SW center), **Gath** (NW center), **Dor** (NW corner on the coast), **Megiddo** (N), **Beth-shan** (NE corner), **Dothan** (N center), **Shechem, Tirzah, Samaria** (all near center), **Adam** (E center), **Jericho** (SE corner), **Bethel** (between Jericho and Aphek).

2. **Brown write-in:**
   a. In open area between the coast and the International Highway (W of Gath and N of Aphek) = PLAIN OF SHARON.

   b. In open area E of Megiddo = JEZREEL VALLEY (two lines).

   c. In open area between Gath, Dothan and Samaria = WESTERN SAMARIA (one line).

   d. In open area E of Tirzah = EASTERN SAMARIA (one line).

   e. In open area between the cities of Samaria and Hazeroth = CENTRAL SAMARIA (one line).

   f. In open area N of Bethel = HILL COUNTRY OF EPHRAIM (three lines).

DISCUSSION

1. **Western perspectives** (*SMA* studied together with *SMM* Maps 1-5, 1-6 and 8-8.) Locate the **Plain of Sharon** and the features which define it:

   a. In the south **Nahal Yarqon** (Yarqon River) which begins at Aphek and runs to the sea. (Note the name printed in blue in the Mediterranean Sea on *SMA* and *SMM* 1-5.)

   b. In the north **Nahal Tanninim** (Crocodile River) which runs around the southern tip of Mt. Carmel, just southeast of the coastal city of Dor.

   c. In the west the **coastal sand dunes** (dotted gray areas) and coastal ridges above the coastline (brown lines along the coast).

   d. In the east the **edge of the hills** of Western Samaria.

   e. On *SMM* 8-8 note coastal ridges, sand dunes (blown inland from the beaches of the Mediterranean Sea) and the streams and swamps behind them.

Much of the **Plain of Sharon** consists of rolling low hills of brown-red sands, oriented in a north-south direction. Swamps are common in the low-lying areas. In antiquity the region was considered inhospitable because of the difficulty of travel through it and the presence of a forbidding oak forest and briers.

> *I am a narcissus of Sharon, a lily of the plain;*
> *As a lily in the brier, such is my true love among women.*
> (Song of Solomon 2.1-2)

The shepherd, who knew well how to lead his sheep through the rough and dry Wilderness, did not dare to venture far into this region. The foreboding nature of Sharon gave the prophet the illustration he needed to highlight his message: *And Sharon shall become a land of grazing for flocks!* (Isaiah 65.10)

The **International Coastal Highway** through Sharon (printed in red on *SMM* 8-8) hugged the edge of the hills of Samaria. There travel was easier, and rich alluvial soil (carried down from the hills) provided the villagers with abundant farmland, particularly in the north near Socoh, Yaham, Gath and Borim. (This Gath is not the famous *Gath of the Philistines* farther south.)

Branching off from the International Coastal Highway by Aphek, routes climbed into the hills, both northeast to Shechem and southeast to Bethel and beyond to Jericho. Because of deeply eroded and difficult canyons these routes had to stay on or near the top of ridges. You may want to locate these ridges on *SMA* by comparing it with routes on Map 8-8.

Near Socoh on the International Coastal Highway north of Aphek an important valley emerges from the hills of Western Samaria. It is called **Nahal Shechem**. In contrast to the other *nahals* this one can be called a true valley. In the gently ascending floor of this valley the farmer still plows and plants, and the merchant easily ascends to Nablus, the modern Arab city near ancient Shechem. These sites are located at the center of the majestic hills of Central Samaria. Using Map 8-8 find this convenient natural entry on *SMA* (Socoh to Shechem).

Still farther north on the International Coastal Highway, the rich agricultural region of Gath (Gath in Sharon) guards the approach to the important Dothan Pass. This pass leads through low hills to the **Dothan Valley**, then descends to Ibleam and enters the Valley of Jezreel from the south. Once in the Jezreel Valley the route must proceed north to the actual site of Jezreel before descending via the Harod Valley to Beth-shan. Map 8-8 shows the features along this route well. Locate them and the Dothan Pass on *SMA*.

The other great passes in the area (to Megiddo and to Jokneam just off *SMM* 8-8) add to the strategic nature of northern Sharon (note Map 4-7). It is not surprising that in a later period Herod the Great (in the years just prior to the birth of Jesus) took advantage of these factors when he had a great port city built here. To do this Herod's engineers had to overcome the difficulties of the Sharon coastline. He named it Caesarea after the emperor himself. However, once completed it linked his kingdom even more closely to Rome. Both the Coastal and the Transjordanian Highways (in addition to the central Hill Country itself) found in Caesarea an open door to the Mediterranean and to *the ends of the world*. The Apostle Paul, who knew Caesarea well, sailed from this port to make his *appeal to Caesar* (*SMM* 12-10).

North of Sharon rises **Mt. Carmel**, a sentinel along the eastern Mediterranean coastline. Its promontory was known as *the Antelope's Nose* to Egyptians who raided the area four thousand years ago. The top of Mt. Carmel was proverbial for its lush though not extremely tall forests. It was Mt. Carmel that Elijah suggested for that great contest between the Canaanite god Baal and the God of Israel. On Mt. Carmel the Assyrian conqueror Shalmaneser III erected his victory stele. It was to the forests of Mt. Carmel that Elisha retreated during those difficult years of Aramean (Syrian) oppression under Hazael.

Mt. Carmel together with Sharon are examples not easily ignored by the prophets. Greenery there continued to flourish in the summer months when much of the land was dry and thirsty. Mt. Carmel and Sharon gave a glimpse of what the great forests of Lebanon (in Upper Galilee and farther north) or the high and fertile plain of Bashan (east of the Golan Heights) were like. Only God's severe judgment or an upside down world could change their foliage!

> *From Zion the Lord roars; from Jerusalem He projects His voice;*
> *The oases of the shepherds wilt and the top of Mt. Carmel dries up!* (Amos 1.2)

> *Look! Brave men shout complaints in the street;*
> *Those coming with messages of peace weep bitter tears;*
> *The highways are in ruins; traveling has come to a halt.*
> *Agreements are treated as scraps of paper; there is no respect [for law] in*
> *the cities; no one shows concern for his fellowman.*
> *As it wilts the land is depressed! As it fades Lebanon is shamed!*
> *Sharon has become like the dry desert plain [Arabah] and Bashan*
> *and Mt. Carmel are leafless!*   (Isaiah 33.9)

In a brighter strain the prophet used the same region to illustrate better days for the land.

91

The Wilderness and the arid spaces exult;
  the dry desert plain [Arabah] rejoices and sprouts!
Like a daffodil it bursts forth in bloom and rejoices — such joy and singing!
The glory of Lebanon is given to it! The splendor of Carmel and Sharon!
They shall see the glory of the Lord; the splendor of our God!   (Isaiah 35.1-2)

2. Northern perspectives (*SMA, SMM* 1-6, 1-7, 1-9, 8-8 and 9-4)

The regions to the north of Samaria were the object of study in Chapter Two. The strategic value of these regions and of the routes which traverse them is best seen on Map 9-4. In Assyria's push south along international routes Samaria (*Israel* on Map 9-4) was reduced to the Hill Country between the Jordan (Rift) Valley, the Plain of Sharon and the Jezreel Valley. If you need to review this area and its relationship to the northern approaches, compare the central part of Map 9-4 with your *SMA*.

3. Eastern perspectives (*SMA, SMM* 1-10, 1-11, 5-3, 5-4, 6-6 and 8-8)

The Jordan (Rift) Valley is the eastern limit of Samaria. Beyond it lies the uplifted **Dome of Gilead**. Nahal Jabbok (Wadi Zarqa) has cut a deep canyon through this region, passing Penuel, Mahanaim and Succoth, as it descends to the Jordan River near Adam.

The higher area in **Gilead** (shown in yellow-brown color on the *SMA*) rises to over 1,000 meters/3,300 feet. Since the Jordan River by Adam is about 300 meters/1,000 feet below sea level, the difference between the highest parts of the Dome of Gilead and the Jordan River is about 1,300 meters/4,300 feet in the space of a few kilometers! Distinct differences between the highland and the Jordan Valley are also evident in regard to climate and cultivation. On *SMM* 6-6 you will also remember in the story of Jephthah that the *Shibboleth/Sibboleth* distinction in pronunciation became a life or death matter for the Israelites from Manasseh and Ephraim returning home (to the region we are calling *Samaria*) from Gilead. This aspect of the story illustrates the actual physical separation of the Gileadites from Israelites living west of the Jordan.

As you scan the **Jordan (Rift) Valley** east of the Jordan River, other canyons and stream beds become apparent. These not only carry water down to the plains; they also bring rich soil. Thus the plains just east of the Jordan River represent areas of rich farmland. This strip of flat land (east of the river and between it and the mountains) also makes for a certain ease of north-south travel. This region and the slopes behind it (from here to the Dead Sea) became known by the specific administrative name of *Across-the-Jordan* or *Beyond-the-Jordan*. In New Testament times it came into Greek as *Perea*. Map 1-10 shows modern roads in the region, while Map 6-6 presents the natural routes or lines of communication between main cities.

Your next task is to take control of **Tirzah** in Eastern Samaria and the approaches to it. (*SMM* 5-3 and 5-4 are helpful here.) Near the fords of the Jordan at Adam a major nahal/wadi empties into the Jordan from Eastern Samaria. As it descends from the northwest to the Jordan River it follows a valley formed by two parallel geological faults. In Arabic it is called *Wadi Faria*. Its Hebrew name, *Nahal Tirzah*, is taken from the city near the valley's northwestern beginnings. This valley, while not totally empty of obstacles, offers a convenient *back door* to Eastern Samaria from Adam to Tirzah. Note the approach to Tirzah from Beth-shan (northeast of Tirzah). While not as convenient as the Wadi Faria approach, the Beth-shan—Tirzah connection makes use of a number of natural passes through the hills. Try to locate some of these passes on your *SMA*.

Due west of Tirzah the mountains of Central Samaria make travel difficult. However, there are natural passes northwest of Tirzah leading to Dothan and beyond to
international highways. Southwest of Tirzah a pass ascends up to **Shechem**, the
central city of the entire region. The climb from Tirzah to Shechem is about 275
meters/900 feet on a route running just west of a very deep canyon. With *SMM 6-6*
and 8-8 open, reread this paragraph, find the routes mentioned and try to locate where
they would run on the *SMA*.

As you have seen, the hub of Eastern Samaria is Tirzah. Connections from it to
Gilead (via Wadi Faria, Adam and Succoth) are not difficult. Although Tirzah has connections to Beth-shan, it is not on the main highway. Thus, while at the crossroads of
Eastern Samaria and linked to Shechem and to the Jordan Valley and Gilead beyond,
it is not on the path of armies marching between Egypt and Mesopotamia.

For the farmer Tirzah's setting is ideal. The region is spring fed and is bathed in sun-
light most of the time due to its relatively low altitude (225 meters/750 feet above
sea level) and its position behind the mountains of Central Samaria. It could be
regarded as being quite *desirable*, which, in fact, is the meaning of the name Tirzah.
It is not surprising, therefore, that in his search for an adequate figure of speech the
writer of the *Song of Songs (of Solomon)* chose this region.

> *You are as beautiful, my love, as Tirzah, as becoming as Jerusalem . . .*
> *Your hair is like a herd of goats, flowing down from Gilead.*
>   (Song of Solomon 6.4-5)

4. Southern perspectives (*SMM* 1-13, 5-4, 6-7 and 8-8).
For geological reasons, connections between Samaria and Judea via the Hill Country of
Ephraim are not easy. Map 6-7 and the *SMA* show a large system of canyons between
Aphek (on the Coastal Highway) and the region of Shiloh (center of Map 6-7). This
entire system with its northern and southern forks could be called the **Shiloh System**.
It makes north-south travel by any one ridge or valley impossible.

Just south of Shechem there is a small but convenient valley (running north and south
of Michmethath) through which the route passes. However, it is not long before the
road must traverse the upper part of the *Shiloh System* (Map 5-4), a difficult area
the Bible calls *the interior of Ephraim*.

Farther south by Bethel the route emerges from the difficulties of the Shiloh System
out onto a plateau. From here travel again becomes more convenient. Bethel is also
the crossroads for routes between the Jordan Valley (by Jericho) and the Coastal Highway (by Aphek). Therefore, the Northern Kingdom always coveted and usually
controlled this **Bethel Plateau** in spite of its proximity to Jerusalem. The battles
between Israel and Judah over this region form a major part of your later studies.

5. Review and summary (*SMM* 1-10, 5-3 and 8-8)
The question has been often asked, *Is Samaria a region open or closed to trade and
invasion?* You may want to formulate your own answer to this question as you study
the maps of this chapter. At this point it is important to review carefully the various
approaches to Samaria by comparing Maps 5-3 or 8-8 with your *SMA*. The interrela-
tionship of these routes (north-south and east-west) as one navigates around the hills

of Central Samaria provides the basis needed to proceed with the actual map studies. You are now prepared *to call the history of Samaria on stage* in order to illustrate the routes and the regions discussed above. As you do, remember to refer to *SMA* often. What you know about Samaria thus far is best seen there.

S M M 4 – 2

TITLE: **POLITICAL CENTERS FROM THE EXECRATION TEXTS**

DATE: **20TH AND 19TH CENTURIES B.C.** (Underline *MB* in yellow in title.)

INTRODUCTION

Map 4-2 provides an interesting point of departure in your study of the region of Samaria. Limited Egyptian sources and archeological evidence point to the fact that the region of Samaria and sites in it played an important role in the country during the beginning of the second millennium B.C.

DISCUSSION

4-2   The red names on Map 4-2 represent those cities which Egypt felt to be hostile to her interests in the country. In order to express her displeasure and to cast a negative influence on these political centers, small clay figurines were made with the appropriate names and curses. These were then smashed and buried in an Egyptian temple. This action was thought to bring the desired result, the destruction of Egypt's enemies. The texts are today called *Execration Texts*. The absence of Megiddo in these texts may reflect its friendly relations with Egypt or even the presence of Egyptian forces there.

The texts come from the twentieth and the nineteenth centuries B.C. Those from the nineteenth century include the name of **Shechem**, a political center deemed important enough to be cursed, even though it did not lie directly on the main International Highway. It may be that its influence was felt because of its central position in the region and also because it was linked closely to the International Highway via the convenient Nahal Shechem approach. This approach and the centrality of Shechem can be seen clearly on Map 4-2.

Archeological evidence shows that in the late nineteenth century B.C. a large area at the site of Shechem was filled in to create an open public area of some importance. This operation was necessary since the site itself is located in the middle of a low mountain pass between Mount Ebal and Mount Gerizim. (In the following centuries this *platform* was surrounded by a strong wall. Successive courtyard buildings built upon it suggest a religious use, perhaps a sacred area with a courtyard temple.) The strategic Nahal Shechem lies directly west of Shechem. To the east a beautiful plain is nestled between the mountains of Eastern Samaria.

It is not surprising that such a situation, strategically important, agriculturally productive and aesthetically beautiful, developed into a political and religious center which sought to extend its control over the entire region. Massive fortifications and extensive building in subsequent periods testify to the site's central position. Less than two kilometers to the west, in the same pass, residents of a modern city are busy building and expanding on the ruins of the Roman city of Neapolis (which means *New City*). Their political and territorial aspirations do not differ much from those of ancient Shechem as witnessed by current newspaper headlines. This contemporary regional center is the Arabic city of Nablus.

MARKING
1. **Yellow underlining** = *MB* in the printed title of the map.

2. **Yellow HL on route** =
   a. The same routes as HL on Map 4-1.

   b. The route from Megiddo N (via Shimon) and then NW to Acco and E to the Megiddo-Hazor route.

3. **Yellow HL on names**: Cities also mentioned in the earlier Execration Texts (20th century B.C.) = **Ashkelon, Beth-shan, Rehob** and **Jerusalem**. Indicate this marking in a legend at the bottom of the map.

S M M   4 − 3 and 4 − 4

DISCUSSION
Maps 4-3 and 4-4 portray events, places and routes in the lives of the patriarchs. Various views for dating the period of the patriarchs range from the twenty-second to the seventeenth century B.C., or even later. Whichever chronological framework one chooses, the importance of Shechem in the narratives cannot be denied. On Map   4-3 a
4-3 Shechem is the first city mentioned in Abraham's entry into the land (Genesis 12.4-6). It was *the place* at Shechem which appears to have originally attracted Abraham's attention and perhaps prompted him to build an altar there. From Shechem he journeyed to Bethel (Genesis 12.8). On Map 4-3 find the route approaching Shechem from the northeast and connecting it to Bethel.

Later, as seen on Map 4-4, Jacob entered the land via Shechem on his return trip from   4-4 a
Haran in northern Mesopotamia (Genesis 31-33). He approached the country via the region of Gilead, no doubt ascending to Shechem via Wadi Faria and the region of Tirzah. At Shechem, where he was able to purchase some land, a serious problem developed. It concerned the rape of Jacob's daughter Dinah by Shechem, the son of   4-4 b
Hamor, an important civic leader (Genesis 34). In the ensuing discussions the leaders of the city demonstrated their firm control over the area. They were in a position to offer Jacob and his large following land rights throughout the surrounding regions. After two of Jacob's sons settled the affair by force, Jacob quickly departed, again along the so-called *Patriarchal Highway* through the mountains to Bethel.

One last important event on Map 4-4 involves Joseph's unplanned trip to Egypt   4-4 c
(Genesis 37). Joseph's brothers were grazing their herds in the neighborhood of Shechem. Jacob (Israel) was aware that his sons were in this region. He naturally was

concerned about their safety, knowing full well how they had alienated the local population of Shechem in their handling of the *Dinah affair*. To check on their well-being, he sent the one son who was left with him, Joseph, his favorite, from the family center at Hebron north to Shechem.

When Joseph arrived at Shechem, he discovered that his brothers had moved the family's herds farther north to the region around Dothan. The Dothan Valley lies along the main artery leading to the Coastal Highway and beyond to Egypt. It was this move that set the scene for the jealous act of selling Joseph to traders *coming from Gilead, their camels loaded with gum, balsam and fragrant resin, which they were taking down to Egypt* via the Coastal Highway (Genesis 37.25). Thus, Joseph journeyed south again, this time not through the mountains but along the highway to Egypt. Measured in distance he would pass not far from his father Jacob in the mountains around Hebron. In terms of final destination, however, they would be worlds apart.

Centuries later after Israel's sojourn in Egypt and following the great events of the Exodus, the giving of the Law in Sinai and the Conquest of Canaan, Joseph, the savior of the sons of Jacob, was finally laid to rest in the promised land.

> *The bones of Joseph, which the sons of Israel [Jacob] brought up from Egypt,*
> *were buried at Shechem, in part of the field which Jacob had purchased*
> *from the sons of Hamor, father of Shechem, for a hundred weights, for it had*
> *become the inheritance of the sons of Joseph [Ephraim and Manasseh].*
> (Joshua 24.32)

All of these stories above illustrate aspects of the region we have termed *Samaria*: its eastern *back door* via Wadi Faria and Tirzah, the centrality of Shechem situated at the very crossroads of the entire region and the proximity of international thoroughfares to the west. All of these elements are basic to your understanding of Samaria. Archeological finds of this general period (Middle Bronze) highlight the importance of the sites discussed above. Map 2-3 shows sites where significant finds of the period have been uncovered. Note especially Shechem, Tirzah, Dothan and Bethel.

2-3

S M M   4 — 8

TITLE: THE AMARNA AGE: KINGS OF CANAAN AND INTERRELATIONS

DATE: About 1400-1350 B.C. (Underline *LB* in yellow in the title of the map.)

INTRODUCTION

4-5/7

In the fifteenth century B.C. the great campaigns of Thutmose III passed along the International Coastal Highway (Maps 4-5 and 4-7). A century later, and a few decades before the Egyptian campaigns of Seti I and Ramses II (Map 4-1), the Pharaoh Amenhotep IV (also known as Akh-en-Aton) made an all-out attempt to change the religious status quo of Egypt. One god above all others was proposed, the solar disc Aton. This trend was coupled with the physical move of Egypt's religious and political capital to a new site. It was named Akh-et-aton and is known today as El-Amarna.

Some feel that this period of internal religious controversy in Egypt reflected a weak Egyptian foreign policy. However, a lack of Egyptian military action in or through the country was more of a reflection of the stable conditions to the north rather than Egyptian weakness. Egyptian power remained the dominating force in the lands which earlier had come under her control. She did not interfere in local power politics unless they directly threatened Egyptian control in strategic areas. Inter-regional skirmishes and power plays resulting from such a *laissez-faire* policy threatened some local leaders. These leaders often corresponded with officials in Egypt on whom their security and the stability of the region depended.

Some 350 letters written on clay tablets (about one half from kings in Canaan) have been preserved in a royal Egyptian archive found at El-Amarna above the banks of the Nile. The star (or villian) of the letters from Canaan is Labayu, king of Shechem!

In the following marking instructions the kings of the land mentioned in the El-Amarna correspondence will be highlighted in yellow. Egyptian bases, still controlling the main highways of the country, will be boxed in blue. The tentacles of Shechem's expanding control under Labayu are shown in orange.

MARKING

1. **Yellow HL on name:** Kings of the Amarna Age = **Yurza** (S of Gaza), **Ashkelon, Lachish, Gath** (not Gath-padalla), **Gezer, Megiddo, Shimon, Achshaph, Acco, Tyre, Hazor, Ashtaroth, Pehel, Zoar** (S of the Dead Sea), **Jerusalem** and **Shechem.** (A reference to *Sharon* may indicate Aphek. Write in *Sharon* in red (ball point) above Aphek and HL in yellow.)

2. **Blue box around name:** Egyptian bases = **Gaza, Joppa** and **Beth-shan.**

3. **Orange circle around name = Shechem.**

4. **Sweeping orange arrows:** Radiating from Shechem showing her encroachment on other regions and city-states =
   a. To Jerusalem.   d. To Gath-padalla.
   b. To Gezer.   e. To Megiddo.
   c. To Aphek.   f. To Shunem.

5. **Black write-in:** Names of selected kings.
   a. Above Jerusalem = ABDI-KHEBA (small caps and in parentheses).

   b. Above Shechem = LABAYU (small caps and in parentheses).

DISCUSSION

The El-Amarna Letters provide a rich source for the study of main Canaanite cities,   4-8
local politics and areas of Egyptian influence during the early fourteenth century B.C. Through careful translation and research, scholars have added to what is known about this fascinating period of the country's history. Only a few relevant facts will be summarized here.

Shechem, whose greatness in the Middle Bronze Period had subsequently diminished, recovered its strength in the Amarna Age. It appears to have taken control of the territory between Jerusalem, the Jezreel Valley and the Sharon Plain. Shechem's king, Labayu, was pressing Jerusalem, Gezer and cities along the Sharon Plain. He was even accused of destroying Shunem and other cities in the area. Finally Egyptian officials ordered his arrest and transfer to Acco and from there to Egypt for questioning. En route to Acco he escaped and was subsequently murdered near Gina on his way back to Shechem.

During his administration Labayu was also accused of allowing certain *outsiders (Hapiru)* to settle in his territory. Giving aid to these enemies of Egypt was a serious charge laid time and again against Labayu in the Amarna Letters. Rulers of other cities feared that this potentially dangerous influx in the Hill Country might upset the status quo in the region. They expressed their concern directly to Egypt and placed the blame directly on the king of Shechem.

Some scholars feel that these early fourteenth century invaders could be the Israelite tribes under Joshua. It should be stressed here that the name *Hapiru* cannot exclusively stand for *Hebrews* but is a general term used in a wider context for foreigners (in this period Semites) who were moving into settled and stable areas. Other scholars would point to the important fact that the specific name *Israel* is not mentioned in the Amarna Letters. They would place Joshua's campaign later (in the mid-thirteenth century) and claim that the *Hapiru* were simply early waves of Semite migrants who would later be joined by a large influx of Israelites and Arameans.

What is important to note for your regional study is that Shechem played a major political role in the central part of the country during this period. The routes which have been studied so far in this chapter linked this central political center to important regions, highways and cities in all directions. Labayu could fulfill his aspirations as long as they did not interfere with Egyptian international interests along main highways. When they did, the king of Shechem found that Egypt was still willing and able to move in and protect her interests, despite her preoccupation with religious issues back home.

These same principles governed the later history of the region of Samaria. Its proximity to international routes and the ease with which one could reach these routes presented a temptation difficult to resist, especially in a period of apparent big power weakness. However, once a government in Samaria arrived in the international arena, it was only a matter of time before another power again restricted her to the hills or used the same convenient access routes to crush her internal political centers.

LEGEND

> **Yellow HL**   =   King of the Amarna Age.
> **Blue box**   =   Egyptian base.

S M M   5 − 1, 5 − 3, 5 − 4 and 6 − 1

INTRODUCTORY DISCUSSION AND OPTIONAL READING

Map 6-1 was marked in Chapter One. Maps 5-3, 5-4 and 6-2 will be marked and discussed in Chapter Four. All of these maps, together with Map 5-1, portray events from the period of the Israelite Conquest and the period of Settlement and Judges.

The leading personality in this period was Joshua, an Ephraimite who had played an important role with Moses during the years in the Wilderness. The center of control, or at least common meeting ground, for the Israelite tribes was in the territory of the House of Joseph (Ephraim and Manasseh). Together with the territory of Benjamin (Joseph's brother) the region from the Jezreel Valley to Jerusalem can be considered as that of one family unit. (Joseph and Benjamin were both sons of Jacob and Rachel.) The implications of this fact are very relevant to your study in the region of Samaria.

Map 5-3 presents Israelite campaigns in Transjordan and their subsequent entry into   5-3 c
Canaan via Jericho. Map 5-4 is a detail of the entry into Canaan. For your present   5-4
study it is interesting to note the two mountains by Shechem on these maps. The
names of these mountains are printed in red, Mt. Ebal and Mt. Gerizim. It appears
that Moses' specific instructions (Deuteronomy 27) were carried out as soon as was
possible after the initial Israelite campaigns in the land. Joshua directed the Israelite   5-3 d
leaders to Mt. Ebal and Mt. Gerizim, one rising to the north of Shechem and its pass
and the other to the south. Here, on the slopes above this famous political and religious center, the Law was again rehearsed.

> *And then he [Joshua] wrote on the stones a copy of the Law of Moses which he*
> *[Moses] had written in the presence of the sons of Israel, and all Israel . . .*
> *were standing on both sides of the ark . . . half facing Mt. Gerizim and half*
> *facing Mt. Ebal . . . and he recited all the words of the Law, the blessing and*
> *the cursing, all of it as it is written in the Book of the Law.* (Joshua 8.32-34)

Prior to this ceremony Joshua *built an altar . . . to the Lord, the God of Israel,* as the Patriarchs had done centuries before. In this particular geographical and historical setting the ceremony must have made a deep impression on these Israelites, who were just one generation removed from the covenant made at Sinai. It stressed their obliga-tion to the Lord, the God of Israel, now that they were actually in the land — and in a certain sense at its geographical, political and religious center.

For your present study the place of this ceremony is as important as the ceremony it-self or discussions of the dating of the event. While some argue that this area was chosen because waves of Israelites had settled here earlier (prior to Joshua), it does not lessen the importance of the place, its geographical setting and its historical precedents.

On Map 5-1 the red names west of the Jordan River represent various kings of the land   5-1 d
whom Joshua and the sons of Israel conquered (Joshua 12.7-24). While the actual
campaigns of Joshua do not include all of these names, some of them are mentioned
in incidents recorded in the book of Judges. It is interesting to note that the name of
Shechem is not included. It is printed in black on Map 5-1 indicating that it is not in
the roster of defeated kings.

This fact, coupled with the absence of any campaign in the area, cannot be overlooked
in any serious discussion of the period. Some feel that Labayu's policy at Shechem   4-8
(Map 4-8) had something to do with the absence of an Israelite campaign here. Others
deny this. It is not in the scope of your present study to pursue this question. Whatever arguments are put forth in this much-debated question, no one can deny that
these events underscore and highlight Shechem's central position in the region of
Samaria, and indeed in the entire country.

Chapters describing the distribution of tribal land rights or inheritances in the land comprise much of the latter part of the book of Joshua. Cities on tribal boundaries or those listed in the tribal territory itself are shown on Map 6-2 by a numbering system. These numbers are linked to lists on the page directly above Map 6-2. A glance at this map (to be marked shortly) shows that the northern and southern tribes are generally well-represented. Judah in the south has the best coverage. However, there is a conspicuous empty area in the center of the map around Shechem.

6-2

Scholars put forth various explanations for this phenomenon. Again, this discussion is not one of your present priorities. However, it is important to note that this large and strategic region lacks a list of cities or districts (such as are found in Judah). This gap is partially filled in by archeological discoveries (Map 8-8). However, much more is needed to complete the picture of local population centers and administrative organization.

Map 6-1 shows that this central region was given to the strong House of Joseph, Ephraim and Manasseh, the two sons of Joseph. Your later studies will show how these tribes exploited the natural advantages of the region, which were far greater than those of Judah to the south. Although David and Solomon were able to keep the House of Joseph under Judah's control, your studies in Chapter Two revealed that Shechem eventually took matters in her own hands and declared independence.

6-1

Before you put Map 6-1 aside, one very important event in Joshua's life must be discussed. The setting is given in Joshua 23. It gives strong hints that not all Israelites took the recommitment at Mt. Ebal and Mt. Gerizim seriously. The conditions of which Joshua speaks in this chapter no doubt were becoming more and more commonplace. There was also the fact that members of a new generation (the grandchildren of those who had experienced the exodus from Egypt) would soon assume places of leadership. This generation gap meant that renewal was necessary.

It is in this context that Joshua decided to put forth his last and perhaps greatest effort to strengthen and preserve Israel's commitment to the Lord, the God of Israel. Joshua had seen with his own eyes Israel's great deliverance from Egypt. He had followed Moses to Sinai. There, as only a youth, he had become Moses' commanding general in the battle against Amalek, leading the Israelites to victory at a moment when their new found freedom and their very existence were being threatened (Exodus 17.8-16). In some of the most sacred and intimate moments in Moses' relationship to the God of Israel (at the giving of the law and later in the Tent of Meeting), Joshua had been present (Exodus 24.13; 32.15-26; 33.7-11). He had had personal experience with that generation's vacillating spiritual commitment and had heard from Moses' own lips that resounding question, *Who is on the Lord's side?* At Kadesh-barnea (as the representative of the tribe of Ephraim) he had voiced his confidence in the God of Israel upon his return with others from spying out the land and had almost lost his life for his testimony (Numbers 14.6-10). At the end of the forty years of Wilderness wanderings he had heard Moses' final warning to a new generation just prior to his death and to their entry into Canaan under Joshua (Deuteronomy 6-11). Finally, he had lived with this new generation in Canaan and was seeing yet another mature.

Now at the end of his life Joshua saw dangerous trends developing. Some of these concerned interaction with local peoples who did not share his love and respect for the God of Israel. Others had to do with Israel's growing preoccupation with the better life which the land afforded. Considering Joshua's intimate knowledge of Israel's recent history, it is not surprising that he, like Moses before him, assembled the leaders of the nation in order to give them his final discourse and instructions. This time he pressed as hard as he could for an inward commitment as well as an outward confession of the Lord, the God of Israel. In his pointed remarks Joshua again disclosed his prestigious position. He implied that if apostasy continued, his clan (or perhaps even Ephraim) would go its separate way, leaving others to fend for themselves: *Make up your mind here and now. Whom will you serve? . . . I and my house will serve the Lord!*

With this background and with your knowledge of Shechem's role in the maps studied thus far in this chapter, read (not optional) **Joshua 24.1-31**. In this passage the great covenant with Israel is reconfirmed. In terms of the subsequent history of the northern tribes, this chapter is foundational. Historical, political and religious overtones are many, and they reverberate throughout the Old and New Testaments. This great event recorded in Joshua 24 echoes Sinai itself. It happened at Shechem beneath Mt. Ebal and Mt. Gerizim (Map 6-1).

S M M   6 – 2

TITLE: TRIBAL TERRITORIES AND CITY-LISTS IN CANAAN

INTRODUCTION

The history of the country is inseparable from the history of the Israelite tribes which settled it in the latter part of the second millennium B.C. The cities and territories associated with these tribes provide one of the richest sources for the geographical study of the country. In addition, various tribes and the territories allotted to them serve as a framework for many subsequent events on the *playing board* of the Bible. The prominent position of Ephraim (Joshua's tribe) and the strategic position which Benjamin (Joseph's brother) occupied between Ephraim and Judah make this tribal study relevant at this point in your assignments. While your work here represents only a basic introduction to the subject, the map will provide a handy reference for future studies.

Above Map 6-2 territories and city-lists of the Israelite tribes in Canaan appear. Corresponding information on the tribes in Transjordan is listed in the sea area of the map itself. In the text of Map 6-2 (above the map) it is helpful to highlight the names of each tribe. Not all tribal cities have equal coverage. Note the detailed information about the southern tribes of Judah (with its eleven districts) and Benjamin. Ephraim's and Manasseh's lists (the House of Joseph) are totally missing. In the north, coverage improves.

6-2
Text

All known tribal cities are also included on Maps 6-3 through 6-7, and all five of these maps are drawn on the same scale (1:300,000). This allows multiple use of the maps. Not only are the stories of various Judges presented, but they are studied against the essential background of local tribal settlement. Thus, these maps serve a dual purpose. The work done on Map 6-2 provides the overall picture of tribal allotments against the main communication routes throughout the country and in Transjordan.

MARKING

All the marking below should be done with a green pen (tribal borders, names and arrows). It may be helpful to first draw in pencil and then in pen. No shading is necessary. Do not draw through numbers or circles, only between them. In general do not draw borders in straight or angular lines, but gently curve them from one point to another unless directed otherwise. To find the general area of the tribe before marking, refer to Map 6-1. The numbers on the maps correspond to the numbers listed in the text above the map. They do not have to be used, but are useful for reference.

1. **Judah:**
   a. **Northern border:** Begin at the mouth of the Jordan River at the Salt (Dead) Sea, 30, 31, 32, 33, 34, 35, 37, 38, 39, 40, 41, just N of 42 and curving S of 61 to 43, just S of 44 to 45, 46, 47, 48, curving N and following the wadi W around the sand dune to the Great (Mediterranean) Sea.

   b. Write-in S of this border, between 100 and 92 = JUDAH.

   c. Write-in at S edge of the map, between 54, 55 and 56 = SIMEON (whose inheritance was within Judah).

2. **Benjamin** and **Dan** (1st territory):
   a. **Northern borders:** Begin at the Jordan River E of Jericho (111), due W (N of 31 and between Gilgal and 111) to 112, S of 113, N of 126 to 114, curving around to 125, W/NW passing N of 202, then S of 116 and sharply N again passing E of 206 and 207 and N of 209 to 210.

   b. A line running N from 40 (on Judah's northern border) to the other green line with 134 E of it.

   c. Write-in just W of 111 = BEN. (abbreviation for Benjamin).

   d. Write-in on the Coastal Plain between 207 and 205 = DAN 1.

3. **Ephraim:**
   a. **Northern border:** Begin at 118 (NW of Shiloh), E between 119 and 120, S to a point on Benjamin's northern border just N of 111; again from 118 to 123 and then along the wadi winding W from 123 (along the thin broken blue line under 123) to the river W of Aphek and along it to the sea at 210.

   b. Write-in in open area S of 123 = EPHRAIM.

4. **Gad, Reuben, ½ of Manasseh** and **Machir** (son of Manasseh):
   Write-in these names in caps as they appear on Map 6-1.

5. **Manasseh:**
   a. Write-in this name in caps in the open area W of Taanach, Ibleam and Shechem.

   b. Arrows from the name Manasseh showing Manasseh's expansion to the NW (1 cm./½ in.) to the NE (2 cm./1 in.) to the area of ½ Manasseh and Machir across the Jordan Valley.

6. **Zebulun:**
    a. **Border:** Begin at 143, 141, 140, 145 (passing just N of 144), 148, curving W along the base of a mountain ridge and around 149 to 150, W around 152 (to the N and W of it) to 143.

    b. Write-in between 140, 149 and 146 = ZEB. (abbreviation for Zebulun).

7. **Asher, Naphtali, Issachar** and **Dan** (2nd territory):
    a. **Border of Asher:** From 143 along the base of Mt. Carmel NW to the sea (passing W of 163, 166, 169 and just E of 170).

    b. **Border of Naphtali:** From just N of 145, E between 161 and 185, NE between 187 and 159 to 162.

    c. **Border between Asher and Naphtali** (assumed since no details given): From the N border of Zebulun (NW of 149) a line running N which leaves 173, 172 and 176 to the W and 191 and 201 to the E.

    d. Write-in between this line and 174 = ASHER.

    e. Write-in just W of Hazor = NAPHTALI.

    f. Write-in just S of 160 = ISS. (abbreviation for Issachar).

    g. Write-in (N edge of the map) just W of 212 = DAN 2.

DISCUSSION

A glance at Map 6-2 will show you that some tribes are rather well-defined while others remain quite empty of red names or numbers. This is because tribal border descriptions and the list of cities within the territories are not given equal coverage in the Bible (Joshua 15-19). The positions of the northern tribes (especially Zebulun's well-definied territory) serve as an important backdrop to the story of Deborah and Barak (the next episode discussed when the marking of Map 6-2 is complete).

In the south the information available on the tribe of Judah is the most complete of all tribes (Joshua 15). Ephraim (to our great surprise) lacks any type of city-list, and Manasseh is hardly mentioned at all. Benjamin, on the other hand, is given full coverage. This is perhaps due to its strategic position (between Ephraim and Judah) and its later forced alignment with Judah and Jerusalem. The ensuing conflict over who would control this small territory of Benjamin is one of the most important issues in the geopolitical history of the Israelite tribes.

Map 6-2 will now be completed by highlighting the main routes of the country in yellow. As this is done, note which tribes lie in the path of these routes. Mention has already been made of the influence of these routes. Try to come to your own conclusions regarding the relationship of these routes to the potential opportunities or insecurities of each tribe.

MARKING
1. **Yellow highlighting on the following routes:**
    a. All routes printed in red on this map (in Transjordan, along the Coastal Plain and in the north).

    b. The other two passes from the International Coastal Highway (in the Sharon Plain) to Ibleam and to Jokneam.

    c. The Megiddo—Beth-shan route, the Megiddo-Ibleam route and the Ibleam—Beth-shan route.

    d. The two routes to the E and NE of Beth-shan going off the E edge of the map (as highlighted on Map 4-1).

    e. The Acco-Hazor route (via 149) and the Megiddo-Hazor route (via 149).

2. **Blue write-in** (as on Map 6-1).
    a. In the Coastal Plain in open area E of Ashdod = PHILISTINES.

    b. In Transjordan, in SE corner of the map, E of highlighted highway = MOAB.

    c. In Transjordan, just below (W) the name Rabbah = AMMON.

DISCUSSION

Sit back and compare Map 6-2 with your *SMA*. Try to locate the tribes outlined above on the full color map. If you were a Danite would you be pleased with your original territory? Why or why not? Do you see potential problems in your second choice? Can you see problems arising between Judah, Ephraim and the Philistines over control of the coastal regions? Why would they all be interested in this area? Since Jericho (No. 111) is the link to Transjordan from the Hill Country, is it apparent why Judah and Ephraim both are interested in Jericho (which actually was allotted to Benjamin)? All of these questions and more will be discussed in subsequent map studies.

S M M   6 − 5 and 6 − 6

INTRODUCTION

The two maps in this section (6-5 and 6-6) were marked in Chapter Two. The events on these maps come from the period of the Judges. Map 6-1 provides the important geographical and tribal context for this study. Refer to it when necessary.

During the years which followed the death of Joshua and his contemporaries, much of what this famous leader had feared actually happened. The following selected portions of Judges 2.10-3.2 provide the best commentary on the period.

> *And another generation grew up . . . who did not know the Lord nor the acts which He had performed for Israel . . . . And the sons of Israel . . . left the Lord, the God of their fathers, who had brought them out from the land of Egypt . . . . He then gave them over to raiders who overran them . . . to the point that they were no longer able to put up any resistance against their invaders . . . . The Lord established champions [or heroes, defenders, protectors, judges] who delivered them out of the clutches of those who had overrun them — but they did not even take note of their champions . . . veering off the path which their fathers had followed. . . . So the Lord said, '. . . from here on I will not evict any more of the nations which were left when Joshua died,' using them in order to test Israel. Would they keep to the path of the Lord, walking in it as their fathers did, or not?*

Here, in the book of Judges (Champions), the writer underscores the principle that this land is *God's testing ground of faith*. As apostasy set in, the non-Israelites who remained in the country put pressure on Israel. To make matters worse, Israel, whose first priorities were family and tribal ties, had not yet developed national institutions. The political leadership needed to meet these mounting threats to her security was sadly missing. Her own internal disunity was one of her greatest enemies.

Given this disquieting atmosphere and the trend toward spiritual apostasy, Israel was entering a very difficult period in her history. The writer of the book of Judges summarizes general conditions and attitudes when in the closing sentence he states, *In those days Israel had no king [human or divine]; each person did what he felt like!* This type of living and the chaotic conditions which it encouraged directly contradicted the strong divine injunction to *love your neighbor as yourself — I am the Lord!* (Leviticus 19.18).

DEBORAH AND BARAK AGAINST THE FORCES OF SISERA

DISCUSSION

Some of the champions of this period are mentioned only briefly, as Tola of Shamir and Abdon of Pirathon, both of whom came from the Hill Country of Ephraim (Map 6-7). The brave actions of others are well-documented. Such is the colorful story of Deborah and Barak, studied on Map 6-5 (Chapter Two). You remember that the   6-5 a Canaanites, under the leadership of the King of Hazor, had made life unbearable for the northern tribes. Deborah, whose counsel was famous throughout Israel, had centered her activity at a place *between Ramah and Bethel in the Hill Country of Ephraim* (Judges 4.4-5).

This region, seen well on Maps 6-7 and 6-1, was claimed jointly by the House of Joseph (the tribe of Ephraim) and Benjamin (Joseph's brother). Very early in the period of Israelite settlement the House of Joseph established an important foothold in the region when they captured and rebuilt the city of Bethel (Judges 1.22-26). Located at the very southern and strategic edge of Ephraim's tribal territory, it was near a number of important internal routes (seen on Maps 6-7 and 6-1). In addition the region had strong religious associations with the Patriarchs. Dramatic events had occurred near Bethel, including far-reaching promises concerning the land (Genesis 28, 35 and Map 4-3). In fact the Deborah of Map 6-5 was *staying under 'Deborah's Palm'* named after an earlier woman (Rebekah's nurse) who had died nearby (Genesis 35.8). Considering the historical and covenantal ties in the region, its geographical centrality and convenience, and Ephraim's prestigious role among the tribes, Deborah made a wise choice when she established herself *between Ramah and Bethel in the Hill Country of Ephraim.*

The deteriorating situation in the north demanded immediate action (Map 6-5). Barak, the son of Abinoam, was summoned by Deborah to the Hill Country of Ephraim. There he agreed to mobilize Israelite forces only if Deborah herself traveled north and lent her popular support to this crucial action. This support and careful preparation were needed to meet the well-equipped and organized army of the Canaanites.

Deborah and Barak no doubt spent time on their way to the Jezreel Valley gathering support among the common rural folk of the hills. For part of the way they probably followed the same route Abraham and Jacob had used centuries before. They would have had to pass through the territory of the House of Joseph and by Shechem, where Joshua had preached renewal and a recommitment to the Lord, the God of Israel. It would have been natural for them to recall events in the life of Joshua, Moses' young Ephraimite commander, who had led a newly independent Israel in its first fight for survival at the battle against the Amalekites in Sinai. Such an example of the weak and untrained defending themselves against the strong must have helped greatly in recruiting volunteers. The opening verses of Deborah and Barak's Song of Victory after the battle allude to these past victories of the Lord, God of Israel (Judges 5.1-5). Together with the northern tribes, Ephraim and Benjamin are mentioned in this vivid, poetic description of the battle (Judges 5). Ephraim leads the list of participating tribes in contrast to other tribes who did not join this semi-united front. Benjamin, located just south of Ephraim, probably was dragged into the conflict because of the close family relationship with Ephraim.

> *. . . then the people of the Lord descended to the gates [of the Jezreel Valley];*
>
> *Awake! Awake Deborah! Awake! Awake! Sound out a song!*
> *Up Barak, and take captive your captors, son of Abinoam!*
> *Then a remnant went down against the mighty;*
> *The Lord's people, for my sake, went down against the strong.*
> *I sent Ephraim, whose fame (origin) is in Amalek.*
> *You were followed by Benjamin, a member of your own family.* (Judges 5.11-14)

It should be noted in summary that Ephraim had every reason to be concerned about conditions in the north where Canaanite centers were threatening Israelite interests. Ephraim's place of leadership was at stake in addition to her own internal security and Israelite economic development. She would naturally be the first to respond to Deborah's call to arms, which was first issued on her southern border *between Ramah and Bethel*. It was, after all, her duty to lead, both in the north and, as we shall see later, in the south when Benjamin's interests were threatened.

GIDEON AND THE MIDIANITES

DISCUSSION

6-6 b   The events portrayed on Map 6-6 again illustrate the prominent part played by the House of Joseph during the early period of Israel's settling the land. The main *champion* of this map comes from Manasseh, Ephraim's brother to the north. His name is Gideon, son of Joash the Abiezerite.

This time the threat to the north (and to the southern coastlands near Gaza) came from the Midianites and the Amalekites, desert raiders from the southeast. They had invaded the grain lands for a period of seven years. Infiltration from the desert was not unusual in times when internal political institutions were weak. Preachers of repentance raised their voices, but few listened.

In such periods farmers in the hills were less likely to be trampled in the path of the invading herdsmen. However, those who had ventured out to till the plains and the valleys were the first to be overrun, being forced to retreat back into the hills for refuge. The best description of such a difficult period is found in Judges 6.1-10. It presents a sharp contrast to Deborah and Barak's Song of Victory in the preceding chapter.

In the midst of these hard times, while secretly threshing wheat in a wine press, Gideon was confronted with a type of annunciation which was difficult to accept: *Strong hero, the Lord is with you!* You may judge Gideon's response for yourself by reading the conversation recorded in Judges 6.11-16. Gideon realized all too well the impossible situation which had plagued Israel for seven long years.

Gideon claimed that his was the weakest clan in the tribe of Manasseh and that he himself was the least important member of his family. The clan lived in Ophrah at the edge of the Jezreel and Harod Valleys (just west, or, as some believe, just east of the Hill of Moreh) in an area which bordered on, or belonged to, the tribe of Issachar. Gideon's apparently humble statement may simply have been a convenient excuse for the moment or may have reflected his actual standing in the larger House of Joseph.

When the next desert invasion took place herdsmen again overran the Jezreel Valley. In response Gideon assembled his own clan (the Abiezerites of Manasseh). He then *sent messengers throughout all of Manasseh, and they also joined ranks with him.* After this initial mobilization Gideon *sent messengers to Asher, Zebulun and Naphtali, and they came out to meet him* (Judges 6.33-35). It therefore appears that the tribe of Manasseh (not Ephraim) played a key role in the planning and execution of this great victory in the north.

The final preparatory measures and the actual battle confrontation were discussed in Chapter Two. In your current study it is the retreat of the desert invaders and the subsequent tribal argument which are more important. Although Gideon had been assured of his victory, he had made a very calculated decision prior to the operation itself. In order to insure against future incursions by these raiders, their leaders had to be destroyed as they retreated. This tactical move of *heading them off at the pass* was carried out as the invaders were leaving the country. Although the exact location of Beth-barah is not known, try to recreate the retreat on Map 6-6 as you read Judges 7.24, 25.

> Gideon had sent messengers throughout all of the Hill Country of Ephraim saying, 'Get down to head off Midian and take control of the Jordan and its fords (waters) as far as Beth-barah.' So all the men of Ephraim who had been mobilized took control of the Jordan and its fords as far as Beth-barah. They took prisoner the two Midianite chiefs, Oreb and Zeeb, killing Oreb at what became known as 'the Rock of Oreb' and Zeeb at the 'Wine Press of Zeeb.' They kept on the tail of Midian and brought the heads of Oreb and Zeeb to Gideon, who was already across the Jordan.

This incident may have involved Midianite forces retreating from the north or invaders fleeing from other areas. One would like to have more details about the extent of the Midianite infiltration and the exact location of some of the places or features mentioned in the account. What is known illustrates the attractive entrance into the Jezreel Valley from the east via the Beth-shan and Harod Valleys. It also shows Ephraim's and Manasseh's concern with affairs to the east, beyond the Jordan. Ephraim's response to Gideon's last minute request illustrates her regional concerns and her ability to act quickly to protect her interests.

The writer of Psalm 83, in a later period, uses this event and the victory of Deborah and Barak as the background for one of the Bible's greatest pleas for help in times of national crisis. The psalm is well worth reading in the context of Maps 6-5 and 6-6.

The psalmist may add another piece of geographical information, depending on how the Hebrew word *Adam* is translated (the city *Adam* or the word *earth*). If the city is intended, note its location on Map 6-6.

> *Make them like Midian — like Sisera, like Jabin in Nahal Kishon;*
> *They were wiped out at En-dor; they became dung at Adam [or for the earth].*
>   (Psalm 83.9-10)

The most important part of this story for your regional study is the attitude expressed by the men of Ephraim toward Gideon and his troops. The strong words of the men of Ephraim indicate that their place of leadership in the House of Joseph had been challenged. Quick thinking and a little flattery on the part of Gideon averted what could have been a serious family feud.

> *What have I done through all of this compared to you? Aren't the*
> *few grapes left on Ephraim's vines after the harvest better than an entire*
> *season's pickings for Abiezer [Gideon's clan in Manasseh]? . . .*
> *What could I do in comparison with you?* (Judges 8.1-3)

This short exchange after the battle represents a much larger reality. Ephraim's prestigious standing should have caused Gideon to think twice before initiating such an operation. After all, the defense of the surrounding regions had been by and large Ephraim's responsibility. Gideon had overstepped himself by not consulting Ephraim during the initial planning stages. Being called at the last moment was beneath her position. One might say that *God chose the weak . . . to put to shame the strong* (1 Corinthians 1.27). However, in the final analysis the incident went far beyond the House of Joseph itself. Ephraim's rich heritage and prominent position demanded the respect of Manasseh — and of all of Israel.

The epilogue of the story contains both good and bad news. Gideon's popularity, despite Ephraim's complaint, grew until popular support called on him to establish himself and his family as the ruling house in Israel. Wisely Gideon refused stating, *I will not govern you nor will my sons govern you; the Lord will govern you!* (Judges 8.23). More than a millennium after Gideon (the famous champion of the north) this declaration again echoed throughout the hills of Galilee in Jesus' preaching on *God's rule (the Kingdom of God/Heaven).* The inference to God's great deliverance through Gideon, the son of Joash the Abiezerite, must have been clear to His hearers.

Gideon's triumph, however, turned into a spiritual defeat for Israel. His supporters changed his victory trophy into an object of worship in Ophrah *where all of Israel lusted after it; it even lured Gideon and his family!* (Judges 8.22-28)

JEPHTHAH AND THE AMMONITES

DISCUSSION

6-6 c Another example of Ephraim's superiority complex is found in the story of the champion Jephthah on Map 6-6 (Judges 10.6-12.7). Again it is not the background of the story (Ammonite oppression in Transjordan) nor Jephthah's victory over the oppressors but Ephraim's reaction after Jephthah's victory which should draw your attention.

And the men of Ephraim mobilized and crossed over to Zaphon. They said to Jephthah, 'Why did you go over to fight with the Ammonites and didn't ask us to join you? We'll burn your house down with you in it!' (Judges 12.1-2)

Jephthah's answer (unlike that of Gideon earlier) was anything but diplomatic. He claimed, and rightly so, that Ephraim was a type of *big-mouth-but-do-nothing*. She had sat back, enjoying the security afforded by the Hill Country west of the Jordan, and had neglected her responsibility in Gilead, east of the Jordan. Ephraim had no excuse, and Jephthah had no other choice than to carry out the rescue operation. Name calling was the next step in this family feud, not an uncommon order of events in this part of the world, where damaging one's honor is as effective as physical blows.

Gilead, you're just a bunch of renegades from Ephraim and from Manasseh!

These remarks finally led to physical confrontation in which the Ephraimites were the losers. In their retreat back across the Jordan their superiority complex (which may have even extended to their *better* Hebrew accent) was a definite liability (Judges 12.5-6).

S M M   6 − 7

TITLE: INTERNAL CONFRONTATION: ABIMELECH AND THE BENJAMINITE CIVIL WAR (AND EHUD)

DATE: THE PERIOD OF THE JUDGES

INTRODUCTION

Your study of the region of Samaria now concentrates on internal Israelite problems. The first occurred within the House of Joseph (Abimelech's campaign at Shechem). The second (the Benjaminite Civil War) is seen in the context of Ephraim's total policy to the south. An attack by Moab on Ephraim's southwestern approach (via Jericho) is also discussed.

THE RISE AND FALL OF ABIMELECH, SON OF GIDEON

DISCUSSION AND READING

The story of Abimelech is found in Judges 8.29-9.57. Its background, however, is   6-7 b
the celebrated victory of Gideon. Following his triumph over the Midianites and Amalekites it appears that Gideon led a rather affluent life which could support a large family. He had *many wives* and *seventy sons* plus a certain son Abimelech by his concubine in Shechem (Judges 8.29-32).

Apostasy again set in throughout Israel, especially after the death of Gideon. This time it resulted in what could be termed *kingdom building* by Gideon's Shechem-based son, Abimelech. In their degeneracy they first showed a lack of love and respect for God, and this led to a lack of concern for others.

Abimelech capitalized on his late father's popularity and on the political and geographical centrality of Shechem. He had grown up in the Shechem area and knew the true potential of the city (**Judges 9.1-3**). He appears to be a fast talking politician who was able to convert the Shechemite's natural tendency toward *kingdom building* into his own financial support. With this support he was able to hire a band of murderers who helped him eliminate any form of resistance from his seventy half-brothers, the legitimate sons of Gideon. Only one of his brothers escaped the sword by hiding himself during the massacre, Jothan, Gideon's youngest son (**Judges 9.4-6**). He later made his way to the area of Shechem to speak out against Abimelech (**Judges 9.7-21**). His speech from the slopes of Mt. Gerizim is one of the most satirical passages in the Bible. It is especially striking if you recall that it was there, on the slopes of Mt. Gerizim and Mt. Ebal above Shechem, that Joshua had required Israel to recite the blessings and the curses, including the following:

> *Cursed is he who secretly strikes down his brother . . .*
> *Cursed is he who accepts a bribe to shed innocent blood . . .*
> (Deuteronomy 27.24-25)

It was also here at Shechem that the people of Israel affirmed, *We will serve the Lord our God. We will obey His voice.* In his own way Gideon, the father of Jothan and Abimelech, had confirmed this covenant by declaring *I will not govern you and my sons will not govern you. The Lord will govern you!* However, Abimelech of Shechem won the day through fast talking and violence and by exploiting Shechem's natural tendencies.

It took three years for the people of Shechem to realize their mistake. Abimelech had no more respect for them than he did for his own brothers. The story of intrigue and bloodshed involving Abimelech and his followers is recorded in **Judges 9.22-49**. There in Shechem, below Mt. Gerizim and Mt. Ebal, the local inhabitants learned the lessons that Jothan had tried to teach them. To escape Abimelech's fury they sought refuge in the great Tower of Shechem and in the House of the God of the Covenant. This structure may actually have been built on *the place at Shechem* which Abraham first visited when God led him into the land (Genesis 12.6). The tower and temple became an inferno for the Shechemites trapped inside after Abimelech organized its destruction by fire.

Misguided political aspirations and a self-centered *kingdom-building* attitude had yielded their fruits — total disregard for God and for others. Shechem, with all of its latent greatness, had become the victim of its own potential by allowing a person like Abimelech to take matters into his own hands. However, the folly of the Abimelech episode was not Shechem's greatest failure. The worst was yet to come (Map 8-2).

Following Abimelech's ruthless act in Shechem, he turned his wrath on Thebez, probably another name for the site of Tirzah. If this was the location, it explains Abimelech's tactics, since Tirzah controls the main route to Transjordan (via Adam) and the route northeast in the direction of Beth-shan. Again the people took refuge in a tower of the city, and again Abimelech decided to destroy them by fire. However, *a certain woman* (with apparently a very good aim) turned out to be the *champion* of the story. She threw down a millstone which landed directly on the head of Abimelech. His last command (given to avoid shame in his death) was to one of his followers who took his sword and killed him. Thus ended the kingdom of Abimelech (**Judges 9.50-57**).

MARKING
1. **Yellow HL on name** (keeping off the dots) =
   a. **Aphek** and **Gezer** (along the Coastal Highway on the W edge of the map).

   b. **Thebez, Shechem, Shiloh, Bethel, Mizpah, Ramah, Gibeah, Jerusalem/Jebus** and **Bethlehem** (sites along the center of the map from N to S).

   c. **Jericho** (SE center) and **Jabesh-gilead** (NE corner).

2. **Yellow HL on route** =
   a. The International Coastal Highway (printed in red in the NW corner of map).

   b. From Shechem NW to the International Coastal Highway.

   c. From Shechem to Thebez.

   d. From Thebez to Adam (on the Jordan River).

   e. From Tirzah NE (by Bezek) toward Beth-shan (just off the map to the N).

   f. From Shechem S to Michmethath and then SW and W to Aphek on the International Coastal Highway.

   g. From Shechem S to Bethlehem (via Lebonah, Bethel and Ramah).

   h. The Aphek-Jericho connection via Timnath-serah (Joshua's inheritance), Bethel, Ai, and from Ai the two possible routes descending to Jericho.

   i. The Jericho-Shechem route via Ophrah, already mostly highlighted. With a normal pencil draw a connecting route from this route (beginning 1 cm./½ in. NW of the *O* of **Ophrah**) SW to join the highlighted route just N of Bethel. HL this connection.

   j. All routes from Gezer to Jericho, including the Beth-horon and Kiriath-jearim connections. Both of these join at Gibeon before crossing the Central Benjamin Plateau to Ramah and continuing E to join one of the Bethel-Jericho routes. (Add and HL a small portion of road above the *A* of **Aijalon**.)

   k. The Jerusalem-Jericho route via the Ascent of Adummim.

3. **Red circle around name:**
   a. One circle around Shechem and Mt. Gerizim (not including Michmethath).

   b. One circle around Thebez.

4. **Green write-in:**
   a. Between Thebez/Tirzah and Dothan = MANASSEH.

   b. In the center E of Shiloh = EPHRAIM.

   c. In the S in the open area between Bethlehem and Bether (W of Bethlehem) = JUDAH.

EPHRAIM'S SOUTHERN FLANK

DISCUSSION

Your study of Map 6-7 now turns to an area which many would not regard as being Samaria proper. It is true that the area's geographical link to Samaria is weaker than that of the regions discussed thus far in this chapter. However, historically Samaria-based tribes and governments considered the region to be of utmost importance and vital to their political and economic interests. Since the history of the region dramatically illustrates this concern, Ephraim's southern flank is studied as part of this chapter.

A glance at Map 6-7 shows that most action (indicated by the names printed in red) occurred along the main north-south route through the Hill Country, from Shechem to Bethlehem. Looking at the map you will see that this route passes from Shechem in Manasseh via Michmethath in Ephraim to Bethlehem in Judah. Between Ephraim and Judah lies the tribal territory of Benjamin. You will remember that there was an especially close family relationship between the House of Joseph (Ephraim and Manasseh) and the tribe of Benjamin (both sons of Jacob and Rachel). Considering Ephraim's prominent position in this family and her concern regarding developments to the north and to the east of the family territory (Maps 6-5 and 6-6), it would be very surprising if the same interest did not extend southward to include the territory of Benjamin.

On her southern flank Ephraim was faced with a special situation (Map 6-1). It centered around the question of tribal leadership and her relationship to the tribe of Judah. Although Joseph and Benjamin were their father's favorites, and although Joseph's son Ephraim occupied a place of special importance among the tribes, it was Judah, of all the sons of Jacob, who received the coveted patriarchal blessing from Jacob before his death in Egypt.

> *And you Judah,*
> *Your brothers shall praise you . . .*
> *Your father's sons shall bend the knee before you . . .*
> *The scepter [governing authority] shall never depart from Judah,*
> *Nor the commander's staff [place of leadership] from between his feet —*
> *Until the rightful [leader] appears,*
> *He who [deserves] the people's allegiance.*   (Genesis 49.8-10)

Given this promise to the tribe of Judah and, at the same time, the prestigious position of leadership acquired by the tribe of Ephraim (also foretold by Jacob in Genesis 48), it is not difficult to see that these two tribes were on a collision course — and Benjamin was caught in the middle. Benjamin's close proximity to Judah only heightened Ephraim's concern in the region.

Back on Map 6-7 run your finger along the north-south route between Shechem and Bethlehem. Note how this route must avoid the *Shiloh System* (canyons draining the area between Tappuah, Shiloh and Bethel), skirting around the most difficult part of this region (called *the remote places* or *the interior* in the Bible). Climbing out of the Shiloh System the route reaches the strategic road center at Bethel on the *Bethel Plateau*. Here it crosses the route which links Jericho with Aphek on the Coastal Highway.

South-southwest of Bethel a convenient ridge between deep canyons allows access onto the main plateau in central Benjamin, which you will come to know as the *Central Benjamin Plateau*. This small but important region is outlined by the cities of Mizpah, Gibeon, Ramah and Gibeah. The plateau served as the crossroads between the north-south route and important east-west connections from the Transjordanian Highway and Jericho to Gezer near the International Coastal Highway. Map 6-7 shows that routes in this region form a network of connections linking such important centers as Aphek, Bethel, Jericho and Gezer. Indeed, the entire region can be seen as one unit, with Benjamin's territory (soon to appear on this map) encompassing the strategic plateau just south of Bethel.

In addition to geographical (and therefore economic) realities Bethel has a special place in Israel's religious history. It was in this region that far-reaching promises were made and dramatic events occurred in the lives of Abraham and Jacob (Genesis 13, 28.10-22 and 35.1-21). In his earlier years while seeking a wife in northern Mesopotamia Jacob was reminded that *I am the God of Bethel!* (Gen. 31.13). In Egypt, on his death bed, the promises and the events of Bethel are still uppermost in his mind as he prepared to pronounce his final blessings. *God Almighty appeared to me at Luz [Bethel's original name]* (Genesis 48.3).

Considering all of these factors, it was natural for Ephraim to look upon the region of Bethel and the strategic territory just south of it with special concern. Religious connotations (Patriarchal promises), potential economic opportunities (trade) and political/military considerations (defense) made Ephraim's southern flank high on her list of priorities.

In the early years of Israelite settlement during the distribution of tribal inheritances, 6-2 a Benjamin and its territory played a very interesting role. After the tribe of Judah and the House of Joseph received their territory (Joshua 15-17), the leadership of Israel gathered at Shiloh (in Ephraim) in order to decide on the distribution of land among the other tribes. Joshua (of Ephraim) gave the instructions to the tribes.

> *Just how long are you going to sit around before going out and possessing the land which the Lord, the God of Abraham, gave to you! Give me three men per tribe, and I'll commission them. They'll get up and out into the land and bring back to me their survey which can be used for land distribution [for the remaining tribes west of the Jordan]. They should make seven divisions, **Judah remaining in its limits to the south and the House of Joseph remaining in its limits to the north**.* (Joshua 18.3-5)

In Joshua's remarks there is a hint of potential trouble between the stronger power centers of Judah and the House of Joseph. The important question was which remaining tribe would receive the strategic territory between these two larger units. When the survey was completed, Joshua cast lots *before the Lord in Shiloh* (Joshua 18.9-10). The results of that moment were to affect all later history of the region. The die was cast in the very first decision of our record.

> *Then the lot of the tribe of the sons of Benjamin, according to their families, came up. As it turned out the territory of their lot was **between the sons of Judah and the sons of Joseph**.* (Joshua 18.11)

6-2 b i   Joshua 18.12-18 gives a rather detailed description of the territory of the tribe of
Benjamin, including its cities (noted in the center of the page above Map 6-2). In some
regions the boundary between Benjamin and Ephraim is difficult to distinguish,
especially in the area of Bethel. According to the boundary description the city is in
Ephraim. However, it is also included in the list of Benjamin's cities. The city of
Ophrah also presents a problem. However, these seemingly overt contradictions may
be explained by the fact that the Ephraim-Benjamin border was probably never
meant to be totally clear-cut. It may also reflect military campaigns in the region discussed in later map studies. Irrespective of proposed solutions, it should be underscored here that Ephraim's concerns in the region of Bethel and its strong ties to the
territory of Benjamin are basic for all later studies in this region.

MARKING

    1. **Brown write-in:**
        a. Find the nahal system which drains from Shiloh (center of the map) to the area
          of Aphek (W edge of map) together with its various tributaries. Along this nahal,
          just E of Aphek = NAHAL SHILOH. (You may want to read the next write-in
          before marking this one.)

        b. W of Lebonah, between the three routes = THE REMOTE PLACES.

    2. **Green border and write-in:** The territory of the tribe of Benjamin.
        a. Benjamin's southern border with Judah beginning in the SE corner of the map at
          the Jordan River SE of Beth-hoglah (with your green pencil) = From the Jordan
          River to the dot of Beth-hoglah and the dot of Beth-arabah, W and then SW into
          the hills (running just S of the route) to the *t* of Ascent and the last *m* of
          Adummim, along the ridge and curving around to the dot of En-shemesh, and
          around the *n* of En-rogel, from the *u* of Jerusalem NW to the dot of Waters of
          Nephtoah, W/SW through the *z* of Mozah, the *E* of Mt. Ephron and *Z* of Zobah
          to the dot of Kiriath-jearim.

        b. Benjamin's northern border with Ephraim beginning at the Jordan River just E
          of Jericho (with your green pencil) = From the Jordan River W between the dots
          of Gilgal and Jericho (S of the dot for Gilgal and N of the dot for Jericho),
          continuing W on a ridge into the hills and then bending slightly NW (toward the
          dot of Ataroth-addar) to the yellow highlighted route just S of Bethel, and then
          SW through the last *r* of Ataroth-addar to a point W of the *G* of Gibeon, crossing
          the highlighted route and immediately turning W (running just S of this route)
          until finally curving sharply S to the *K* of Kiriath-jearim.

        c. After checking your work, mark these borders with your green pen (without
          running through letters). With your green pencil shade in the inside of all of
          these lines to indicate that they delineate the approximate limits of Benjamin's
          control. (Although Bethel and Ophrah are mentioned in the city list of Benjamin
          in Joshua 18.23, the region belongs to Ephraim according to the border descrip-
          tion.)

        d. In the open area between the dot of Jericho and Beth-aven, and not too close to
          either city = BENJAMIN (written with one letter under the other).

     3. **Blue underlining:** Unconquered Canaanite centers from Map 6-1 = **Beth-shemesh**
      (Har-heres), **Aijalon, Shaalbim** (all in Dan) and **Gezer** (in Ephraim).

4. **Blue box around name**: Unconquered Canaanite center of special importance = **Jerusalem/Jebus** (in Benjamin).

5. **Orange underlining**: Gibeonite cities studied in Chapter Four = **Gibeon, Beeroth, Chephirah** and **Kiriath-jearim.**

6. **Black write-in** (small caps): Between Gibeon and Chephirah (in three lines) = FOUR GIBEONITE CITIES.

DISCUSSION

Having completed the background marking for Map 6-7, sit back and take a good look at your work. As it stands now the map presents one of the best statements on Ephraim's southern priority in and around the territory of Benjamin. You might want to compare it with Map 6-2 in order to see the extent of Ephraim's official territory. It is interesting to note that the main places of tribal assembly (political and religious) were in the territory of the House of Joseph: Gilgal, Shechem, Shiloh and Bethel (No. 113 on Map 6-2).

On Map 6-7 find Shiloh in Ephraim. Somewhat isolated but centrally located, it served well as the tribal and religious headquarters until the days of Samuel. From Shiloh there was a direct link to Bethel and from Bethel southwest to Gezer near the International Coastal Highway. Gezer was included in Ephraim's inheritance. However, the Bethel-Gezer connection passed along the edge of the tribal territory of Benjamin.

To the east of Bethel the Jericho oasis (an all-important link to the Transjordanian Highway) and Gilgal (another tribal meeting place and religious center) provided a door for expansion in that direction. One of the keys to eastern and western control was the Central Benjamin Plateau (the area between Gibeah, Ramah, Mizpah and Gibeon), the *crossroads of Benjamin.* Just south of the plateau the Jebusite area (around Jerusalem) still had not been occupied by Israelites.

The one most important factor on Map 6-7 is the strategic unity of the Jericho-Gezer region, especially in the central region where north-south and east-west routes intersect. Ephraim dared not neglect this southern flank which, together with the regions east, north and west of Shechem, comprised its natural economic and political areas of interest.

You will remember that the introductory chapter of the book of Judges presents very important regional information relating to tribal settlement. Two facts about Ephraim and Benjamin should be underscored here. The first is in Judges 1.22-26, which states that Ephraim conquered and settled Bethel. Ephraim's strong presence in this strategic area was therefore an early established fact. The region is sometimes referred to in later history as the *Hill Country of Ephraim,* although this term was also used in a general sense for all the Hill Country of Ephraim and Manasseh. (This terminology lends weight to the importance of Ephraim within the House of Joseph.)

The second fact is found in Judges 1.8 and 1.21. These verses state that early in this period Jerusalem was attacked by Judah (Judges 1.8), perhaps in a move to match Ephraim's presence at Bethel. However, Judah appears to have stopped short of occupying the city and its territory.

But the sons of Benjamin did not drive out the Jebusites living in Jerusalem, and so to this day the Jebusites are still living with the sons of Benjamin [in Benjaminite territory] in Jerusalem. (Judges 1.21)

6-3 f
These two facts, an Ephraimite presence at Bethel (north of Benjamin) and the undecided fate of Jerusalem (on Benjamin's southern border with Judah), prepared the *playing board* for some of the most decisive moves in Biblical history. These moves had far-reaching political, religious and economic significance. It was in the interests of Ephraim, and to a great degree within her power, to control Benjamin. The fact that Benjamin (or the House of Joseph) did not move to settle the Jebusite area is no doubt explained by Judah's own interests in this area on her northern border. In fact, the Jebusite enclave may have developed after the time of Joshua and could have served as a type of *buffer state* between Judah and the House of Joseph. No doubt political analysts of the day already realized that it was only a matter of time before each of these tribal power centers would challenge the other for the position of leadership in Israel and the control of the tribe of Benjamin. It was finally David of Bethlehem in Judah who decided the fate of the region, claiming Jerusalem for his new political and religious capital (Map 7-7). Had he not made this move, Jerusalem may have remained just another city along the north-south highway in the hills.

EHUD AND THE MOABITES

DISCUSSION

6-7 a
Because of the strategic importance of Benjamin, its territory was often the scene of conflict resulting from internal tribal disputes or from invasions by surrounding nations. One of these attacks came from Moab, a nation in Transjordan (just off the southeast corner of Map 6-7) which had enlisted the support of the Ammonites and Amalekites.

The oasis of Jericho (or as our story calls it, *the city of palms*), served as the *back door* to Benjamin, to Ephraim/Manasseh and to Judah. The Israelites knew this well, since it was at Jericho that Joshua had led the children of Israel to victory in their opening campaign in Canaan. Therefore, events along this main eastern approach could never be ignored by people living in the central Hill Country.

The importance of Jericho may explain why it was included in Benjamin's territory and not assigned to one of the stronger neighboring tribes. This would have helped to keep a sense of balance in the region. The question of tribal control faded, however, during the Moabite occupation of *the city of palms*. It is not difficult to imagine what this Moabite presence in Jericho meant for those living along the routes of the Hill Country. *For eighteen years the people of Israel toiled for Eglon, the king of Moab* (Judges 3.14). The Moabites knew the strategic value of Jericho, for it served them well as a main base for the exploitation of Israel. Centuries later Israel would use this same base in her exploitation of Moab.

It was *Ehud, son of Gera from Benjamin, a left-handed man,* who finally made a move. Details of his well-thought-out plan of action while presenting his taxes to the king of Moab make interesting reading in **Judges 3.12-30.**

MARKING
1. Brown write-in:
a. Between Adam and the Dead Sea, just E of the river = JORDAN RIVER.

b. In the Dead Sea, just S of the mouth of the Jordan River = FORDS OF THE JOR-DAN (small caps) with arrow pointing to the nearest E-W route crossing the Jordan River.

2. Blue write-in and sweeping arrow and circle:
a. Just off the map, E of the mouth of the Jordan River = MOAB.

b. Circle around names of **Gilgal** and **Jericho**.

c. Arrow from Moab to Jericho region.

3. Black write-in: In convenient open area by Jericho = CITY OF PALMS (small caps) with small arrow to Jericho.

4. Flight (blue) and chase (green) arrow = Pointing SE to Moab across Jordan River. (Note red circle below.)

5. Red circle = Around the Fords of the Jordan (on part of the flight-chase arrow).

AN ATROCITY AT GIBEAH LEADS TO CIVIL WAR IN BENJAMIN

DISCUSSION
Up to this point much of our study on Map 6-7 has emphasized 1) the special position of Benjamin between the stronger tribes of Judah and Ephraim, 2) the strategic importance of the territory of Benjamin on Ephraim's southern flank, and 3) Ephraim's legitimate concern over developments in and around Benjamin. With these important factors opens one of the most tragic episodes in the history of the region, the tribal civil war in Benjamin, which reduced the tribe to a mere six hundred fighting men.

6-7 c

The story occurred rather early in the period, since Judges 20.28 states that *Phinehas the son of Eleazar [the nephew of Moses] was still officiating.* It is, however, reserved for the closing chapters (19-21) of the Book of Champions (Judges), although no champion is mentioned in it. Unlike most of the accounts in this book, the story is entirely an internal problem. There are no Philistines, no Moabites nor any Canaanites mentioned. No famous deliverer like Samson or Deborah emerges. The person who precipitates the drama is known only as *a certain Levite* in the opening verse (19.1). The closing phrase (21.25) underscores the lack of central authority in the country when *there was no king and each person did what he felt like.*

One of the main causes of moral decadence was a self-centered attitude resulting in a complete lack of concern for others. The warm Near Eastern hospitality seen in Bethlehem of Judah is contrasted with the indifference of the Benjaminites to the needs of a stranger in their midst. The words of the Levite who lived in Ephraim, spoken to another Ephraimite in the open square of Gibeah, present a clear testimony against this city of Benjamin and its inhabitants.

> *We are crossing [through Benjamin] from Bethlehem in Judah to the interior*
> *of the Hill Country of Ephraim where I live. I went to Bethlehem in Judah, and*
> *I am now on my way home — but no one offers me a place to stay.* (Judges 19.18)

READING

Read **Judges 19**. As you do, keep an eye on Map 6-7 taking careful note of the geographical information (cities, routes, etc.) and references to the tribes of Ephraim,
Judah and Benjamin. This chapter introduces one of the Bible's most graphic stories,
recounted a number of times in detail with little disguised or excused. It casts a long
shadow over subsequent Benjaminite history and creates a situation which affects
Benjamin's ability to withstand the mounting pressures on her small but strategic
territory.

DISCUSSION

The next chapter (Judges 20) describes the civil war between the Benjaminites and
all of Israel, sparked off by the Levite's report and the evidence of the *Gibeah affair.*
The resulting united tribal front against Benjamin (including support from Gilead
across the Jordan) is rarely seen in Israelite history. It appears that no tribe wanted
to be missing at this most important moment in Israel's geopolitical history. One
could venture to say that the Gibeah affair was only a convenient excuse to get the
real issue out on the table — who would ultimately control the territory of Benjamin?

In addition to external threats from surrounding nations, internal pressure on Benjamin
had resulted from her location between Ephraim and Judah. Now in the Gibeah affair
Benjamin was confronted with a united tribal front (including tribes from Gilead in
Transjordan), mobilized at Mizpah on the northern edge of her rather undefined
border with Ephraim. (In this same region, *between Ramah and Bethel,* Deborah and
Barak earlier had issued their call to arms against the Canaanites of the north.)

Internally Benjamin was faced with other problems. Geographically she was anything
but isolated, situated at the crossroads of highways coming from all points of the
compass. On her southern flank the Jebusites were potentially a *fifth column* who
could not be trusted. There were also the Gibeonites, who occupied the all-important
western approaches from the Coastal Highway. Their trick on Joshua (Joshua 9) had
made it possible for them to remain in the very heart of Benjaminite territory.

Before you read the account of the conflict in Judges 20, a few specific notes on Map
6-7 should prove to be helpful.

1. The Bethel-Bethlehem route passes through various regions. It leaves the strategic
   area around Bethel and in a few kilometers descends to Mizpah. Here it emerges
   out onto the Central Benjamin Plateau, outlined by the cities of Mizpah, Ramah,
   Gibeah and Gibeon. Although covered by low hills, this plateau provides the
   ease of travel not available in any of the eroded regions around it.

2. Gibeah is situated on a narrow watershed ridge just south of the Central Benjamin
   Plateau. To the west, and particularly to the east and the northeast of the city,
   deep canyons define Gibeah's prominent position on one of the most important
   internal highways in the Hill Country. These canyons are the subject of many
   discussions about the hiding place of *the men in ambush who sped and rushed
   upon Gibeah* during the conflict.

3. A number of place-names mentioned in the story are not yet identified (Gidom, Baal-tamar and Nohah). They all may not represent actual cities but some regional features in the area. The text also speaks of hand to hand conflict *along the highways, one of which goes up to Bethel and the other in the direction of Geba off the beaten track.* (Some prefer to read *Gibeah* or *Gibeon* instead of *Geba* which would change the scene of part of the conflict. *Off the beaten track* literally means *out in the country*, which better fits the setting of Geba, east of the Central Benjamin Plateau on the edge of the Wilderness. (The name *Geba* appears in black by mistake on Map 6-7 in the first printing of the *SMM*.)

4. Some comment must be made regarding the large numbers in this chapter. The discussion centers around the translation of the Hebrew word *eleph*. This word often is translated *thousand* but can also mean a *family, clan, or military unit of fighting men* (such as a squad of ten to twenty soldiers). The *twenty-six, twenty-two, eighteen, ten,* should not be thought of as so many *thousand* men but as so many *units* of men, each unit consisting of somewhere in the neighborhood of ten to twenty fighting men each. (A unit of ten is mentioned specifically in verse 10.) This interpretation does not detract from the authority of the Scriptures in any way. It simply attempts to understand what the Bible actually says. Certainly it places the other numbers in the chapter in a reasonable context.

> . . . *seven hundred picked men who were left-handed* (verse 16).

> . . . *about thirty men of Israel* (verses 31 and 39).

> . . . *one hundred men of Benjamin, all of whom drew the sword* (verse 35).

> . . . *six hundred men [who] turned and fled toward the Wilderness to the rock of Rimmon* (verse 47).

READING
With this background **read Judges 20**, giving special attention to geographical information and possible markings on Map 6-7.

MARKING
1. **Sweeping green arrows and write-in** =
   a. From just NE of Bethel to Mizpah (just E of the road) with TRIBES MOBILIZE written along the arrow in small caps.

   b. From Mizpah to Ramah (small arrow to show the Israelite advance toward Gibeah.)

2. **Orange on dot**: Center of Benjaminite defense = **Gibeah**.

3. **Yellow HL on name** = **Geba** (printed in black by mistake in the first printing of the *SMM*).

4. **Red confrontation marks: ✳** =
   a. On road halfway between Ramah and Gibeah with a small *1* and *2* beneath it in red (separated by a comma).

   b. Between Ramah and Geba with a small *3* just N of it in red.

5. **Sweeping orange arrow**: Benjaminite retreat after the third encounter with the unified Israelite forces = From the region of Geba to the E and the NE toward Rimmon.

6. **Brown write-in**: E of Rimmon = **Rock** (small caps).

DISCUSSION

A very interesting chapter brings to a close this final episode of the book of Judges. The tribes of Israel appear to wake up to the fact that the conflict in which they had just participated had been costly. Benjamin had been seriously weakened, and tribal energies had been depleted. Now they were faced with a much greater peril. If Benjamin were allowed to disappear altogether, a vacuum would be created in the region. This could trigger a civil war on a much greater scale than anyone wanted to imagine. It would pit Ephraim against Judah for the control of the region. Some sort of an arrangement had to be negotiated in order to avoid such an eventuality.

To replenish the tribe of Benjamin, wives were sought for the six hundred men of Benjamin who survived the conflict. When the first solution (decided on at Bethel) did not provide enough wives to go around, a second is devised. It centered around Shiloh in Ephraim, one of the main gathering places for tribal activities. Shiloh was a central and secure place in which the Ark of the Covenant was kept, although it was taken out to other places (like Bethel) for an unspecified length of time.

Nestled high in the Hill Country of Ephraim, Shiloh was protected on the west by the rugged Shiloh System (the *interior* or *remote places of Ephraim* as the Bible calls it). To the east the steep descent into the Jordan (Rift) Valley created a drop of 1100 meters in ten kilometers (3600 feet in six miles). Unlike the open and vulnerable Central Benjamin Plateau with roads in all directions, the isolated, beautiful Shiloh Valley offered all the security needed for the Ark and its attendants.

It was in these hills of Ephraim, in the midst of their own family (the House of Joseph), that the remaining Benjaminites found wives to repopulate their tribal inheritance. Perhaps there are even geopolitical overtones in this story as technicalities are overcome by an apparently fair (and amusing) arrangement with the Benjaminites.

READING

In light of all of the political and moral implications discussed above, read **Judges 21**. Remember that it brings to a climax a period of external threats and internal apostasy. It was in this context that Samuel was born, that spiritual leader from Ramah in Benjamin who grew to manhood at Shiloh.

MARKING

1. **Yellow HL on name and red underlining** = **Jabesh-gilead** (NE corner of map).

2. **Orange circle around name**: Finding wives for the Benjaminites in Judges 21 = **Jabesh-gilead** and **Shiloh**.

3. **Black write-in** (small caps):
   a. Just W of orange circle of Jabesh-gilead = 400 WIVES TAKEN FOR BENJAMINITE REMNANT (small caps, two lines).

   b. Between the orange circle of Shiloh and the HL route = OTHER WIVES TAKEN.

DISCUSSION

The gruesome details of this final story in the book of Judges may have left you with mixed feelings of contempt and despair. This is no doubt the perspective which the Biblical writer wished to convey. Certainly one of the hallmarks of the Bible is that *it tells it the way it was*, recording at times a side of human nature which we would rather forget.

In addition to preparing us for Samuel's ministry of revival on Map 7-3, this perspective may provide us with part of the context for St. Paul's remarks in the New Testament over a millennium later. In his letter to the Romans this *chief of sinners*, as he describes himself, carefully builds a case for God's judgment over all, Jew and Gentile alike (Romans 1-3). In spite of this seemingly hopeless situation, he goes ahead to illustrate the fact that *where [man's] sin increased [God's] grace abounded even more* (Romans 4-8). He then deals with one of the main issues of his letter, the relationship between the growing Gentile church and its original Jewish stock (Romans 9-11). In the middle of this discussion the Apostle, a well-trained and former zealous Pharisee, makes the following statement regarding God's grace. Could he have had in mind the sad events portrayed on Map 6-7 as he gave us details on his own personal background?

> *Concerning Israel he [Isaiah] says, 'I have stretched out my hands all day to a disobedient and a hostile people.' Can I say, therefore, 'Hasn't God rejected his people?' Never! I myself am an Israelite, a descendant of Abraham, from the tribe of Benjamin!*   (Romans 10.21-11.1)

LEGEND
Blue underlining or blue box = Map 6-1.

S M M   7 – 3

TITLE: SAMUEL'S MINISTRY

DATE: 11TH CENTURY B.C.

INTRODUCTION

Your study of Map 6-7 concluded with the discussion of the civil war in the region of Benjamin. This reflected the continuing struggle of Ephraim and Judah for the coveted area between them. Potentially this internal tension could harm Israelite interests far more than pressures on them from the outside. We are told that in this period *each person did what he felt like*. If such self-centered and covetous desires (exhibited in the actions of the men of Gibeah in Judges 19.22-26) were to dictate tribal policies, Israel was indeed in trouble.

As if all of the problems seen on Map 6-7 were not enough, a new threat had emerged on the Coastal Plain, frustrating Israelite tribal interests in the region. It was, however, forcing the tribes to consider ways and means of meeting the common need of defense.

This threat came from the Philistines, who had taken control of the southern Coastal Plain around 1150 B.C. From their five main centers (cities in blue boxes on Map 6-1) they were in the process of extending their political and economic control both along the strategic Coastal Highway and eastward into the Hill Country. In the contemporary story of Samson (Judges 13-16) the fear of Philistine retaliation echoes in the question put to him by the men of Judah after one of his raids on the Philistines.

Don't you realize that we're under the control of the Philistines?
Look at the mess you've gotten us into now!   (Judges 15.11)

MARKING

1. **Yellow HL on route** = Coastal Highway (printed in red) from the SW corner of the map to the N edge of the map (via Gath, Ekron, Gittaim and Aphek and then N off the map) and from Aphek W off the map.

2. **Yellow HL on name:**
   a. Along the Coastal Highway = **Gath, Ekron** and **Ashdod** (three of the five Philistine cities) and **Aphek.**

   b. Along the N-S route in the Hill Country = **Shechem, Bethel, Mizpah, Ramah, Bethlehem** and **Hebron.**

   c. In the Jordan (Rift) Valley = **Gilgal** (the religious center by the oasis of Jericho which assumed importance during this period).

3. **Blue write-in:** In the open area between Ekron and Timnah (avoiding the road) = PHILISTINES.

4. **Blue on dot** = **Jerusalem/Jebus.**

5. **Green write-in:**
   a. In the open area between Bethel and Tappuah = EPHRAIM.

   b. In the open area between Bethlehem and Hushah = JUDAH.

   c. In the same general location as on Map 6-7 = BENJAMIN. (The actual territory of the tribe of Benjamin can be seen on Map 6-2.)

6. **Green border** (first in green pencil and then in green pen):
   General limit of Israelite settlement but not implying there was Israelite control = Beginning in the SW corner of the map and running N between the names of Gaza and Lachish, then NE via the name of Moresheth-gath but W of Azekah and Shaaraim, then N between Aphek and Ebenezer but stopping 1 cm./½ in. before the Aphek-Ebenezer route, beginning again 1 cm./½ in. N of this same route, continuing N off the map. Shade in the E side of this line with green pencil.

SAMUEL'S BIRTH AND CHILDHOOD AT RAMAH AND SHILOH

DISCUSSION AND READING

7-3 a   Within the context of tribal friction, internal religious corruption and Philistine domination, the Bible introduces a remarkable figure. He was born of a Levitical family which had settled in Ephraim. The family actually lived at Ramah, on the edge of that well known region between Ephraim and Benjamin. The area *between Ramah and Bethel in the Hill Country of Ephraim* had been famous since the days of Jacob

(Genesis 35.5-21 with 1 Samuel 10.2 and Jeremiah 31.15). It was here that Deborah ministered (Judges 4.4-5) and the Israelite tribes mobilized (at Mizpah) during the Benjaminite civil war (Judges 20.1-3). North from Ramah, along this route which had seen so much sadness, beneath the hill of Mizpah and through the important center of Bethel came Hannah on her way to Shiloh. She was one of the few bright lights in this otherwise gloomy period. Aware of the corruptions in the religious establishment she nevertheless came to present her request in simple trust. In the year following her prayer of faith and her song of praise she brought forth that *champion of the faith*, who had been so sorely needed in the closing chapters of the book of Judges. Samuel, the prophet and priest, would preach repentance and personal commitment to an apostate generation. In the midst of the winds of political change he also would anoint the first and second kings of Israel, Saul and David.

Skim **1 Samuel 1-3**, noting some of the themes mentioned above and the context in which Samuel came of age.

PHILISTINE VICTORY AT EBENEZER BY APHEK

DISCUSSION
Philistine control of the International Coastal Highway was only a prelude to an ex-   7-3 b
pansionist policy which included some of the country's main routes. We have already seen (Map 7-4) that in the north Philistine control ultimately reached the Jezreel Valley and Beth-shan via Megiddo. The limited Israelite tribal forces had no hope of winning a battle in these areas.

The only way Israel could possibly frustrate Philistine ambitions was to choose the right place in which to attack, a place where all Israelite forces could emerge from the hills and quickly concentrate on one objective. This place was near Aphek on the Coastal Highway.

The *Geographical Preview* to this chapter discussed the setting of Aphek at the head of the Yarkon River. Here the swamps produced by large springs forced coastal traffic inland through a narrow *funnel* of land (between the springs and the Hill Country of Ephraim). Nearby, in the low hills overlooking Aphek and its rich agricultural plain, a site has been tentatively identified with Ebenezer. In this region the Israelites mobilized and set up camp in their bid to overrun Aphek and thereby contain the Philistines.

It is clear that this battle was not another skirmish in the on-going Israelite-Philistine conflict. It was a major offensive by the tribes, a carefully planned *all-or-nothing-at-all* attempt to defend Israelite interests in the land.

It is also interesting to note on Map 6-2 that the strategic region of Aphek was allotted to Ephraim. One wonders if this did not have some degree of influence on the choice of the battle field. From a more practical point of view, the ridge routes east of Aphek led directly into *the remote places of the Hill Country of Ephraim* (the Shiloh System). This region offered convenient hiding places for the Israelites in case of a Philistine victory.

It is not hard to imagine the disappointment when the first Israelite attack met with strong Philistine resistance and failed. At this moment of frustration the Israelites reaped the fruit of decades of apostasy — they put God on trial. Ascending to Shiloh they thought that they could *take control of God.* Carrying the Ark through the most difficult part of the Hill Country of Ephraim was certainly a formidable task, one which may have given them a certain sense of satisfaction. Arriving at the edge of the Hill Country, above Aphek, they must have had a certain feeling of security and impending success in the air, mixed with those shouts of triumph.

READING

You may want to complete the marking below before reading **1 Samuel 4.** The end of this tragic story shows the consequence of the *God-in-a-box* attitude. The episode is a warning to all who feel at one time or another that they can *package God* or control Him by any man-made device or system. Moses himself, who had every reason to feel that he had an edge on God's revelation, thought it wise to warn Israel of this danger when he said, *Never put the Lord your God on trial* (Deuteronomy 6.16).

MARKING

1. **Blue box around name:** Philistine camp = **Aphek.**

2. **Green box around name:** Israelite camp = **Ebenezer.**

3. **Sweeping blue arrow:** Philistine mobilization = From Gittaim to Aphek.

4. **Sweeping green arrows:** Israelite mobilization =
   a. From Pirathon along the ridge to Ebenezer.

   b. From Timnath-serah to Ebenezer.

   c. From Shiloh, curving to the N of Tappuah and then W to Ebenezer.

5. **Red confrontation mark** in the open space between Ebenezer and Aphek = ✱ .

6. **Green flight arrows:** Israelite retreat = Short arrows from Ebenezer back to Pirathon, Timnath-serah and Shiloh. (No Philistine chase arrows are required.) Although archeological remains indicate that Shiloh was destroyed in this period, it is not known if this was by the Philistines, or which route they may have taken to Shiloh. Red on the dot of Shiloh would indicate its destruction.

THE ARK IN PHILISTIA AND ITS RETURN VIA BETH-SHEMESH

DISCUSSION AND SUGGESTED READING

7-3 c   The sequel to the battle of Aphek and the loss of the Ark of the Covenant is found in **1 Samuel 5.1-7.2.** In short, the lesson to be learned (with all due reverance) is that *God can take care of Himself.* Happenings in Philistia demonstrated that indeed God's power to deliver had not changed but that it was in some way linked to the attitude in man's heart. This message was not new to Israel. It echoed both the words of Moses to the children of Israel prior to their entry into the land and of Joshua's farewell challenge to the tribes at Shechem.

> *And now, Israel, what does the Lord your God ask of you? It is this —*
> *[first and foremost] to recognize who the Lord your God is, [and then] to*
> *walk in all His ways, to love Him and to worship (serve) the Lord your*
> *God with all your heart and with all your soul.*   (Deuteronomy 10.12)

*And now [Israel] recognize who the Lord is and worship (serve) Him
with all [that is within you] and with sincerity [of heart].*   (Joshua 24.14)

All of the events studied thus far on Map 7-3 occurred during Samuel's early years at Shiloh. They must have made a deep impression upon him. Later in his life, the lesson of the battle of Aphek and the return of the Ark from Philistia may have served as the background to his preaching and ministry in the main religious centers in Benjamin and in southern Ephraim (1 Samuel 7.15-17).

*If you are coming back to the Lord with all your heart . . . then
fix your heart firmly on the Lord, worshipping Him alone,
and He will deliver you from Philistine domination.*   (1 Samuel 7.3)

We should not be surprised that Jesus preached the same message to a Samaritan woman beneath Mt. Gerizim. Had He not passed Ramah (Samuel's home), Mizpah, Bethel and Shiloh on His way through the territory of Benjamin and Ephraim to Jacob's well, a stone's throw from the ancient site of Shechem and the Tomb of Joseph?   `12-5/6`

*The hour will come — and in fact it is here already — when true
worshippers will worship the Father **in spirit and in truth**, for that
is the type of worshipper the Father desires. God is a spirit, and those
who would worship Him must worship **in spirit and in truth**.*   (John 4.23-24)

This is the message which rings through the hills and the history of Samaria.

MARKING

1. **Yellow HL on name** = **Beth-shemesh** and **Kiriath-jearim**.

2. **Yellow HL on route** = The route from Ekron to Kiriath-jearim via Beth-shemesh.

3. **Sweeping orange arrow**: The Ark taken to Philistia = From Gittaim to Ashdod.

4. **Orange arrows**: Travels of the Ark in Philistia (five arrows) = From Ashdod to Gath, from Gath to Ekron, from Ekron (via Timnah) to Beth-shemesh and from Beth-shemesh to Kiriath-jearim (via the highlighted route).

5. **Orange on dot**: Cities in Samuel's preaching circuit = **Bethel**, **Gilgal**, **Mizpah** and **Ramah**.

DELIVERANCE FROM THE PHILISTINES AT MIZPAH

DISCUSSION AND READING

Samuel's ministry had a definite impact on the national conscience. He appears to have concentrated his efforts in the established religious centers of southern Ephraim and Benjamin. In this same region Deborah had ministered during the period of the Judges (Map 6-5), *between Ramah and Bethel in the Hill Country of Ephraim.* (Shiloh was probably in ruins by this time.)   `7-3 d e`

The success of Samuel's efforts presented a direct challenge to Philistine domination. His ministry consolidated the people of Israel in a religious revival which could not be separated from political and territorial aspirations. (The current history of the Middle East is the best example of this phenomenon.)

The Philistines were quick to recognize this threat to their control and moved to break up public meetings which could turn into national independence movements. It was again at Mizpah, in that area *between Ramah and Bethel in the Hill Country of Ephraim,* that Samuel's spiritual mobilization took place. There he demonstrated God's power to deliver Israel — but only after a period of repentance and renewal. The full story should be read in **1 Samuel 7.3-14.**

MARKING

1. **Yellow HL on name = Beth-car** (at Lower Beth-horon).

2. **Yellow HL on route** = From Mizpah SW across the plain (not printed on the map) to join the ridge route W of the name Gibeon to Beth-car, Gezer and Gittaim.

3. **Sweeping blue arrow**: Philistine advance to Mizpah = From Gezer via Aijalon and Beth-car to about 2 cm./3/4 in. W of the site of Mizpah.

4. **Red confrontation mark**: Just W of Mizpah between the city and the point of the blue arrow = ✳ .

5. **A flight (blue) and chase (green) arrow** = From Mizpah to Upper Beth-horon.

6. **Three blue flight arrows** = From Beth-car to Gezer.

LEGEND

Orange arrows	= Travels of the Ark and its return.
Orange dot	= Cities in Samuel's circuit.

S M M 7 − 4 , 7 − 7 and 7 − 1

INTRODUCTION

Map 7-4 (Saul's beginning and end) was partially completed in Chapter One. Some marking will be added in this chapter but finished in Chapter Four. Map 7-7 (David's reign) will also be marked in Chapter Four. Map 7-1 (David's census and Solomon's reign) was marked and discussed in the first two chapters.

While these three maps contain many details which relate to Ephraim's southern flank, time will not be spent discussing them in this chapter. What will be stressed is Benjamin's transition from a dependent position under the shadow of Ephraim to an integral part of Judah's northern defenses. The shock of this change was felt for centuries to come in the skirmishes and battles of the region. One period of the region's history, the first fifty years of the Divided Kingdom (930-880 B.C.), could even be termed the *battle for Benjamin.*

MARKING (Map 7-4)

1. **Yellow HL on name = Bethel, Mizpah, Ramah, Gibeah, Jerusalem** (stay off the dot), **Bethlehem** and **Hebron.**

2. **Green write-in:** In the open area N of Bethel = EPHRAIM.

3. **Blue on dot** = Jerusalem.

DISCUSSION

Ephraim's influence over Benjamin had been evident since the period of tribal settlement. Ephraim carefully monitored events on her important southern flank, which was her frontier with Judah via Benjamin. The main center of this surveillance was Bethel. In the eleventh century B.C. the area south of Bethel served as the home territory of Samuel, who played a significant role in those transitional years between the period of the Judges and the rise of the monarchy.

The background and the accounts of Samuel's involvement in the choice of Saul as the first king of Israel are given in 1 Samuel 8-10 (Map 7-4). Unfortunately, specific information on certain journeys and city names is not provided. However, it appears that the main activity again took place *between Ramah and Bethel in the Hill Country of Ephraim.* Also the site of Mizpah is again given a prominent place as the point of gathering for important discussions on the matter of the monarchy. Its position, overlooking the strategic Central Benjamin Plateau (including Samuel's home in Ramah and Saul's village at Gibeah), provided an appropriate stage for these discussions (1 Samuel 10.17-27).   7-4 a b

In this setting it would be surprising if Ephraim did not play an important role during the discussions. The choice of the unknown Saul of Benjamin must have come as a surprise (or perhaps a relief) to many attending this important meeting. During the drawing of lots (1 Samuel 10.20-24) one is almost forced to hold his breath as the name of the tribe of Israel's first king is announced. When the name *Benjamin* was heard, there was no doubt a sudden hush, and there were certainly many unspoken questions.

Could this reflect an advantage for Ephraim? Would Judah accept it? Could a man from Benjamin be trusted in the light of the events leading up to the civil war there? What kind of leader would this weakened tribe produce to meet the threat of Philistine domination? It is no wonder that Saul (who appears to be aware of the final outcome before it was announced) took the opportunity to slip away and to hide in the baggage which tribal VIP's had brought to the conference.

The following lots pointed to Saul who lived — of all places — at Gibeah. While some of the delegates felt that God's choice was their choice, others scorned what they felt to be a totally wrong decision. It would be interesting to know their tribal backgrounds.

The entire episode, set as it is in potential tribal friction, was anything but encouraging for Saul. He must have had many second thoughts on his way back to Gibeah. The first test of his abilities came when the Ammonites in Transjordan attacked Jabesh-gilead, from where four hundred of Benjamin's ancestors (wives after the civil war) had come (Map 7-4). Then there were his major opponents the Philistines, who still persisted in their goal of controlling the Central Benjamin Plateau and thereby dividing the tribes of Judah and Ephraim.   7-4 c

In the midst of these external threats from the east and from the west, there was always the difficult balancing act of meeting Judah's security needs in the south while satisfying Ephraim's desire to keep her prominent position in the north. Both of these tribes were facing increasing Philistine pressure to which Saul would have to respond.

Given these challenges and the limited tribal resources Saul accomplished much in his reign, as we learn from 1 Samuel 14.47-48. However, through all of this it was Saul's response to the spiritual challenge which concerned Samuel. Could Saul, unlike some of Israel's earlier *champions,* stand up to the pressures and continue 7-4 d e   *to fix [his] heart firmly on the Lord* (1 Samuel 7.3)? During two campaigns, one against the Philistines in Benjamin and the other against Amalekites on Judah's southern flank (1 Samuel 13-15), Saul fell short of Samuel's expectations. These campaigns are discussed in Chapter Four when Map 7-4 will be completed.

7-4 h   With the death of Saul and his son, the crown prince Jonathan, in that fateful battle at Mt. Gilboa, the whole question of who would lead Israel was again opened. Had Saul of Benjamin demonstrated a balanced policy between Ephraim and Judah? Would his successor be strong enough to keep the Philistines out of the Hill Country and consolidate the successes of Saul? Were there contenders in Judah who could effectively challenge the Benjamin-based monarchy and create *a more even-handed policy* in respect to the House of Joseph? As it turned out, it was the task of David from Bethlehem in Judah to respond to many of these questions. In David we find both an astute military/political leader and a person with the spiritual qualifications which God desired, *a man after His own heart* (1 Samuel 13.14).

The life of David is studied in Chapter Four (Maps 7-5 through 7-7). It is not possible in our present discussion, however, to ignore some of the new facts in Benjamin which David created during his reign. Even without marking Map 7-7 we can use it to make these facts clear.

7-7   On Map 7-7 find the main north-south route in the Hill Country from Shechem to Hebron. Note again the east-west connection from Jericho via Bethel to Aphek (just off the map in the west, beyond Ebenezer). Also follow the route from Jericho to Ramah on the Central Benjamin Plateau, and from there the routes on to Gezer in the west. [In the first printing of the *SMM* the arrow for Gezer points the wrong direction.] Also note the proximity of Jerusalem (south of Gibeah), where a Jebusite enclave still served as a type of buffer between Judah and the Ephraim/Benjamin territory. Finally, compare all of these links (in and around the Central Benjamin Plateau) with the more isolated setting of Hebron, farther south in the Hill Country of Judah.

David came to appreciate the strategic importance of the Central Benjamin Plateau. This small region had far-reaching geopolitical significance during his lifetime. He may have recognized this during his stay with Saul and Jonathan at Gibeah. If, as a simple shepherd boy, he did not know of it, his recent experience with Goliath and the Philistines provided ample reason for considering the land's defenses and regional realities.

David quickly grasped Benjamin's strategic position. Effective control of the plateau was more than a factor in discouraging renewed Philistine campaigns in the hills. It also provided the springboard for Israel to expand out to the International Coastal Highway (via Gezer) and over to the Transjordanian Highway (via Jericho).

There were, however, certain problems related to David's emerging plan to take over Benjamin. What was the future of the present Benjamin-based regime (the House of Saul)? What action could serve as an excuse to start the process leading to Judah's takeover of the Central Benjamin Plateau, an action which would appear to be a legitimate move by Judah? Finally, and most important, what would Ephraim's response be to all of this?

The first response came with the death of Saul and Jonathan. Subsequently the re- | 7-7 a
maining supporters of the Benjamin-based monarchy had to be contained. This was perhaps one of David's most difficult tasks, one which his supporters carried too far at times. The excuse which David needed to start his takeover of Benjamin was not hard to find. It lay in the Jebusite enclave at Jerusalem, just across a small canyon | 7-7 b
from Judah. After all, the men of Judah had already campaigned there (Judges 1.8), and for years Benjamin had not laid claim to the area (Judges 1.21). Being north of Hebron (David's first capital) and more centrally located, Jerusalem would serve well as a new capital for Israel — one which required as its first line of defense the Central Benjamin Plateau.

Ephraim's response to these moves may have been expressed in its support for Saul's successors in the north and in Transjordan. However, David's lightning tactics soon won him the support (if only outward recognition) of all the tribes. By the time Ephraim realized what had happened, David was already established, and there was nothing effective she could do.

Distrust and rebellion smoldered in the north during David's rule. There the only major flare-up recorded was when Sheba, the son of Bichri of Benjamin, issued his call to arms, and the northern tribes attempted to break away from David. However, David's security forces soon had the situation under control. Solomon, David's son, was able to capitalize on his father's achievements as we saw summarized on Map 7-1 | 7-1 c
in Chapter One (which would be well to review at this point). At the same time Solomon appears to have had the wisdom to appoint a separate officer over the district of Benjamin (1 Kings 4.18), thereby giving the appearance that Benjamin was still, to some degree, independent of Judah.

The real battle for Benjamin was yet to come. The smoldering coals would break out | 8-2 a
into flames as soon as Solomon was off the scene. Ephraim could not allow this intolerable situation to continue. It is here that we again meet *Jeroboam, son of Nebat, from Zeredah in Ephraim* (1 Kings 11.26). With the encouragement given him during his exile in Egypt this ambitious Ephraimite successfully reversed the trend which David had initiated. The attitude of the House of Joseph during those long years of David's and Solomon's reigns is summarized in that outburst at Shechem. It came when Rehoboam, Solomon's son, decided to apply more pressure on the northern tribes to keep them in line. His decision, taken after a great deal of thought and numerous discussions with his advisors from Judah, provided the impetus which Jeroboam needed. At last Ephraim would throw off the yoke of Judah and return to the place of leadership in the north.

> *What's in it for us to be a part of David?*
> *Are our natural rights dependent on the son of Jesse?*
> *To your tents [back to the good old days], Israel!*
> *And as for you [House of] David, mind your own business [back in Judah]!*
>   (1 Kings 12.16)

S M M   8 — 2

INTRODUCTION

This map was marked in Chapter Two. As a prelude to the discussion below, skim over the discussions for this map in Chapter Two.

DISCUSSION (with Map 8-2 open)

This chapter on the region of Samaria has stressed the importance of Shechem in the political and religious history of Samaria. Geographically its position is second to none in the entire Hill Country. Thus it is not surprising to find that it was at Shechem that Rehoboam met with representatives of the northern tribes in order to reconfirm their allegiance to the Jerusalem-based monarchy.

The outcome of this meeting has been discussed earlier. There are a few points, however, which should be underscored here with Map 8-2 and the *SMA* in view.

1. The revolt of the northern tribes (Israel) was led by a man from Ephraim called
8-2 a **Jeroboam.** His home was in Zeredah in the proximity of Timnath-serah, Joshua's inheritance (seen on Map 7-4 along the ridge between Bethel and Aphek). It would be interesting to know Jeroboam's lineage and possible connections with the family of Joshua, but no information is available. (A Greek supplement to the original Hebrew texts of these chapters in 1 Kings adds a number of details, but it cannot be trusted.)

2. Shechem's centrality had both advantages and disadvantages during Jeroboam's
8-2 b reign. The campaign of Pharaoh Shishak against Judah and Israel would certainly have included Shechem. (The name is missing from Shishak's inscription: however, a portion of the inscription has been destroyed.)

3. Jeroboam moved his capital to Tirzah, but the time of the move is not known. There were certainly considerations of security in this move. However, another major factor was Tirzah's location and its convenient connection with Penuel across the Jordan in Gilead. These two capitals created a certain geographical and tribal unity which Jeroboam no doubt had as one of his top priorities. This, after all, was what Ephraim previously had strived to maintain, tribal unity with Ephraim at the head. On Map 8-2 it is clear that Shishak's campaign attempted to destroy cities along main routes and thereby to discourage political and economic advantages. (The geographical order of the city-list is still a subject of discussion.)

4. Jeroboam purposely disassociated himself (and his kingdom) from the religion of Judah. Jeroboam actually had no other choice, given 1) the promise of leadership to Judah (Genesis 49.8-12), 2) the prominence of the Jerusalem-based monarchy with its representatives throughout the entire country (the Levites of 2 Chronicles 11.14) and 3) his own obvious aspirations for the northern tribal league and Ephraim. It was either a continuation of Judah's dominance or a once-and-for-all break. He chose the latter. We may not condone his choice, but we should try to understand his dilemma.

5. The significance of Jeroboam's building at Dan has already been discussed. Here we should underscore Jeroboam's wisdom in choosing Bethel as a sanctuary and administrative center in the south. Its prestigious position in the past and its strategic location both made it the only logical candidate. However, it stood as a thorn

in the flesh for Jerusalem and as such would become the object of Judah's plan to maintain control of the Central Benjamin Plateau and, if possible, the route ascending to the region of Bethel. Jeroboam's building of Bethel was the first shot in the *Battle for Benjamin* which was soon to break out. This explains why we often read that *military conflicts were always breaking out between Rehoboam and Jeroboam*. In this region *between Ramah and Bethel in the Hill Country of Ephraim* there was no way to avoid this.

The question arises as to who actually benefited the most from these internal conflicts (political, military and religious). In the long run it was certainly not the northern tribal league (Israel) nor the Jerusalem-based monarchy (Judah). The winner was Egypt. *Divide and conquer* was Egypt's principle. As a result Shishak's campaign in the land must have caused many to stop and think. In spite of certain inequities, a united Israel had allowed a certain political stability, great territorial expansion and economic advantages on the scale that Israel and Judah alone would never be able to match. In the wake of Egypt's campaign in the area, lesser nations surrounding Israel and Judah would rise again and claim their share in the profits of this *Land Between*.

8-2 c

Although there were periods of Israelite prosperity, local conflicts and infighting among nations in the region continued for two centuries (about 930 to 730 B.C.), or until Assyria appeared on the scene in the person of Tiglath-pileser III. However, the first fifty years of these two centuries (930-880 B.C.) witnessed very strained relations between Israel and Judah, mainly over the question of who ultimately would control the territory of the tribe of Benjamin and approaches to it from the Transjordanian Highway and the International Coastal Highway.

READING
1 Kings 12.25-33 is such an important passage that it would be helpful to read it again at this time. Its emphasis on Bethel continues into 1 Kings 13, which you may want to skim.

S M M   8 – 4

TITLE: JUDAH-ISRAEL BORDER DISPUTES; ETHIOPIAN THREAT TO JUDAH

DATE: 930-880 B.C.

INTRODUCTION
Around 900 B.C. the *Battle for Benjamin* climaxed in several fascinating diplomatic and military moves. These are portrayed in the northern area of Map 8-4. The other part of the map treats earlier developments in Judah under Rehoboam (930-913 B.C.). It is marked in Chapter Four.

MARKING
1. **Green write-in**: In the open area just W of Bether and Peor (to the W of Bethlehem) = JUDAH.

2. **Orange write-in**: In the open area E of Timnath-serah (W of Bethel and Birzaith) = ISRAEL.

3. **Yellow HL on name** = **Jerusalem, Ramah, Mizpah, Mt. Zemaraim, Bethel, Jeshanah, Ephron/Ephrain** (NE of Bethel), **Tirzah** (name E of Ephron) and **Geba** (E of Ramah).

4. **Green box around name**: capital of Judah = JERUSALEM.

5. **Orange box around name**: capital of Israel (to the N off this map) = TIRZAH.

6. **Yellow HL on route** =
   a. All routes which were HL on Map 6-7 (copied from Map 6-7 noting strategic centers like Jericho, Bethel, Ramah, etc.).

   b. The route from Ephron to Bethel (copied in pencil from Map 6-7 and then HL).

7. **Blue border and write-in** = From the NW corner of the map moving SE between Gittaim and Gibbethon, and between Gezer and Timnah, curving around Timnah (just E of the name) and then SW to the W edge of the map, passing just S of Gath. Shade in the W side of this border and write in PHILISTINES in the open area W of Ekron and Gath.

REHOBOAM'S DEFENSE STRATEGY IN JUDAH

DISCUSSION

8-4 a   After the division of Solomon's kingdom (930 B.C.) there was continuous fighting between **Jeroboam** and **Rehoboam**. Although much of it no doubt related to the area you have just marked (between Israel and Judah), no details are given regarding specific campaigns. It is interesting to note that 2 Chronicles 11.5-12 provides a list of cities which Rehoboam strengthened in and around Judah. However, no specific fortress or military depot is listed for Benjamin, that sensitive area just north of Judah. We only read that Rehoboam strengthened cities in Benjamin and thus *had Judah and Benjamin under his control.* This may reflect the lack of stability in the region during this period and the fact that the border between Judah and Israel was still undefined. Both sides were maneuvering for control of this region *between Ramah and Bethel* where names are highlighted on Map 8-4.

8-4 b   We now turn to the events which occurred just before and after 900 B.C. The first recorded move was made by Rehoboam's son **Abijah** (sometimes **Abijam**) during his short three year reign (913-910 B.C.). A very interesting combination of diplomatic and military moves gave Judah the upper hand in the area of Bethel, which Judah had coveted for some time.

During Abijah's reign the tensions which had characterized relations between Israel and Judah continued. We are told that *a state of war [continued] to exist between Abijam and Jeroboam* (1 Kings 15.7). At some point Abijah was able to negotiate an alliance with Damascus (the two fathers mentioned in 1 Kings 15.19). This type of diplomatic move would have been logical early in Abijah's reign. His concern for the security of the northern tribes and for those in Transjordan (with its capital at Penuel on Map 8-2) may have turned Jeroboam's attention away from his southern border with Judah.

In any event, Abijah felt strong enough to attack the Bethel region via the Central Benjamin Plateau. His well-trained forces met the army of Jeroboam in the region just south of Bethel by Mt. Zemaraim. As can be seen on Map 8-4, the north-south ridge narrows at this point, being constricted by deeply eroded canyons on the east and the west. These canyons provided the cover that Jeroboam's ambush needed as they circled around Abijah's forces. (Today the twin cities of Ramallah/el-Bira cover this strategic ridge.)

Abijah finally gained the upper hand in the battle and then wisely extended his campaign to include the northern and eastern approaches to the Bethel region (Jeshanah and Ephron/Ephrain). This successful offensive must have shocked the Northern Kingdom and Jeroboam's advisors at Tirzah.

READING

Read now the detailed account of this episode in **2 Chronicles 13**. Note how Abijah carefully chooses his words in his dramatic speech prior to the battle. His reference to recent events and to David's accomplishments have strong religious overtones. The geographical setting makes the speech even more relevant. Abijah would have been looking toward the famous (now infamous) religious center of Bethel, one of his prime objectives in this campaign. His religious emphasis, however, may have provided a convenient pretext for other objectives — the political and economic control of the Bethel region. His move should not come as a surprise after all that this region has come to mean to you in your study of this chapter.

MARKING

1. **Red on dot** = Bethel, Jeshanah and **Ephron/Ephrain.**

2. **Green arrows**: Abijah's campaign =
   a. From the Central Benjamin Plateau (just W of the name Mizpah) running NE by the dot of Mt. Zemaraim and pointing to Bethel. (Note the place of the write-in below before marking.)

   b. From Bethel N and splitting into two with one branch pointing to Jeshanah and the other to Ephron/Ephrain.

3. **Green write-in:**
   a. Just below the longer green arrow = ABIJAH.

   b. At the S end of the longer green arrow = *1* (a small number one inside a small circle).

4. **Red circle around name** = Gibbethon (in northern Philistia).

5. **Sweeping orange arrow**: Israel's campaign in northern Philistia (Gibbethon) = Along the Coastal Highway (running just W of it) and pointing S to Gibbethon.

DISCUSSION

When Abijah of Judah died, his son **Asa** became king (910 B.C.). Israel's loss of the Bethel region to Judah had serious repercussions. Perhaps it had something to do with **Baasha's** assassination of Jeroboam's son Nadab, together with all of Jeroboam's family, shortly after he became king at Tirzah. The coup was carried out during a military campaign against northern Philistia. On Map 8-4 note how this campaign reflects Israel's attempt to outflank Judah by expanding her control along the strategic Inter-

8-4 c

8-4 d

national Coastal Highway. In this region there are important connections to the Central Benjamin Plateau. Israel's attempt to take Gibbethon was, therefore, part of a continuous *battle for Benjamin.*

8-4 e During the reigns of Asa in Judah and Baasha in Israel, diplomatic and military activity over the issue of territory between the two nations continued. As the head of a new dynasty at Tirzah, Baasha needed to demonstrate his ability to deliver. 1 Kings 15.19 tells us that he renegotiated a treaty with the king of Damascus. This relieved pressure on the north and allowed him to concentrate on solving problems in the south. We are not told just how he retook the Bethel region, but, like Abijah, Baasha was not satisfied with Bethel alone. He extended the campaign to include the southern approaches of Bethel, the Central Benjamin Plateau with its strategic crossroads at Ramah. This automatically isolated Jerusalem and produced an intolerable situation for Judah. The implications in Baasha's move are summarized well in one of the headlines of the day.

> *Military clashes between Asa [of Judah] and Baasha [of Israel] were occurring all the time. At one point Baasha, king of Israel, mounted an attack against Judah. In it he was able to fortify Ramah and thereby cut off all of Asa's [northern] links to the outside world (allowed no one to go out or to come in to Asa, king of Judah).*   (1 Kings 15.16-17)

MARKING
1. **Sweeping orange arrow** = From the area between Jeshanah and Ephron/Ephrain running SW, passing just E of Bethel and pointing to Ramah.

2. **Orange box around dot**: Baasha's fortification = **Ramah.**

3. **Orange write-in:**
   a. On the orange arrow = BAASHA.

   b. At the N end of the orange arrow = *2* (a small number two inside a small circle).

DISCUSSION
It is not difficult to see that the earlier coastal campaign (at Gibbethon) was related to the struggle for the Central Benjamin Plateau around Ramah. (We later find Israel again attacking Gibbethon in 1 Kings 16.15-16). It appears to be part of a well-thought-out policy of weakening Judah's influence in the region and thus allowing Israel to return to its dominant position. These battles again underscore the importance of Ephraim's southern flank in the history of Israel.

READING
Just as the ruling family at Tirzah could not tolerate Judah's control of Bethel, the Jerusalem-based monarchy was now forced to respond to the loss of Ramah and the Central Benjamin Plateau. **1 Kings 15.16-22** outlines the diplomatic and military moves taken by Asa of Judah. Read this passage carefully with Map 8-4 open before
8-5 a you. Verse 20 refers to Map 8-5, which you should turn to at that point.

MARKING
1. **Small green triangle on dot** (filled in): Asa's fortifications on the border with Israel = **Mizpah** and **Geba.**

2. **Green border**: Stabilized border between Judah and Israel, which divided up the
territory of Benjamin between them = From the edge of the map (below the *m*
of Kingdom in the map title) running W to the *m* of Michmash (along the ridge
just S of the Jericho-Bethel route), continuing NW and passing N of Geba, N
of the name Ramah and N of the dot of Mizpah (skipping over other lines which
you have drawn), W via the *dd* of Ataroth-addar, the *r* of both Beth-horons and
the *b* of Shaalbim and joining Philistia's border at a point just S of Gittaim. Shade
in the S side of this border.

DISCUSSION

The border between Israel and Judah which you just drew emerged from decades of
conflict. The strategic nature of the region was at the heart of the conflict. Both
Israel and Judah saw the territory of Benjamin as essential to their vital interests.
From the very beginning, during the distribution of tribal territories, Benjamin's fate
was sealed. The civil war fought there only weakened her ability to withstand surrounding pressures. The Benjamin-based monarchy under Saul did not reflect Benjamin's strong political or military stance. It only underscored her uncomfortable position of being between two stronger tribes and her inferior rank. Benjamin did not
threaten them and therefore served them well.

Now at last the sacrifice of Benjamin was complete. It can be seen by comparing
Benjamin's territory on Map 6-7 with the final border arrangement on Map 8-4. It
is clear that Judah came out ahead. The Central Benjamin Plateau including Mizpah
was under the control of Jerusalem. Also Judah had been able to keep control of the
western approaches to the plateau but had lost Jericho on the east. With Jericho she
lost the connections to the Transjordanian Highway.

The process which had begun with David's capture of the Jebusite stronghold at Jerusalem was now complete. Jerusalem and her northern approaches were firmly in
Judah's control and would remain there. Ephraim had lost Benjamin but maintained
control of the area around Bethel.   At last there was a measure of stability in this
region *between Ramah and Bethel in the Hill Country of Ephraim.*

The *Battle for Benjamin* and its approaches, together with the enmity which emerged
from it, was not soon forgotten. Subsequent strained relations between Judah and
Israel were always seen in the light of this struggle. Thus it is not surprising to hear
the echo of this battle in the words of Isaiah the prophet almost two centuries later.

> *Then Ephraim's jealously will be put aside,*
> *And the enmity of Judah will cease to be.*
> *Ephraim will not be jealous of Judah,*
> *And Judah will not be hostile toward Ephraim.*
> *But [together] they shall swoop down over Philistia on their western flank,*
> *And as one they shall plunder the people [nations] on the east . . . .*
>   (Isaiah 11.13-14)

This prophetic promise, like others in the same chapter of Isaiah, stands out as something abnormal and rarely, if ever, seen. The enmity between Israel and Judah and the
struggle for dominance in the region of Benjamin is, therefore, one of the basic factors
in our understanding of Ephraim's southern flank.

LEGEND
Green box   = Rehoboam's fortifications.
Red dot   = Abijah's campaign.
Orange box   = Baasha's campaign.
Green triangle   = Asa's fortifications.

S M M   8 – 5

DISCUSSION

Maps 8-5, 8-1 and 8-7 have already been marked and discussed. For the most part they represent a period (880-840 B.C.) when Israel and Judah *buried the hatchet* and even cooperated in various areas, including military campaigns with joint forces. The following paragraphs summarize several important issues of this period in the history of Samaria. (Map 8-8 is a useful reference for the following discussion.)

1. Background

8-4 f Shortly before 880 B.C. another coup took place at Tirzah. 1 Kings 16.8-13 describes the assassination of Elah, Baasha's son, by **Zimri**, the commander of half of the kingdom's chariots. In his brief seven day reign, Zimri also wiped out the entire royal family and its political associates. Among other things this coup reflects dissatisfaction with the way Baasha handled the *Benjamin affair,* a concern for Ephraim's deteriorating status in the region and a general loss of confidence in the family's ability to lead the nation. Asa of Judah had outmaneuvered Baasha, and Israel had lost Benjamin

8-5 a for good. Tirzah's alliance with Damascus was dissolved and replaced by a Damascus-Jerusalem agreement. This created the real possibility of renewed pressure on the northern tribes and in Transjordan, areas coveted by Damascus. Meanwhile Israel's army was again out on the field, attempting to contain the Philistines at Gibbethon on the Coastal Highway. Given the death of Baasha and his son's lack of concern in matters of state it is not surprising that a high ranking army officer carried out the plot while the new king was *drinking himself drunk in Tirzah.*

8-4 f Another person who was watching the situation closely was **Omri**, the head of Israel's armed forces. When news of Zimri's takeover at Tirzah reached Omri in Gibbethon, his forces immediately proclaimed him as king. The ensuing internal struggle left Zimri dead at Tirzah. However, it took five more years of civil war (Omri against Tibni) to establish Omri as sole leader in the north.

2. The Rise of Omri and Ahab and Developments in Israel's Foreign Policy

The state of affairs inherited from Baasha's reign and the years of civil war left Israel in a weakened position. When Omri finally quelled the internal strife (880 B.C.), he was still faced with the task of rebuilding the country and stabilizing its foreign policy. His response to this challenge demonstrated his political skills and a grasp of the times in which he lived.

8-5 b a. Omri's first move was to leave Tirzah. It was a site to which Jeroboam had retreated and was no longer suitable. A new capital was needed to signal a new beginning for the country. Omri chose a strategic location in Western Samaria with convenient links to the Coastal Highway. His military experience and his campaign at Gibbethon had underscored the importance of this route. (Here it is helpful to highlight in yellow the International Coastal Highway, which is printed in red on Map 8-8.) Omri's new capital at Samaria (Shomeron in Hebrew) allowed him to extend Israel's influence into this strategic area which at this time was not under the control of the Philistines. In addition, it was there that Israel could enjoy the benefits of trade without direct confrontation with Damascus or Jerusalem.

b. Building diplomatic ties and alliances with surrounding nations was a key factor during this period. In some cases conflicting national interest did not allow this. Damascus, for example, had developing interests along the Transjordanian Highway to the east. Only a few years earlier she had stabbed Israel in the back by breaking off relations with Tirzah and attacking the north at the request of Jerusalem. Israel had also been in open conflict with the Philistines at Gibbethon on the Coastal Highway. This could not be resolved easily now that the capital of Israel was at Samaria.

Israel's conflicting interests with Damascus in the east and the Philistines in the west meant that she was forced to mend fences elsewhere. Thus, during the years of rule by the House of Omri (880-841 B.C.), there is no record of military confrontation between Israel and Judah. To the contrary, we find that the kings of Israel and Judah cooperated in various military campaigns against the Arameans of Damascus (Maps 8-5 and 8-7) and against Moab (Map 8-6, yet unmarked). It appears that after wasting their resources in the *battle for Benjamin,* both Israel and Judah recognized the advantages (and the need) for such cooperation. At last there was peace in the region *between Ramah and Bethel.*

The most important diplomatic move by Israel was the forming of an alliance   8-5 c
with Phoenicia, culminating in the marriage of Ahab, Omri's son, with Jezebel, the daughter of the king of Sidon. The alliance opened the ports of the Mediterranean to Israel and to the goods she could export from the highways she controlled. This was exactly what Israel's economy needed at that moment. We may not condone the religious compromise inherent in such an agreement, but we can understand the reasoning behind the action.

c. The opening of the Mediterranean markets to goods from Israel encouraged the king of Samaria to seek control of important Transjordanian trade routes. In the northern regions this brought him into direct conflict with the king of Damascus. In central Transjordan the control of Moab became his prime objective. In the days of Ahab, after his marriage with Jezebel, we are given a hint of Israel's expansion in the direction of Moab when we read that *Hiel of Bethel reconstructed Jericho* (1 Kings 16.34). This statement almost appears to be out of context or at least insignificant unless Ahab's Transjordanian policy is understood.

The ministries of Elijah and Elisha (Maps 8-1 and 8-7) also reflect Israel's control   8-1 b
of Bethel, Jericho and regions across the Jordan (1 Kings 17.1-7; 2 Kings 2). The   8-7 a
most significant piece of information comes from the opening chapters of 2 Kings where we are told that Moab threw off the yoke of Israel at Ahab's death (2 Kings 1.1; 3.4-5). Thus the new beginning for Israel under the House of Omri was to include political and economic control of as much of the Transjordanian Highway as possible. This meant that a series of wars with Damascus and her allies in Transjordan was inevitable.

The successful combination of all of the factors discussed above was the task of the kings of Israel (the House of Omri) during this period. Measured by man's standards of success these kings did their job well. Few in Israel questioned their ability to lead the nation during this period. From our perspective we make a mistake when we condemn the prosperity and the success of the period in and of itself. We are equally wrong to condone all of the methods used to usher in this new age. When all is said and done, the words of Moses again come to mind. In any discussion of this affluent and yet apostate age, each person must make his or her own application of this message.

> *Be careful in case you say to yourself, 'My power and the might of my own*
> *hand have made me successful!' Remember the Lord your God, since it is*
> *He who gives you strength to succeed in order to carry out His covenant*
> *which He swore to your fathers . . . . But in the event that you totally*
> *forget the Lord your God and pursue other gods, worshiping them and*
> *bowing the knee to them, I warn you right now, you will be wiped out.*
> *Like the nations which the Lord is destroying before you, in the same way*
> *will you be destroyed for not taking seriously the voice of the Lord your*
> *God.*   (Deuteronomy 8.17-20)

READING

8-5 b   The *SCS* for Map 8-5 lists suggested reading for this study which you may want to skim. Of special interest is the summary of events at Tirzah and the move of the capital to Samaria which are related in 1 Kings 16.

S M M   8 − 7, 8 − 8 and 9 − 4

DISCUSSION

Between the years 853 and 841 B.C. the local scene in the land changed drastically. On Maps 8-5 and 8-7 in Chapter Two these changes were discussed. In the following paragraphs developments in the ninth and eighth centuries B.C. are summarized, climaxing in the dramatic campaigns of Tiglath-piliser III of Assyria (734-732 B.C.).

8-5 h   1. See-saw battles between Damascus and Samaria raged toward the end of Ahab's life. Sometimes Judah joined forces with Israel in an attempt to control strategic centers along the Transjordanian Highway. This centered around Ramoth-gilead (1 Kings 20 and 22.1-37). The only respite from these conflicts was in 853 B.C., when all nations in the region joined forces against the Assyrian assault (led by Shalmaneser III) in northern Mesopotamia (1 Kings 22.1).

8-6 c   2. With the death of Ahab (perhaps beginning just prior to it) Moab revolted against Israelite domination. This revolt may well have received encouragement from Damascus. Such developments in Transjordan spelled trouble for Israel's political and economic life. After Judah's and Israel's attempt to put down the revolt (2 Kings 3), Moab organized its own campaign against Judah which failed (2 Chronicles 20.1-30).

8-6 d e

8-6 f   3. Military confrontation between Damascus and Samaria continued into the reigns of Ahab's sons. Meanwhile Judah was faced with revolts in the southeast of Transjordan (Edom) and in the west (parts of Philistia) near the Coastal Highway (2 Kings 6-8; 2 Chronicles 21).

4. These events take you up to 841 B.C. and Map 8-7. In that year the regimes of both   8-7 d
   Damascus and Samaria were toppled by internal coups led by Hazael and Jehu. The
   northern approaches to the country suffered a short-lived but serious attack by
   Shalmaneser III of Assyria, and Judah was plagued by internal division. As a result   8-7 e
   Israel, as well as Judah, was left in a weakened position. Hazael, the new leader in
   Damascus, was quick to take advantage of the situation, penetrating the country's   9-1 d
   defenses and overrunning highways in both the east and the west. There was no
   relief until Damascus was forced to surrender to the Assyrians (Adad-nirari III) a   9-1 e
   generation later (about 806 B.C.).

5. The fall of Damascus was followed by a period of political stability, territorial   9-1/2
   expansion and economic growth in Israel and in Judah. The first half of the eighth   e i
   century (800-750 B.C.) saw a remarkable recovery in both nations. The Samarian-
   based monarchy reached its zenith under **Jeroboam II.** In Israel the feeling of
   success and a false sense of security in the midst of affluency is strongly condemned
   by prophets who knew the times. (Those with more time would find a quick
   reading of the prophets Amos and Hosea very interesting at this point in the study.
   This also is the setting of the book of Jonah.) **Uzziah** of Jerusalem culminated the
   period in Judah. In spite of the good times there was a certain undercurrent of
   distrust and jealousy between the two monarchies. In the one incident preserved for
   us the king of Israel answers a challenge from the king of Judah by sacking Jeru-   9-1 g
   salem (2 Kings 14.8-14; 2 Chronicles 25.17-24). During this affluent period important information on clans and settlement centers around the capital of Samaria
   comes from the *Samaria Ostraca,* sherds with writing on them found at excavations   9-1 f
   at the capital. These are the names which appear in red on Map 8-8.   8-8 b

6. Under the shadow of an Assyria on the move, the years between 750 and 735 B.C.   9-1 h j
   were hectic indeed. Internal political problems in Israel and a vacillating government in Jerusalem did not help the situation. Discussions on how to meet the
   Assyrian threat centered around Jerusalem's decision not to join the Samaria-
   Damascus alliance against the larger enemy. In the light of the final outcome Jeru-   9-4
   salem's decision was wise. In 734-732 B.C. Tiglath-pileser III carried out lightning
   attacks on all major highways of the country leaving little question as to who was
   in control of the situation. The resulting limitation of Israel to the Hill Country
   is dramatically portrayed by comparing the borders of Map 8-1 with those of Map
   9-4. The *good old days* of Ahab or Jeroboam II were gone forever.

S M M   9 – 5

**TITLE: FALL OF SAMARIA, ASSYRIAN EXPANSION UNDER SHALMANESER V
AND SARGON II**

DATE: LATE 8TH CENTURY B.C.

INTRODUCTION

The brief summary completed above takes us up to the final phase in the history of
the Samaria-based monarchy. Israel's borders as seen on Map 9-4 vividly illustrate

the intolerable situation in which she found herself after the campaigns of Tiglath-pileser III. She had no choice other than to bow to Assyrian might and demands. Around her an entirely new administrative world was developing, which would last for centuries after the fall of Samaria itself. The realities of this world crushed all hope of reviving the nation's former glory.

MARKING

1. **Yellow HL on route** = The International Highway (printed in red) beginning in the NE corner of the map by Chinnereth and running to the SW corner of the map via Megiddo, Aphek, Joppa and Ashdod; also the Gibbethon, Ekron and Gath branch.

2. **Red write-in** (small letters in red ball point pen): In the NE corner of the map in the sea area just E of Chinnereth = **Hamath**. (Note the HL below in case you prefer to complete that first.) Add a black arrow by the name pointing N off the map.

3. **Yellow HL on name** = **Samaria** and **Hamath**.

4. **Orange square around name**: Capital city = **Samaria**.

DISCUSSION

9-5 a   With the death of Tiglath-pileser III there was at last a glimmer of hope in Samaria. Israel's desire to break the Assyrian hold was encouraged by Egypt, who had been shocked by the recent demonstration of Assyrian might and her advance into regions leading to the Nile. Any nation in a position to cause problems for Assyria was Egypt's ally. The *Land Between* again became a buffer zone between Mesopotamia and Egypt.

The temptation to revolt was too great for **Hoshea**, Samaria's last king. When the revolt broke out, Assyrian military might moved in. Hoshea surrendered, but the city, with its strong defenses, held out for three years (724-722 B.C.). (The Assyrian king, Sargon II, claimed the victory which probably belonged to his predecessor Shalmaneser V who died in 722 B.C.)

In 722 B.C. Samaria fell, and with it came the end of that separate kingdom which Jeroboam, *son of Nebat from the Hill Country of Ephraim,* had created two centuries earlier. The history of this kingdom had been that of success mixed with defeat and frustration followed by reconstruction. This defeat, however, was different. There was no hope of reestablishing an independent nation. The Assyrian takeover was

9-5 b   irreversible. Assyria was on the move along the Coastal Highway toward Egypt, her ultimate goal. The century following the fall of Samaria was to be her century, one in which Assyrian power and control would reach its greatest extent.

MARKING

1. **Blue write-in and circle**: In the open area between Chinnereth and Gath-hepher (written across the route) = ASSYRIA (in large caps). Put a circle around this word in heavy blue.

2. **Sweeping blue arrow**:
   a. From the NE edge of the map (near Chinnereth) to the circle around *Assyria* (running just W of the HL route, but with no point on the arrow).

b. From the circle around *Assyria* to about 1 cm./½ in. N of Samaria, running between Jezreel and Ophrah and just W of Dothan, pointing toward Samaria. (Note additional red circle around Samaria below.)

3. **Blue write-in:** Above the sweeping blue arrow (beginning S of Jezreel) = SHAL-MANESER V.

4. **Black write-in:** Below the sweeping blue arrow and the name Shalmaneser V = (724-722 B.C.).

5. **Red circle around name** (including orange box) = **Samaria.**

READING AND DISCUSSION

The fall of Samaria receives special mention in the Bible. It served as a complement to   9-5 a
Moses' and Joshua's warnings centuries before. Read the actual account surrounding this important event in **2 Kings 17.1-6 and 18.9-12.** The commentary on the reasons behind this disaster is given in 2 Kings 17.7-41. The Bible also clearly states the Assyrian resettlement policy. The repercussions of these shifts in population were felt in the later history of the region down through the Greek and the Roman periods. A new era had begun. Samaria, with its mixed population, was now part of the Assyrian Empire. An inscription of the Assyrian king underscores our Biblical text: *I placed an officer of mine as governor over them and imposed upon them tribute as for Assyrian citizens.* Thus ended the history of the Northern Kingdom of Israel.

DISCUSSION

Rumblings continued to be heard along the road to Egypt. In the north the strate-   9-5 b
gic center of Hamath led a revolt which reached from Damascus to the Mediterranean (720 B.C.). Cities in the coastal region of Philistia mobilized (no doubt with Egypt's encouragement again) and attempted to stem the tide of the mounting Assyrian aggression (713-712 B.C.). Perhaps they were also prompted by similar revolts in Babylonia to the east.

Sargon II of Assyria met both revolts with Assyrian might. The strategic coastal region suffered the same fate as Samaria a decade before: *I reorganized these cities and settled therein people from the regions of the East which I had conquered personally. I installed an officer of mine over them and declared them Assyrian citizens . . .* The Assyrian king even boasts that the king of Ethiopia (who controlled Egypt in that period) made overtures to Assyria and established trade links.

During the next decade Judah, under Hezekiah, organized yet another revolt in the   9-6 a
area. Incidents surrounding this famous revolt receive special prominence in the Bible and are studied in Chapter Four.

Assyrian administrative control of conquered areas was effectively established during the late eighth century B.C. Assyrian provinces (created at various intervals) are indicated in blue in the following marking. Orange now becomes the color for Egypt in contrast to blue for Assyria.

MARKING

1. **Yellow HL on name** = Gibbethon, Ekron, Gath, Ashdod, Ashdod-yam/Asudimmu, Gaza, Raphia, Laban, Megiddo, Dor, Bethel and Jerusalem.

2. **Red on dot** = Gibbethon, Ekron and Gath.

3. **Red circle around name** (avoid other names and arrows) = **Ashdod** (where one revolt was centered) and **Raphia** (the site of an important battle between Egyptian and Assyrian forces).

4. **Red on arrow** = On each arrow in the SW corner of the map.

5. **Sweeping blue arrow** (Assyrian campaigns under Sargon II) =
   a. From the region of the Megiddo Pass (running just W of the HL route) S via Aphek and then splitting into two branches, one running W by Joppa and on S toward Ashdod, and the other from the Aphek region S and pointing to Gibbethon.

   b. From Gibbethon to Ekron.

   c. From Ekron to Gath.

   d. From Gath to Ashdod.

6. **Blue write-in**: On the blue arrow somewhere N of Aphek = SARGON II.

7. **Black write-in**:
   a. On the blue arrow from Joppa to Ashdod = (720 B.C.).

   b. On the blue arrow from Aphek to Gibbethon = (713-712 B.C.).

8. **Blue write-in**: Assyrian provinces (heavy caps)
   a. In Galilee just W of Gath-hepher = MEGIDDO.

   b. In the Sharon Plain just N of Migdal = (DOR) (which was later attached to Samaria).

   c. Just S of the city of Samaria = SAMARIA.

   d. In the open area between Ekron and Ashdod = ASHDOD.

   e. In the extreme NE corner of the map (partially in the sea area) = KARNAIM.

   f. On the E edge of the map, just N of Succoth = GILEAD.

   g. On the E edge of the map, just NE of the Dead Sea = AMMON (with a small black arrow pointing NE from the name).

   h. In the extreme SE corner of the map = MOAB.

   i. On the S edge of the map in the Dead Sea = EDOM (with a small black arrow pointing SE).

9. **Orange write-in**: In the SW corner of the map, written vertically above the map number = EGYPT (with a small black arrow pointing SW).

10. **Brown write-in**: On the W edge of the map in the sea area W of Joppa and H. Yavne Yam = BROOK OF EGYPT (with a small black arrow pointing to the SW).

11. **Green box around name = Jerusalem.**

12. **Green write-in**: Just SE of Jerusalem = JUDAH.

13. **Green border** = Copied from Map 9-4 (round off the corner by Lower Beth-horon). Shade in the Judah side of this border.

LEGEND (Map 9-5)
Large blue words = Assyrian Provinces

DISCUSSION
Sit back and compare Maps 8-1, 9-4 and 9-5. (Although Map 8-1 is from the period of Elijah, it could also represent Israel in the days of Jeroboam II.) These three maps vividly show the effect of three decades of Assyrian campaigns and penetration to the Brook of Egypt in Northern Sinai. The affluence and prosperity of an earlier period had changed into a nightmare of destruction and despair. Judah was left alone in the Hill Country, surrounded by Assyrian provinces. It was from this perspective that Isaiah the prophet did much of his preaching and Hezekiah planned his revolt.

At Bethel, just north of Jerusalem, a priest of Samaria, who had been sent back from   9-5 a
Assyria, ministered. In the midst of a hopeless political situation and growing religious unorthodoxy a voice was calling for repentance and renewal again. We know little about this priest except that he challenged his hearers *to recognize who the Lord is* (2 Kings 17.28). This was the only echo of Moses' and Joshua's preaching still heard in the Hill Country of Ephraim.

REVIEW ASSIGNMENTS

At the close of this study questions arise as to the nature of Samaria itself. What are the region's natural defenses? How far does Samaria's natural sphere of influence extend? Does the history of the region help answer these questions? How is the Biblical message linked to these regional perspectives?

The *Geographical Preview of Samaria and Surrounding Regions* in the opening pages of this chapter answers some of these questions. It would be helpful to review this preview at this point in your study with the *SMA* in clear view. Try to come to your own conclusions now that you have completed the assignments in this chapter.

A glance at the *SMA* shows Samaria's position in the central Hill Country. There is a question as to terminology (hills or mountains) for this terrain which reaches heights of over 900 meters/3000 feet. A much more important discussion concerns the nature of this Hill Country, its approaches, defenses and sphere of influence. The following paragraphs raise some of the important issues in such a discussion. Read them with both the *SMM* and the *SMA* handy.

1. Samaria is surrounded by plains or valleys on all sides except in the south. In the northwest, where Samaria is joined to the Carmel range, the Plain of Dothan with its international highway tends to separate Samaria from the range. While the plains surrounding Samaria are not totally open to travel and trade, they do provide the general perspective of open territory on three sides of the region. Activity on these plains can be seen by glancing at Maps 4-4, 4-5, 4-6, 4-1, 4-9, 6-2, 6-6, 7-3, 7-4, 8-2, 8-5, 8-7, 9-4 and 9-5.

2. In the region of Samaria the Hill Country is not uniform geologically. Types of rock and structural changes have resulted in a pattern of valleys and smaller plains which usually lead conveniently from one to another. (The main exception is the descent from Shechem to Tirzah.) These can be easily seen on the *SMA*. On the other hand, throughout most of Samaria travel along ridges is inconvenient. Only in the southwest (from the valley south of Shechem to Aphek on the Coastal Highway) do the uplifted and deeply-eroded limestone hills force routes to stay on the more convenient mountain ridges. Glance at the following maps and locate these various types of natural routes (valleys and ridges) in Samaria: Maps 4-3, 4-4, 4-8, 6-6, 6-7, 7-3, 7-4, 8-2, 8-5 and 8-8.

3. Various important centers in and around Samaria have been stressed in this chapter. The most important of these are **Aphek, Dothan, Samaria, Tirzah, Shechem, Bethel** and **Jericho**. After finding each site on your *SMA*, attempt to explain the significance of its location by answering the following questions about the site and the region in which it is found:
   a. What importance does it have to Samaria's defenses?

   b. What are potential external threats to the site or the region from international or surrounding local powers?

   c. Does the region in which the site is located lead to anywhere significant? In other words, is the site important in terms of Samaria's natural sphere of influence? Does Samaria's control of the region create a state of confrontation with surrounding nations? In this exercise do not forget the overlying importance of the International Coastal Highway and the Transjordanian Highway.

4. In light of your studies of Samaria (including the above review assignments) how would you summarize Samaria's natural defenses and sphere of influence? What do you see as necessary ingredients for the political and economic success of a Samarian-based monarchy? Consider the following (with the *SMA* in view) in answering this question.
   a. The International Coastal Highway and approaches from Philistia.

   b. The advantages of links to Phoenicia with its maritime trade contacts across the Mediterranean Sea.

   c. The Transjordanian Highway with links eastward from Beth-shan and from Jericho.

   d. The need to contain the expanding Aramean kingdom (based in Damascus) by fortifying various northern approaches to the country (Maps 8-5 and 8-7).

e. Rising Moabite nationalism, no doubt encouraged by Damascus.

f. Relations with Judah and the need to maintain control of the Bethel region and, if possible, the territory of the tribe of Benjamin.

CONCLUSION

The review assignments above have underscored the advantages and disadvantages of ruling the region of Samaria. This should make you more sensitive to policies of the kings of Israel in the tenth to eighth centuries B.C. It also helps explain why the Northern Kingdom was doomed to inevitable downfall when international powers again came on the scene.

Biblical writers knew the approaches to Samaria well. They used them as illustrations in their preaching and teaching to accentuate their message. Amos, a prophet from Judah sent to Israel, makes use of Samaria's position (the city) as he speaks of sending word out along the International Coastal Highway to Egypt. He also alludes to the city's position on a lone hill surrounded by higher hills on two sides, an almost theater-like setting facing the west.

> *Announce it throughout the strongholds in Ashdod [some prefer Assyria]*
> *and throughout the strongholds in the land of Egypt, and say, 'Get*
> *together on the hills [around] Samaria and see the confusion which is*
> *within her and the oppressions she contains.'*   (Amos 3.9)

Hosea, another prophet to Israel, emphasizes Samaria's strategic priorities in the agriculturally productive Valley of Jezreel. His words illustrate potential disaster and yet God's faithfulness.

> *On that day I will break Israel's bow in the Valley of Jezreel [just*
> *where it is needed most!].*   (Hosea 1.5)

> *'On that day I will respond,' says the Lord,*
>   *'I will respond to the heavens,*
>   *and they will respond to the earth,*
>   *and the earth shall respond to the grain, to the new wine and*
>   *the fresh oil,*
>   *and they will respond to God's sowing (Jezreel),*
>   *and I will sow her [Israel] to Myself in the land . . .'*
>   (Hosea 2.21-23)

Amos speaks of Israel's interests east of the Jezreel Valley, along the Transjordanian Highway. Success in that area and its approaches (at Karnaim and at Lo-debar) gave a false sense of security in a time when Assyria was beginning to stir again.

> *You who rejoice over Lo-debar and say, 'Didn't we — in our own*
> *strength — take Karnaim for ourselves?' But look [beyond Karnaim],*
> *O House of Israel, because I am raising up a nation against you, says*
> *the Lord, the God of Sabaoth. They will oppress you from Lebo-*
> *hamath to the nahal of the Arabah [from north to south and along the*
> *entire Transjordanian Highway].*   (Amos 6.13-14)

145

Connections between Shechem and Gilead via Adam and Succoth (as well as links to Moab) are implied in Psalm 60.6-8 (or 108.7-9) and in Hosea 6.7-10.

To the south the constant friction between Israel and Judah over the region between them is the background of one of Isaiah's great expectations as he contemplates a better time to come.

> *Then Ephraim's jealousy will be put aside,*
> *And the enmity of Judah will cease to be.*
> *Ephraim will not be jealous of Judah,*
> *And Judah will not be hostile toward Ephraim.*
> *But [together] they shall swoop down over Philistia*
> *   on their western flank [the International Coastal Highway],*
> *And as one they shall plunder the people [nations] on the east*
> *   [along the Transjordanian Highway] . . . .*   (Isaiah 11.13-14)

The potential for trade and expansion in and around the region of Samaria was great indeed. Given this potential it is surprising that the central site of Shechem did not continue to dominate the history of the region and the entire Hill Country in later years. The site has aptly been called *the uncrowned queen of the hills.* It is just that.

Your study in this chapter was concerned with the regions which surround Shechem. They served well as *God's testing ground of faith* in this *Land Between.* Over the centuries, and in spite of the ministries of prophets like Elijah, Elisha, Amos and Hosea, the leaders of the region failed *to recognize who God is.* Preferring to create their own kingdoms and their own gods, they persisted in *the sins of Jeroboam.* Finally, invasion, destruction and exile followed the same routes which earlier had brought trade and affluency. The changing fortunes of the House of Joseph (together with Benjamin) are summarized in **Psalm 80**, one of the Bible's most poignant and appropriate prayers to read at the close of this chapter. It echoes the days of Moses, the exodus and the covenant at Sinai, all of which Joshua the Ephraimite experienced. Joshua's attempt, late in his life, to reconfirm this covenant at Shechem and Samuel's persistent call to renewal at the close of the period of Judges are also heard in the psalmist's moving words of repentance.

Jesus and His disciples walked these same routes of Samaria. At least once, at Jacob's Well near ancient Shechem at the foot of Mt. Gerizim, the subject of a heartfelt response to God's call was discussed (John 4.1-43). It is not difficult to imagine that this theme was often the subject of Jesus' conversations with His disciples as they reviewed the history of this region through which they passed. The words spoken in the affluent days of Jeroboam II by a prophet to Israel must have penetrated their spirits.

> *For I delight in unchanging love, not sacrifice,*
> *The recognition of who God is, rather than burnt offerings.*
>   (Hosea 6.6)

CHAPTER FOUR

JUDAH AND SURROUNDING REGIONS

INTRODUCTION

The aim of the assignments in Chapter Four is to explore Judah (Judea) and the regions which surround it. The name *Judea* is a later Greek form of the Hebrew word *Judah*. The latter is a much more appropriate term to use in this period of history. The Bible gives detailed information about this area which also came to include Jerusalem, the city which David appropriated and transformed into the capital of his expanding kingdom.

The core of Judah, called the *Hill Country of Judah*, is a rather narrow ridge of uplifted limestone approximately 40 kilometers/25 miles long and 16 kilometers/10 miles wide. This Hill Country is surrounded by three regions: the Shephelah (Lowland) in the west, the Negev in the south and the Wilderness in the east. These regions are clearly seen on the *SMA* (northern and southern sheets joined) and on the key map which introduces Section One of the *SMM*. To the north of the Hill Country of Judah lies Benjamin (Ephraim's southern flank discussed in Chapter Three).

The *SMA* and the key map to Section One also provide a larger geographical context for Judah. Indeed, Judah's rich historical record must be understood in light of this larger context. While surrounding regions like the Coastal Plain (Philistia), Moab and Edom are important in their own right, their relationship to Judah is emphasized in this chapter because of Biblical priorities. The complexity of regional relationships and the historical record in this chapter demand constant reference to all available aids, including the *SMA* and Appendix II of the *Guide*.

The basic historical setting for the study of Judah has already been covered on maps marked and discussed in previous chapters. It is often useful to review discussions in earlier chapters as these maps appear again in this chapter. Consult the *Index to SMM Maps in the Guide* (inside back cover) for page numbers of earlier discussions. Thirty-one maps make up the bulk of this chapter, some of which are already marked. An asterisk indicates that the map was completely marked in previous chapters of the *Guide*.

S M M   4 — 2

DISCUSSION

Map 4-2, marked and briefly discussed in Chapter Three, appears at the beginning of Chapter Four as a reminder of Egypt's ever present concern with this *Land Between*, especially the International Coastal Highway and the links from it to northern Mesopotamia. Little historical information is known about conditions in this country during the early second millennium B.C., the period of the Execration Texts. These texts (curses placed on certain political centers along the country's main highways as well as on Jerusalem and Shechem in the Hill Country) reflect Egyptian priorities in areas where her presence was actively resisted. Megiddo and **Pa-Canaan/Gaza** (which can be written in on this map **in black** from Map 4-1) stand out as exceptions, no doubt because they served as secure Egyptian bases.

Egypt has always regarded this country, and especially its southern approaches, as her natural first line of defense. Your studies of Judah and the regions which surrounded it often reveal Egypt's desire to control the Coastal Plain and local power centers in the country. This is seen clearly on Map 4-2 (reflecting a situation in the twentieth and nineteenth centuries B.C.) through Map 9-7 (which closes this chapter in the sixth century B.C.).

Egyptian interests during these centuries were expressed in military, economic and political terms, sometimes through intensive diplomatic activity. This type of involvement was still evident in the late second millennium A.D., both in the nineteenth and in the mid-twentieth centuries A.D. when Egyptian military forces entered the country. In the 1970's Egypt engaged in both military and peaceful exchanges with the modern State of Israel which controlled both the Coastal Plain and the approach to it from Northern Sinai.

S M M   4 — 3

TITLE: **THE PATRIARCHS: ABRAHAM AND ISAAC**

DATE: There are various views about the general date for the events on this map. Many place it in the **EARLY 2ND MILLENNIUM B.C.** which means that it would fall in the Middle Bronze Period. Therefore, underline *MB* in yellow in the title of the map. (Some place it even earlier, in the late third millennium B.C.)

INTRODUCTION

Genesis 12-50 describes events in the lives of the patriarchs, Abraham, Isaac and Jacob (and his son Joseph). These chapters are basic to both Old and New Testament history. The dates of the patriarchs (and links to contemporary and subsequent events) are still the subject of much discussion. However, the geographical information in these passages illuminates the regional aspects studied in this chapter and serves as a convenient introduction.

MARKING

1. **Brown write-in**:
   a. In the open area between the names Bethlehem/Ephratha and Beth-zur (about 4 cm./1½ in. long beginning W of Jerusalem) = HILL COUNTRY.

   b. S center of the map, between the names Arad, Hormah and Beer-sheba and continuing W of Beer-sheba = NEGEV (N = west of Arad, EG = west of Hormah and EV = west of Beer-sheba).

   c. In the open area in the extreme S of the map (S of Beer-sheba and just S of the road printed in red) = WILDERNESS.

   d. In the open area in the extreme SE part of the map, just E of the main Transjordanian Highway which is printed in red = MT. SEIR.

   e. In the large body of water near the center of the map = DEAD SEA.

   f. In the large valley just N of the Dead Sea = JORDAN VALLEY.

2. **Blue write-in**: SW corner of the map, just N of the route printed in black, 5 cm./2 in. from the edge = EGYPT with a small black arrow pointing W.

READING

Abraham (Abram) had left the region of Ur and settled in Haran (northern Mesopotamia). He was called to leave Haran and his father's house for a land promised to him by God. While his point of entry is not known, his early travels in the land are described in detail in **Genesis 12 and 13**. Read these two chapters, noting place-names   4-3 a b and routes on Map 4-3.

MARKING

Yellow HL on road and names: Important sites and route in the early patriarchal period = **Shechem, Bethel/Luz, Ai, Hebron/Kiriath-arba** and **Beer-sheba**. HL the route connecting (or running near) these sites, from Shechem S and off the map to Egypt.

READING

4-3 d-g
4-3 c
Genesis 12-26 describes events in the lives of Abraham and Isaac. If time allows, it would be helpful to skim these chapters. Especially note **Genesis 18-23 and 25-26.** Chapter 14 is also interesting since it is the first military campaign in the country recorded in the Bible. This campaign (red on dots in marking below) took place along the Transjordanian Highway and in the Wilderness south of the Negev.

DISCUSSION

In contrast to international travel, Abraham and Isaac appear to have kept to the main north-south route, which runs through the Hill Country from Shechem to Hebron and on to Beer-sheba. Some have called this the *Way of the Patriarchs*. Places mentioned in these chapters were or became important local centers in other periods.

At this point it is necessary to define a new term which appears on Map 4-3 as the *Negev*. The term is properly spelled *Negeb*. However, since the *b* is pronounced as a *v* in modern Hebrew, the term *Negev* is preferred.

Today this term is applied to most of southern Israel, from the Hill Country to the Red Sea and Sinai. In the Bible, however, it is used in a much more restricted sense. There it designates the area between the Hill Country (in the center of Map 4-3) and the Wilderness (to the south of Map 4-3). To the west it consists of a generally flat region (between the Mediterranean Sea and Beer-sheba). To the east it is made up of two broad basins between higher hills. On Map 4-3 and on the *SMA* (northern and southern sheets joined) the region can be seen by first locating *Nahal Besor,* which drains from the southeast into the Mediterranean Sea just south of Gaza. Farther inland this nahal divides. One branch turns to the east via Beer-sheba, Hormah and Arad. Here it is called *Nahal Beer-sheva,* which appears on the *SMA*. By locating the tributaries to this central drainage system, you can generally define what is termed the *Biblical Negev*.

The region of the Biblical Negev is covered with fine wind-blown soil (called *loess*). In terms of rainfall it can be considered a semi-arid *marginal region,* south of the better watered Hill Country. Annual rainfall is very uncertain but averages 200-300 milli-meters or 8-12 inches. In good years the region supports crops of grains. However, in drought years, which are frequent, the farmer can lose everything.

The combination of a powdery-like soil (which absorbs water with difficulty), sudden cloudbursts (which create problems of quick run-off and soil erosion along stream beds) and the uncertainty of sufficient rainfall for crops all make up the setting of a later psalm. The writer uses the image of a sudden, swelling torrent through the Biblical Negev in his prayer for those returning from exile in Babylon. An unspoken request for sufficient rain lies behind his comparison of the sowing season (in late fall) and that of the harvest (in the spring).

> Let the captives [which were taken from the land by the Babylonians]
>   be gathered back, like the stream beds of the Negev.
> For those who sow in tears, the same shall reap with joy.
> He who goes back and forth weeping, carrying [and sowing] all the seed he has,
> The same shall surely come with joy, carrying his sheaves [from the harvest].
>   (Psalm 126.4-6)

Over the centuries the Biblical Negev (and the wilderness to the east, south and west of it) has been the home of various bedouin tribes. In times of a strong central government, settlement increased, and the region was built up, becoming a southern line of defense for the local power in the Hill Country. Without such security the region was exposed to attacks by desert raiders (such as the Amalekites in the Bible) who swept in from the neighboring Wilderness to the south.

Once in the control of a strong local government (like the Southern Kingdom of Judah), the Negev served as a stepping stone to Edom on the Transjordanian Highway and to the important Red Sea with its trade links to East Africa. This expansion frustrated Edom's independence as well as Egyptian interests in the same southern trade routes. All of these factors are illustrated on later *SMM* maps.

MARKING

1. **Orange circle around name**: Places where special events took place = **Jerusalem/Salem, Gerar** (NW of Beer-sheba) and **Zoar** (S of Dead Sea).

2. **Orange sweeping arrow**: Movements by Lot and Hagar =
   a. From the Bethel region toward Jericho.

   b. From Hebron SE along the route toward the S part of the Dead Sea.

   c. From Beer-sheba S toward the Wilderness.

3. **Black write-in** (small caps):
   a. By the orange arrow pointing to Jericho = LOT.   4-3 b

   b. Just E of the orange circle around Jerusalem = MELCHIZEDEK.   4-3 c

   c. By the orange arrow SE of Hebron = THREE MEN TO SODOM AND   4-3 d
      GOMORRAH.

   d. Beside the orange circle of Zoar = LOT.

   e. By the orange arrow S of Beer-sheba = HAGAR.   4-3 e

   f. Just E of the orange circle around Gerar = ABIMELECH.

4. **Red on dot or arrow**: Sites mentioned in the campaign of the northern kings begin-   4-3 c
   ning in the NE corner of the map = **Ashtaroth, Karnaim, Ham, Kiriathaim, Kadesh-barnea** (SW corner of the map), **Tamar** and **Zoar**. After this campaign in which Lot
   was taken captive, Abraham rescued Lot at Dan. Write (in red) the name DAN (red
   ball point if possible) just E of Beth-shan with a black arrow pointing due N. Put
   the name in parentheses.

5. **Green sweeping arrow**: Main movement of Abraham.
   a. From the NE pointing toward Shechem.   4-3 a

   b. From the region of Beer-sheba pointing SW toward Egypt (running just W of the
      HL road).

4-3 b   c. From Egypt pointing toward the region of Beer-sheba (running just E of the HL route).

4-3 e g   d. From the region of Beer-sheba toward Gerar.

LEGEND
   Yellow HL = Main places and routes in the patriarchal narratives.
   Orange   = Places where other important events happened.
   Red on dot = City mentioned in the campaign of the northern kings (Genesis 14).

S M M   4 – 4

TITLE: THE PATRIARCHS: JACOB AND JOSEPH

DATE: **18TH – 16TH CENTURIES B.C.** (Underline in yellow *MB/LB* in the title of the map.)

INTRODUCTION
   The places and events studied on this map are related to events in the lives of Jacob and his son Joseph. The full account of those events is found in Genesis 25-50 and includes details concerning happenings in Haran (northern modern Syria), in Egypt and in the *Land Between*. One of the important events which relates directly to Map 4-4
4-4 a b deals with Jacob's departure to and return from Haran. Skim **Genesis 28, 32, 33 and 35**, noting place-names which are in red on Map 4-4. The marking instructions below may be completed before or after reading these chapters.

MARKING
   1. **Brown write-in:**
      a. In the same position as on Map 4-3 = NEGEV and MT. SEIR.

      b. In the N center of the map, in the open area W of Bethel/Luz = CANAAN (in larger caps, spread out about 10 cm./2 in.).

      c. In the NE part of the map, find the river canyon which runs between the two possible sites of Mahanaim. To the S of this canyon write NAHAL JABBOK with a small brown arrow pointing N to the canyon.

      d. In the open area N of the Nahal Jabbok, between the two possible sites of Mahanaim = GILEAD (in large caps).

   2. **Yellow HL on names = Penuel** and **Mahanaim** (only the Mahanaim near Penuel), **Shechem, Bethel/Luz**, and **Hebron/Kiriath-arba**.

   3. **Yellow HL on routes** = Shortest route between Penuel and Shechem, and then along the same route as HL on Map 4-3 (off the SW corner of the map to Egypt on the road printed in black).

   4. **Sweeping green arrows** (along HL routes):
      a. Along the road from Succoth to Shechem.

   b. From Hebron to Beer-sheba.

   c. From Beer-sheba off the map to Egypt with the note ISRAEL TO EGYPT (small
      black caps) on the arrow.

DISCUSSION AND READING

In contrast to Map 4-3, Map 4-4 includes one interesting event which brings the Coastal   4-4 c
Highway into the picture, the selling of Joseph into Egypt in Genesis 37. The key
site in the story is Dothan, situated on the side of a valley which carries the main
international route as it passes from the Jezreel Valley to the Sharon (Coastal) Plain.
(Compare Map 4-7.) Once Joseph had been sold into the hands of the Ishmaelite
traders, his path to Egypt was along the Coastal Highway — far away from his father's
home in the Hill Country around Hebron. Years later the truth was revealed, much to   4-4 e
the shame of his brothers. This event, however, was destined to save the house of
Jacob. Read these stories in **Genesis 37 and 45.1-46.7**, either before or after completing the following marking instructions.

MARKING

   1. **Yellow HL on route** = From the Transjordanian Highway in Gilead to Egypt via
      Pehel, Beth-shan, Ibleam, Dothan, Gath, Aphek, Joppa, Gaza and off the map toward
      Egypt along the Coastal Highway.

   2. **Orange circle around name** = Dothan.

   3. **Sweeping blue arrows** by HL route:
      a. From Beth-shan to Dothan.

      b. From Dothan to Aphek.

      c. From Joppa along the Coastal Highway toward Egypt. On this arrow write in
         JOSEPH (green) TO EGYPT (blue).

DISCUSSION

Maps 4-3 and 4-4 have served as an introduction to the geographical setting of the
patriarchs. Events in their lives were concentrated along the north-south route
between the important center of Shechem in the Hill Country and Beer-sheba in the
Negev. A survey of the broader world in which they lived and a thorough discussion
of the chronological issues of the era (Early, Middle and Late Bronze Periods) are
beyond the scope of your present study and not directly related to its objectives.
However, you would be wise to consult available libraries or your instructors for
up-to-date information on these subjects.

It should be stressed here that the world of the patriarchs was that of a developed and
organized society and not what is usually regarded as a simple pastoral-bedouin existence. Throughout Genesis 12-50 there are connections to Mesopotamia and to Egypt
as well as negotiations with local political centers (Shechem, Salem and Hebron) as
well as Gerar in the Western Negev on a branch of the Coastal Highway.

Much of the theological relevance of the patriarchs is based upon the fact that there
were other more attractive lifestyles available to these early Biblical figures. The
option they chose gave them few of the advantages they could have enjoyed elsewhere,

4-3 f

especially in Mesopotamia where their family was established. In light of this fact and the great promises made to Abraham during his lifetime, his remark to the leaders of Hebron after the death of his wife, Sarah, takes on new meaning.

> *I am only a stranger, an immigrant here with you. [At least] allow me*
> *to have some place to bury my dead [wife Sarah].*   (Genesis 23.4)

The option he chose is best summarized in the New Testament book, *The Letter to the Hebrews.* In it the writer summons Old Testament figures to illustrate the faith of those who *recognized who God is* — and chose to follow Him. One passage concerns Abraham and Sarah and stands out in the impressive list of Hebrews 10.32-12.2.

> *All these died in faith — without gaining what had been promised . . .*
> *confessing that they were only 'strangers and migrants on the earth.'*
> *People who speak like this make it clear that they are looking for a real*
> *home. If they had in mind [the home] from which they had come, the*
> *opportunity to return was theirs. However, they set their heart on some-*
> *thing better — heaven itself. This is why God is not ashamed to be called*
> *their God. After all, He did have a city ready for them.*   (Hebrews 11.13-16)

LEGEND   See Map 4-3.

S M M   4 — 6

TITLE: **DETAIL: CAMPAIGN OF THUTMOSE III (SOUTHERN)**

DATE: **MID-15TH CENTURY B.C.** (Underline in yellow *LB* in the title of the map.)

INTRODUCTION

At this point in the study of Judah and surrounding regions, we turn again to the International Coastal Highway. The importance of this route was seen in the maps just studied. The concentration of events in the Hill Country on Maps 4-3 and 4-4 was seen against the commercial importance of the coastal trade route along which Joseph was taken to Egypt. Major geographical features along the route are introduced here.

MARKING

1. **Yellow HL on name = Gaza, Pa-Canaan** in the S and **Aphek** in the N.

2. **Brown write-in:**
   a. Along the coast, S of Joppa in the darker areas = SAND DUNES.

   b. In the open areas W of Gibbethon and Gath and E of Ashdod = COASTAL PLAIN.

   c. E center of the map, just W of Beth-shemesh and Jarmuth and E of Timnah = SHEPHELAH (LOWLAND).

   d. In the S of the map, between the right edge of the map and the names Ziklag and Gerar = WESTERN NEGEV (letters running from E to W).

e. In SW corner of the map, along the large nahal which runs on the map from the region of T. el-Farah (South) and passes Yurza before emptying into the sea by Sharuhen (T. el-Ajjul) = NAHAL BESOR (written along the nahal, just E of it).

f. In the N of the map find the river which runs from Aphek to the sea. After **tracing it in blue, write in its name in brown** = YARQON RIVER (just S of the river with a **small brown arrow** pointing N to the river).

DISCUSSION

The name *Coastal Plain* can be used for any plain which borders the sea. The *SMA* and the map which introduces Section One of the *SMM* give the various names for the coastal regions. In the north it is called the *Plain of Acco*. In the central region it is known as the *Plain of Sharon*. In the south (the region now under study) the name *Coastal Plain* is used. This region, later settled by the Philistines, is called *Philistia* by some. Compare the key map to Section One with Map 4-5, noting these three coastal regions. On Map 4-5 locate the specific region now under study and covered on Map 4-6.

The Coastal Plain on Map 4-6 is geographically varied. In the south the great Nahal Besor cuts a path across the Western Negev and empties into the sea just south of Gaza. This natural feature serves as a southern boundary of the country. One could say that the Coastal Highway officially enters the country (from the southwest) when it crosses Nahal Besor. For this reason the region of Gaza plays a key role in various historical periods. Gaza's connection to Transjordan via the Negev is also an important factor. This port city served as the main outlet to the Mediterranean Sea for the Negev and even for trade from Edom. To the present day this small region (known as the *Gaza Strip*) retains its importance and its cultural ties to Egypt.

In the north of Map 4-6 the Yarqon River creates another natural boundary. The river and resulting swamps force coastal traffic eastward to Aphek, a site situated by the bountiful sources of the Yarqon, only a mile away from the hills (just east of the site). An important region between three cities south of the Yarqon River could be termed the *Joppa-Aphek-Lod Triangle*. Rich agricultural lands border this triangle of routes.

Another attractive agricultural area is found east of Ashdod. It has been filled with rich soil deposited by run-off from the hills. Drainage directly to the sea is hampered by coastal sand dunes. Between Ashdod and Gerar (in the south) the map shows a slightly raised region which is located between the Coastal Plain and the Western Negev. East of the Coastal Plain, low foothills begin, called in the Hebrew Bible the *Shephelah* (Lowland).

Main international routes in this coastal region can be seen printed in red on Map 4-6. Note the strategic importance of the Gaza region in the south and the area of Aphek in the north. These two regions (south and north) are linked by two main highways. The western route serves sites located on or near the sea between Gaza and Aphek. The eastern route turns inland and runs at the foot of the Shephelah (Lowland). It touches various important centers where routes from the Hill Country of Judah and the Shephelah enter the Coastal Plain. Sites and routes in this region play a major role or serve as an important background for all later history of the area.

In the sixteenth century B.C. Egypt was in the process of throwing off the yoke of   4-5 a
foreigners they termed *Hyksos*. Pharaoh Ahmose I (of the Eighteenth Dynasty)

succeeded in reaching Sharuhen, south of Gaza, which Egyptian forces *besieged for three years*. Subsequently, Egyptian control spread northward along the main Coastal Highway and the northern approaches to the country. However, administrative control of various Canaanite centers was maintained at Gaza, the closest major city to Egypt, called *That-Which-the-Ruler-Seized* by the Egyptians.

4-5 b

In the mid-fifteenth century B.C. rebellion broke out in Canaan and reached as far south as Yurza (south of Gaza). An Egyptian garrison held out in Sharuhen, but Egypt's foothold in Canaan was seriously threatened. Such was the background of one of the greatest campaigns in the country's history, documented in the Annals of Thutmose III. (It was introduced on Map 4-5 in Chapter One). Pharaoh Thutmose III reestablished a strong Egyptian presence at Gaza as a prelude to his march to Megiddo via the Coastal Plain and Aphek.

Most of the red names on Map 4-5 represented place-names from the impressive list of Thutmose III on his temple wall at Karnak in Upper Egypt. It appears that Thutmose III or his commanders conducted a number of campaigns in this part of the Coastal Plain, such as the alleged capture of Joppa by means of soldiers hidden in gift baskets sent to the city. Therefore, all names on Map 4-6 appear in black except Sharuhen, Gaza and Yurza, which have been mentioned above in relationship to specific campaigns or revolts.

MARKING

1. **Yellow HL on route** = the same routes as highlighted on Map 4-5.

2. **Red on dot**: limit of Canaanite rebellion = Yurza.

3. **Blue box around name** = Gaza, Pa-Canaan.

4. **Blue write-in**:
   a. Above blue box around Gaza = MAIN EGYPTIAN BASE.

   b. In the same place as found on Map 4-5 = EGYPT (with black arrow pointing W).

5. **Sweeping blue arrows**:
   a. From the direction of Egypt to Gaza.

   b. From Gaza to Aphek running E of Ashdod and W of Lod.

6. **Blue write-in** along the Gaza-Aphek arrow = THE ADVANCE OF THUTMOSE III TOWARD MEGIDDO.

DISCUSSION

Compare this map with Map 4-5 to reinforce in your mind the Coastal Plain's strategic position along the main International Highway. Also open to Map 4-1 (studied in Chapter One) and note the same Coastal Plain. There a description of Canaan by an Egyptian scribe (orange dots) speaks of the dangers of travel in Canaan and the possibility of breakdowns on difficult roads. This highlights a positive note regarding the availability of workshops for chariot repairs (service stations) at Joppa. Distances from Gaza and Raphia to the border of Egypt are presented as basic information for any Egyptian courier to foreign lands. Pharaoh Merneptah's victory statement (also on Map 4-1) underscores the strategic importance of this coastal region to Egypt: *Plundered is Canaan with every evil; carried off is Ashkelon; seized upon is Gezer!*

4-1 c
4-9 c

4-1 d
4-9 c

The Philistines took control of this strategic Coastal Plain in the twelfth century B.C.   6-1 b
and from it expanded their influence along the Coastal Highway and into the Jezreel
Valley. The Bible speaks of the connection from Egypt to the Coastal Plain as *the*
way of the Philistines. Control of this region allowed the Philistines to exploit their
commercial potential. However, increased nationalistic feelings in Israel ultimately
clashed with Philistine objectives. Thus this part of the Coastal Plain will play an
important role in later studies, especially as the theme of Israelite-Philistine relations is
developed on maps in Sections Six and Seven of the *SMM*.

S M M   5 – 2

TITLE: WILDERNESS WANDERINGS

DATE: ABOUT 1400 B.C. (Many prefer a thirteenth century B.C. date.)

INTRODUCTION

Maps 5-2 through 5-5 form a sequence of four maps. Map 5-2 begins with Moses and
the children of Israel in the Wilderness and Transjordan (south and east of Canaan).
Map 5-5 ends with Joshua's campaigns in central Canaan. The opening map (5-2)
gives you an opportunity to explore the regions to the south and to the east of Judah.

MARKING

1. **Brown write-in:**
   a. In the same position as on Map 4-3 and 4-4 = WILDERNESS and NEGEV.

   b. In the N of the map, N of Hebron and just E of Gedor = HILL COUNTRY
      (in two lines).

   c. In the N of the map, in the open area between Libnah and Lachish = SHEPHELAH
      with its English equivalent under it in parentheses = (LOWLAND).

   d. In the body of water in the NE part of the map = SALT SEA (DEAD SEA) (in
      two lines).

   e. In the NE corner, the large river canyon running into the Dead Sea (between
      Dibon and Ar = NAHAL ARNON (written in just W of Ar with a brown arrow
      pointing N to the canyon).

   f. SE of the Dead Sea, the large river canyon running into the swamps by Zoar =
      NAHAL ZERED (written in SE of Zoar with a brown arrow pointing N to the
      canyon).

   g. In the great valley between Edom and the Wilderness, W of Rekem = RIFT
      VALLEY (ARABAH) (in two lines).

2. **Blue on river, blue write-in and blue on dot:**
   a. Bring out the main rivers in the canyons of Nahal Arnon and Nahal Zered by
      tracing them in blue. The Arnon splits into two just S of Aroer.

b. Between Nahal Arnon and Nahal Zered just S of Ader = MOAB.

c. S of Nahal Zered, just E of Punon and Rekem = EDOM.

d. **Blue on dot** of Late Bronze centers in the southern Coastal Plain, the Shephelah and Hill Country = **Ashkelon, Gaza, Deir el-Balah, Yurza, T. el-Farah** (south), **Gerar, Ziklag, Eglon** (both possible sites), **T. Zippor, Lachish, T. Beit Mirsim** and **Debir.** In the open area just E of Gaza write (in blue) = LATE BRONZE CANAANITE CITIES (small caps).

3. **Yellow HL on name** = **Kadesh-barnea** (in the Wilderness) and **Hebron** (in the Hill Country).

4. **Green write-in:** By Kadesh-barnea = ISRAELITE CAMP (in two lines).

DISCUSSION AND READING

The route by which the Israelites reached the region of Kadesh (-barnea) is not part of this study. Traditional sites (such as Gebel Musa above St. Katharina's Monastery) and routes in southern Sinai can be noted on the map inside the back cover of the *SMM*. The long march to Canaan had taken many months. Daily sustenance of manna ceased to be appreciated as the Israelites reached the crucial crossroads in the journey at Kadesh. The book of Numbers records the general feeling of the people.

> *Who can find us some meat to eat? Oh! Remember the fish we used to eat in Egypt for nothing — and the cucumbers, the melons, the leeks, the onions and the garlic? And now look what we've got to fill our starving stomachs — just this manna!* (Numbers 11.4-6).

By the springs of Kadesh, on the edge of Canaan, various options were open to the Israelites. The Coastal Highway (stressed in the last map study) was geographically attractive. However, the presence of strong Canaanite cities (blue dots) would make this route questionable to say the least. In order to gain more information about the land, Moses sent twelve spies into Canaan. With Map 5-2 open, read **Numbers 13.1-24.** Note the tribal representatives of Ephraim (Hoshea/Joshua) and of Judah (Caleb).

5-2 c

MARKING

1. **Sweeping green arrows:**
   a. From Kadesh-barnea to Hormah via Mt. Hor (the road printed in red) and then NE around into the Negev by Hormah (the road printed in black). Along this arrow write (in brown) WAY OF ATHARIM.

   b. From the region of Hormah to Hebron (via NE and then N).

2. **Red circle around name** = Hormah.

DISCUSSION AND READING

As we noted earlier, the Biblical Negev is the region just south of the Hill Country and Shephelah on Map 5-2. If the region's fluctuating rainfall permits, the farmer can make use of this area for cultivating grains. The region also serves as grazing land for the herdsman. While not the most attractive part of the country, the Negev offers more advantages than most of the Wilderness farther south. The spies must have noted these improved conditions as they entered the area from the Wilderness.

North of the Negev one ascends to the Hill Country, dominated by the important center of Hebron. Here the hills rise to 1000 meters (over 3000 feet), and rainfall is sufficient to sustain vines and orchards. The climb to Hebron must have been exciting for the spies, especially since it was the season for the first ripe grapes (July/August). Caleb was so impressed with this region that 45 years later he convinced Joshua to give it to him for an inheritance. **Numbers 13.25-14.45** records the outcome of this trip.   6-3 b

The decision not to enter the land had serious consequences. A later attempt by some   5-2 d
Israelites to storm the Hill Country via the Negev ended in defeat. As you would
expect, local leaders gathered their forces to resist this invasion (much like Saul and   7-5 a
David did later in order to protect Judah's southern flank against Amalekite incur-   7-6 a
sions). A request to pass through Edomite territory east of the Rift Valley by way of
Ezion-geber (southern edge of Map 5-2) and the Transjordanian (King's) Highway was
also rejected. (Questions concerning the nature of the Edomite population at this time
and the extent of its influence are beyond the scope of this study.)

Finally, after about 38 years a course was set, beginning from the region of Kadesh   5-2 e
and moving eastward across the Rift Valley, making the steep ascent to the Transjordanian highlands via Zalmonah and Punon and reaching the Nahal Zered via northern
Edom. From there it touched Moabite territory before crossing Nahal Arnon to the
Wilderness of Jahaz and Dibon. The tableland (Mishor) north of Nahal Arnon and
Dibon was the scene of the great battle with Sihon, king of Heshbon (Map 5-3). Some
of the very interesting happenings along this route can be noted by skimming **Numbers
20.1-21.15 and 33.37-44.**

MARKING

1. **Green write-in**: In open area between Kadesh-barnea and Ezion-geber (S edge of the
   map) = WILDERNESS WANDERINGS.

2. **Sweeping green arrows**:
   a. From the region of Mt. Hor (NE of Kadesh-barnea), E to Ije-abarim/Iyim via
      Punon (running S of the red road and then NE from Punon and across the
      Transjordanian plateau).

   b. From Ije-abarim/Iyim to a region just E of Kedemoth (NE around the most
      difficult part of Nahal Arnon).

READING

The prayer in **Psalm 90**, one of the most expressive of all the psalms, has been attributed to Moses. Within the setting of the Wilderness wanderings and the passing
of an entire generation it takes on new meaning. Read it slowly and thoughtfully in
the light of the events of this map.

S M M   5 – 3

TITLE: CAMPAIGNS IN TRANSJORDAN AND ENTRY INTO CANAAN

DATE: **ABOUT 1400 B.C.** (Many prefer a thirteenth century B.C. date.)

INTRODUCTION

The events studied on this map continue from Map 5-2. On Map 5-2 Nahal Arnon is seen in the northeast corner. On Map 5-3 it appears in the southeast corner, next to the edge of the map. Marking various geographical features on Map 5-3 will prove very helpful as this study develops.

MARKING

1. **Brown write-in:**

   a. In the body of water in the S of the map = SALT SEA (DEAD SEA) in two lines.

   b. Along the Jordan River, S of the city Adam, running just E of the river = RIVER JORDAN.

   c. At the extreme S of the map, E of the Dead Sea, find the deep river canyon = NAHAL ARNON (in the open area just W of Dibon, with a small brown arrow pointing to the canyon).

   d. In. the Transjordan, just E of Succoth, the deep river canyon running into the Jordan from the NE and E of Adam = NAHAL JABBOK (with arrow).

   e. In the SE corner of the map, in the open area between Bezer, Jahaz, Kedemoth and Almon-diblathaim = MEDEBA PLATEAU with (MISHOR) written in just W of it.

   f. In the open area just NE of the Dead Sea, between the Dead Sea, the Jordan River and (Beth-) Nimrah = PLAINS OF MOAB (in three lines).

   g. In the open area between the Dead Sea and Bethlehem = WILDERNESS.

   h. In the open area between Bethlehem and Hebron, just E of Gedor = HILL COUNTRY.

   i. In the open area just NW of Bethel = HILL COUNTRY.

   j. In the open space W of Adullam and Keilah = SHEPHELAH.

2. **Blue write-in** or **blue on river:**

   a. In the open area, W center of the map, W of Mt. Gerizim and Bethel but not too close to them = CANAAN (in larger caps, W or E of the word HILL COUNTRY).

   b. In blue, trace the Jabbok River in the Nahal Jabbok from the E side of the map to Adam.

   c. In blue, trace the Jordan River from the N (by the word Dan) to its mouth at the Dead Sea.

d. In blue, trace the Arnon River in Nahal Arnon from the SE side of the map to the Dead Sea.

DISCUSSION

Map 5-2 introduced the southern approach to the Hill Country via the Biblical Negev. 5-2 d
Map 5-3 is one of the best maps to demonstrate the eastern approach to the Hill Country, or what has been called its *back door*. (The *front door* is by the western approach from the Coastal Highway.) In studying the eastern approach it is helpful to look at the key map which introduces Section One of the *SMM* and to open to the full color *SMA* (with north and south sections joined). These maps provide an overview of the southern, eastern and western approaches to the central Hill Country (termed the *Hill Country of Judah*). The main objective of this study is to introduce the eastern approach.

Map 5-2 brought Moses and the children of Israel up to Nahal Arnon in Transjordan. 5-2 e
Map 5-3 continues the story north of this great natural boundary, on to what the Hebrew Bible calls the *Mishor*, in English termed the *Medeba Plateau*. This plateau is the traditional staging ground for attacks on central Canaan from the Transjordanian Highway.

Obstacles which define this eastern approach are 1) the waters of the Dead Sea itself (almost 400 m./1300 ft. below sea level), 2) the steep slopes on the east of the Dead Sea (rising almost 1200 m./4000 ft. above its eastern shore), and 3) sheer limestone cliffs to the west of the Dead Sea (up to 400 m./1300 ft.). All of these features can be seen clearly on *SMA* but are not fully appreciated until one views them in person.

These difficult obstacles help define a much more attractive region just north of the Dead Sea. Here in the Lower Jordan Valley, ridges descending into the valley from the Medeba Plateau are easier to navigate. Instead of the Dead Sea, the valley floor is broken only by the Jordan River, today a meandering stream. In antiquity it would have presented a serious obstacle during flood stage. On both sides of the larger valley rich farm lands result from the combination of sun, soil and water in the region. To the west the limestone cliffs are broken by areas of chalk and chalk ridges, allowing easier ascents to the Hill Country. The key to the entire region lies in the control of the strategic oasis of Jericho, west of the Jordan River at the foot of the Wilderness. Explore this eastern approach from the Medeba Plateau to the Hill Country via Jericho on *SMA*.

Turning again to Map 5-3, note the routes descending from the Transjordanian Highway (especially from Heshbon on the edge of the Medeba Plateau) to the Plains of Moab and crossing the Jordan River to Jericho. The strategic position of Jericho in the Lower Jordan Valley is highlighted by the number of routes which link it to the Hill Country farther west. Routes connect it with Jerusalem, Bethel and the region of Gibeon. From Gibeon important routes descend to the *front door* of central Canaan (the Aijalon Valley) and the Coastal Highway, beyond the limits of Map 5-3. This cross-country route (from the Transjordanian Highway to the Coastal Highway) carried some of the most famous events in the Bible and is important enough to be included on the *Introductory Schematic: The Playing Board*. While it was already introduced on Map 6-7 in Chapter Three, this is an appropriate moment to review various aspects and features along this east-west connection.

MARKING

    1. **Yellow HL on names**:

        a. In Transjordan = **Heshbon, Jazer** (not Jahaz), **Pisgah** and **Edrei** (NE corner).

        b. In Canaan = **Jericho, Gilgal, Ai** and **Bethel.**

    2. **Blue border and write-in** = Begin on the E edge of the map, between Rabbah (Rabbath-ammon) and Bezer, move NW and then N passing just E of Jazer, turning NE and passing just E of Jogbehah and continuing NE to the E edge of the map. Shade in the inside of this border with blue pencil and write in = AMMON.

    3. **Red circle around name** = **Jahaz, Heshbon, Jazer** and **Edrei.**

    4. **Sweeping green arrows**:

        a. From the extreme SE corner of the map to Jahaz.

        b. From Jahaz and the Medeba Plateau to Heshbon.

        c. From Jazer NE along the route toward Ramoth-gilead (Edrei is farther NE, off the map).

READING

5-3 a

    The Israelite campaigns in Transjordan and the settlement of some of the tribes there (especially on the strategic Medeba Plateau) provide a background for later events in the region. With this in mind read **Numbers 21.13-22.1, 32.1-42 and Deuteronomy 34.**

DISCUSSION

5-3 c

5-5 a
5-3 d

    Joshua's line of advance into Canaan via Jericho and Ai is introduced in the following marking. Details and reading assignments are given on Map 5-4. Inhabitants of the hills (at Gibeon and at Jebus/Jerusalem) no doubt watched Joshua's advance with deep concern. Their reactions are noted when you study Map 5-5. After this initial campaign Joshua summoned Israelite leaders to Mt. Ebal and Mt. Gerizim (by Shechem). There the law was read, apparently in a peaceful setting. This leads one to assume that the inhabitants of that region offered no resistance or perhaps even cooperated with the Israelites on the basis of an earlier affiliation. Consult Chapter Three for a more detailed discussion of this event.

MARKING

    1. **Blue on dot and blue write-in** (just above the name of Jerusalem) = JEBUSITES (small caps).

    2. **Orange on dot and blue write-in**: the four Gibeonite cities in the SW center of the map = **Gibeon, Beeroth, Chephirah** and **Kiriath-jearim.** Write in the open area between these four cities = GIBEONITES (JOSHUA 9.17) in small blue caps in two lines.

    3. **Yellow HL on route** = From Heshbon to Jericho and then the northern of the two routes from Jericho to Ai.

    4. **Red circle around name** = **Jericho.**

    5. **Red confrontation mark**: .5 cm./¼ in. E of Ai on the highlighted route =   ✳

6. **Sweeping green arrows:**
   a. From the Plains of Moab to Jericho.

   b. From Jericho to the red confrontation mark by Ai (along the highlighted route).

7. **A green circle** = Around the entire region of Mt. Ebal, Mt. Gerizim and Shechem.

S M M   5 – 4

TITLE: DETAIL: ENTRY INTO CANAAN AND INITIAL CAMPAIGNS

DATE: About 1400 B.C. (Many prefer a thirteenth century date.)

INTRODUCTION AND READING

With firm control of key Transjordanian regions, the Israelites now turned their attention to Canaan itself. The instructions given by Moses at this point provide valuable background information on the character of the land itself, a *Land Between,* which was to become *God's testing ground of faith.* Read **Deuteronomy 1-11**, especially noting 6-11. Jesus quoted exclusively from these instructions of Moses during His temptation in the Wilderness (Matthew 4.1-11).

Israel's entry into Canaan signaled a time of renewal and a moment of new beginnings   5-3 c
in the life of the nation. Joshua of Ephraim took command, the Israelites crossed the Jordan, the supply of manna ceased, the feast of Passover was celebrated and Jericho was conquered. All of these events are described in Joshua 1-5. These chapters also record geographical data about Jericho itself and the surrounding region, including its position west of the Jordan River and yet its proximity to the hills, seen clearly on Map 5-4.

The story of Joshua's two spies who conspired with Rahab of Jericho illustrates Jericho's setting. The spies must have hid somewhere west of the city, either in the deeply eroded and lonely chalk hills or in one of ·the isolated canyons cut through the limestone cliffs.

> *When they left [Jericho] they made straight for the hills [west of the city].*
> *There they remained for three days until those who were after them [gave up*
> *and] returned to Jericho. Their pursuers had combed all the [escape] routes,*
> *but with no success. The two men [in hiding] then turned back [toward*
> *Jericho], and descending from the hills, crossed over [the Jordan] and came*
> *to Joshua son of Nun. They told him all about what had happened to them.*
> (Joshua 2.22-23)

The most remarkable feature of the region of Jericho is the oasis itself. Springs appear in several places in the area. The two most prominent springs are noted as small solid blue dots on Map 5-4, one at some distance northwest of Jericho (called the Naaran Springs). Due to the combination of water (emerging from underground springs fed by the limestone hills farther west), soil (deposited on the plain from the same hills) and climate (warm and sunny during most of the year), the region is known for all types of agricultural products, especially dates and balsam (used in ancient ointments).

4-3 b
Jericho's fame begins in the New Stone Age when, according to archeological findings at the site, a society organized into what is thought to be the world's first city. It is not surprising that Lot, who with Abraham had lived for a short time in the lush Nile Valley of Egypt, *looked out [from the hills] and saw all the wide open spaces of the Jordan — all under irrigation . . . like the garden of the Lord, just like Egypt . . . so Lot chose [to move out into] these open spaces of the Jordan [Valley]* (Map 4-3, Genesis 13.10-11). His choice appears to have been made from the mountains northeast of Bethel, with a view of the Jericho oasis or the Plains of Moab.

12-2 a

12-5
In the first century B.C. the region of Jericho was Anthony's special gift to Cleopatra. When King Herod gained control of the area, he used its natural resources to develop a beautiful winter palace with all the supporting facilities. Destroyed at his death, it was rebuilt by his son Archelaus. During this period Jesus often passed through this affluent and historic region. On His last visit He encountered Jericho's chief tax collector, Zacchaeus, who had become rich by exploiting his important position in this coveted area. All of this points to the unique character of Jericho and its surroundings.

5-3 c
In Joshua's conquest of Jericho two statements stand out against this background. The first has its seasonal context in the spring at Passover.

> *The Israelites set up camp at Gilgal and kept the Passover on the eve of the fourteenth day of the month, there on the plains of Jericho. Starting the day after Passover, right on that day, they ate what came from the land itself — unleavened bread and roasted [grain]. And the day after they ate off the land, the manna ceased. The Israelites had no more manna, and that year they ate the produce of the land of Canaan.*   (Joshua 5.10-12)

The second statement was Joshua's interdiction on the resettlement of the site. He must have seen it as potentially dangerous for the people, especially considering Lot's fate after he separated from Abraham and the warnings Moses had just issued.

> *Cursed be the man — before the Lord — who shall come out here and reconstruct this city Jericho. On [the life of] his oldest son he shall lay its foundations, and on [the life of] his youngest son shall he set up its gates.*
>   (Joshua 6.26)

8-6 a
Hundreds of years later in the days of the apostasy of Israel, Jericho's allurement, its affluency and its position on the important trade route to Transjordan could not be resisted. *In his [Ahab's] days Hiel of Bethel rebuilt Jericho* (1 Kings 16.34).

With this background in mind, skim **Joshua 3-6** before completing the following marking.

MARKING
1. **Brown write-in:**
   a. By comparing Map 5-4 with Map 5-3 = RIVER JORDAN, PLAINS OF MOAB.

   b. In the large eroded area NW of Bethel, between roads = HILL COUNTRY.

   c. SW corner, between Bethlehem and Manahath = HILL COUNTRY.

   d. In the open area between Jericho and Jerusalem, just W of the names of W. Qilt and W. Mukallik = WILDERNESS.

e. In the open area just NE of the dot Gibeon = C.B.P. (small caps between the two routes). This is an abbreviation for the *Central Benjamin Plateau,* a term used for this region, later given to the tribe of Benjamin as seen on Maps 6-2 and 6-3.

f. Just NW of the dot of Bethel = B.P. (small caps). This is an abbreviation for the *Bethel Plateau,* a term used for the region west and northeast of Bethel.

2. **Blue on dot** = **Jericho** (do not cover blue dot), **Ai, Bethel** and **Jerusalem.**

3. **Blue write-in**: Just E of Jerusalem = JEBUSITES.

4. **Orange on dots = Gibeon** and **Beeroth** plus write (in blue) GIBEONITES (small blue caps) just E of Gibeon and Beeroth.

5. **Yellow HL on names = Jericho** and **Gilgal.**

6. **Yellow HL on route:**
   a. From the SE corner of the map, via Beth-jeshimoth to Jericho.

   b. The main north-south route through the Hill Country from Shechem to Bethlehem via Bethel and Jerusalem, passing off the map SW of Bethlehem.

7. **Small green square (solid green) with green write-in:** Joshua's camps = On the dot of Gilgal with JOSHUA'S CAMP written in just NE (in two lines).

8. **Sweeping green arrow** = From the Plains of Moab to Gilgal.

9. **Red circle around name = Jericho.**

DISCUSSION (It is helpful to study the maps as someone reads this discussion.)
With the fall of Jericho, routes to the Hill Country via the Wilderness were open to the   5-3 c
Israelites. The detail in Map 5-4 shows some of the obstacles facing anyone approaching the Hill Country from the east. Note various features on this map as they are described in this discussion. Then find them with *SMA* and/or Map 1-4.

Jericho lies at 260 meters/850 feet below sea level. The mountains around Bethel rise to almost 900 meters/slightly under 3000 feet above sea level. This means that one must climb 1150 meters/3800 feet from Jericho to the Bethel Plateau. Try to imagine this difference while looking at the routes between Jericho and Bethel. The regions of Gibeon and Jerusalem are approximately 100 meters/328 feet lower than Bethel.

The route between Jerusalem and Bethel generally follows higher ground between eastern and western watersheds (drainage systems). Most of Map 5-4 shows drainage to the east reaching the Jordan River or the Dead Sea. The beginning of the western watershed can be seen at the western edge of the map. Keeping to the line of least resistance, the main north-south internal communication link south of Bethel can be seen between these two watersheds. This is the same route as was highlighted on Maps 4-3 and 4-4 showing the travels of the patriarchs. Our study now turns to the connections between this internal route and the important city at the oasis of Jericho.

Between the Jerusalem-Bethel ridge road and the region of Jericho, a number of large stream beds have cut deep canyons through the Wilderness as they descend to the Jordan Valley. You will remember that such a stream bed (dry except during heavy rains) is called a *nahal* in Hebrew and a *wadi* in Arabic.

One major wadi system called Wadi Suweinit begins at Bethel. From there it runs south and then southeast creating a major obstacle to travel. The sides of this wadi are at times 200 meters/650 feet above the actual dry stream bed. W. Suweinit empties into the larger W. Qilt, together with another major tributary (W. Farah, not printed on Map 5-4). W. Qilt presents one of the most impressive obstacles to travel in this part of the Wilderness.

The next major wadi system to the north of the Qilt begins just north and northeast of Ai. It also creates a major obstacle to travel, as it cuts a deep path in the region just north of Jericho where it is called W. Nueima. Farther up the wadi in its most rugged part it is called *W. Makkuk*. It would be helpful for future reference to **write in the name W. Makkuk in small blue letters** along the most rugged part of the wadi, halfway between Ai and Jericho.

These two major obstacles (W. Qilt system and the W. Makkuk), together with other surrounding difficulties, define natural communication links from Jericho to the Hill Country. Note on Map 5-4 how routes tend to stay on ridges and out of the wadi systems. When one must cross over to another ridge, the route is not easy. However, the crossing occurs at the least difficult point along the wadi — in a place the Bible calls a *pass* (discussed on Map 7-4 later in this chapter).

With these factors in mind, study the various routes between Jericho and the Hill Country on Map 5-4. Note various options in order to ascend from Jericho to Ai and Bethel. Note how the Jericho-Gibeon route must cross over a pass in W. Suweinit to reach the Central Benjamin Plateau or make a long detour via the Bethel Plateau. The Jericho-Jerusalem link must also cross a wadi (W. Mukallik) before making a final ascent along a ridge to the Mt. of Olives and Jerusalem.

After debriefing the spies he had sent out, Joshua decided that an important foothold in the central Hill Country could be established by taking control of a plateau-like region just southeast of Ai. This strategic area, between routes to and from other regions, served as the first line of defense for the strategic crossroads of Bethel. It also opened the attack route across the important W. Suweinit pass to the Central Benjamin Plateau and Gibeon, a basic prerequisite for control of the entire central Hill Country. Joshua's spies also returned with an interesting report on conditions around Ai and the force needed to take the region.

> *Don't send all the men up [in the hills]. Only about two or three fighting units [should be enough] to go up and mount the attack on Ai. Certainly don't put all the men through that [climb] since there are just a few of them [up there].*   (Joshua 7.3)

Joshua 7 records the defeat of the Israelites in this first attempt on Ai. The cause of this defeat and its remedy are explained. The inhabitants of Gibeon and Jerusalem must have felt a sense of relief at the news of the Israelite defeat. The question of large numbers in these stories was discussed on Map 6-7 in Chapter Three under the *Civil War in Benjamin*. Here it is sufficient to recall that the Hebrew word *eleph* can mean *thousand, clan, family* or *unit of fighting men (squad of 10 or 20)*. The last option makes very good sense in Joshua 7.2-6 and in Joshua 8. Certainly losing 36 fighting men (Joshua 7.5) out of 3000 could not have been considered a crushing defeat. On the other hand, the loss of 36 out of about 50 (three times a unit of 15 to 20 men) would have been disasterous. The original estimate of the enemy force is also important to remember: *There are just a few of them up there* (Joshua 7.3).

READING
Joshua 8 provides interesting details concerning the second attack on the region of Ai. Since this chapter is one of the most detailed descriptions of an attack in the Bible, it is helpful to read it before completing the marking on Map 5-4. However, you may want to complete the first item of the marking before reading the chapter. Note possible battle details on the map as you read, and compare with the marking below.

MARKING
1. Wadi Makkuk has already been written in, according to instructions given in paragraph six of the above discussion. One important tributary of Wadi Makkuk was omitted on Map 5-4 in the first printing. It is an east-west ravine just to the north of Ai. It may be added in blue ballpoint pen as a **thin broken blue line** leaving the wadi at the turn, just east of the *A* of Ai. From this turn it should run west via the *A* of Ai and then toward the dot of Bethel, stopping .5 cm./¼ in. east of this dot. This is a deep canyon which creates a definite barrier between the Ai ridge and the region north of it. It has a local name, W. Jaya, but is part of the Makkuk system. (Other tributaries to the Makkuk or Qilt systems may also be drawn.)

2. **Yellow HL on route** = From Jericho NW and then W into the hills, crossing Wadi Makkuk and climbing the ridge to Ai and Bethel.

3. **Yellow HL on names** = Ai and Bethel.

4. **Small green square (solid green) with green write-in:** Joshua's forward camp = 2 cm./ 3/4 in. E of Ai, just W of the fork in the highlighted route and N of where this route crosses Wadi Makkuk. Write in JOSHUA'S CAMP (green and in two lines) just N of the square.

5. **Sweeping green arrow:** From Jericho to Joshua's camp N of W. Makkuk.

6. **Red confrontation mark:** On the Ai ridge about halfway between Ai and Joshua's camp N of W. Makkuk = ✳ (on the route itself).

7. **Small blue arrows:** Defender's advance.
   a. From Bethel to Ai.

   b. From Ai to the red confrontation mark. (Keep off the yellow.)

8. **Short green arrow:** Israelite advance = From Joshua's camp N of W. Makkuk to the red confrontation mark S of the wadi.

9. **Green write-in and arrow:** 2 cm./3/4 in. S/SW of Ai, just SE of Bethel = AMBUSH (small caps with green arrow pointing to Ai).

10. **A green circle** around the region of Mt. Ebal, Mt. Gerizim and Shechem indicating the reading of the law in apparently peaceful surroundings by Shechem.

DISCUSSION

5-3 c   As stated earlier, Joshua's campaign against Ai as recorded in the seventh and eighth chapters of the book of Joshua provides one of the most detailed regional descriptions in the Bible. When this description is compared to the actual terrain in that part of Map 5-4 which you have just marked, the correlations are dramatic. Some of them are listed here to reinforce your understanding of the dynamic of this region. Compare them with Map 5-4 as you read.

1. The natural routes between Jericho and the strategic Bethel Plateau avoid the deep canyons which make up the Makkuk and Qilt wadi systems. These routes tend to stay on ridges. One natural *pass* across Wadi Makkuk allows access to the Jericho-Ai ridge route from the ridge route north of Wadi Makkuk. The pinching of the ridge route by Ai on Map 5-4 makes it a natural *first line of defense* for the Hill Country around Bethel. Therefore, tactically speaking, the strategic importance of the region and routes around Bethel (discussed in your earlier studies) and Bethel's natural eastern approach from Jericho via Ai explain Joshua's choice of this region and this site as his first objective in the Hill Country. This basic fact cannot be ignored in any discussion of the identification of the location of Ai.

2. In the Bible Ai is inseparably linked with Bethel. This connection is made in the narrative of Joshua 8.17 where it is stated that during Israel's second attack on Ai *no one stayed back in Ai and Bethel who did not go out after Israel.* Your studies in Chapter Three of the *Guide* have already illustrated Bethel's prominent position on the north-south ridge route through the Hill Country. The repercussions of the Israelite victory in the region of Ai and Bethel had to have a profound impact on the inhabitants of the Central Benjamin Plateau (the Gibeonites) since they realized that their area was the next objective of the Israelite advance. Joshua 9 reflects their attitude of *if you can't beat them join them.* Thus Ai's key position east of Bethel and the shadow which the Israelite victory at Ai/Bethel cast over the Central Benjamin Plateau must also be seen as part of Joshua's overall strategy in his attack on the Hill Country. Meanwhile, as these events transpired, there must have been increasing alarm in Jerusalem as you will discover in your study of Joshua 10 on Map 5-5.

3. East of Ai on Map 5-4 one route descends due east to the pass across Wadi Makkuk. This pass affords the last crossing before the wadi deepens into a major canyon and obstacle. From there on, the unified stream bed of the wadi cuts a twisted path through the uplifted limestone resulting in rocky scarps of up to 200 meters or 660 feet before continuing east through the rough chalk wilderness. The difference between this rugged region and the pass just west of it is very dramatic. It may reflect what the Biblical writer states in Joshua 7.5 when he says that the defenders of the Hill Country pursued the Israelites *as far as the broken/fractured area (shebarim), striking them down along the descent [to the pass].* (If this first attack came from the route southeast of Ai, the word *shebarim* may point to the same type of broken terrain, but the *descent* would refer to the steep slope off the eastern side of the uplifted limestone where this route to Jericho turns due east.)

4. To the north of the route east of Ai, the deep Wadi Jaya/Wadi Makkuk has created a natural barrier. This barrier underscores the importance of the pass across Wadi Makkuk noted above and demonstrates Joshua's tactical wisdom when the Israelites made their approach the second time, *arriving over against the city and setting up camp to the north of the Ai [ridge]* in Joshua 8.11.

5. Along the route immediately southeast of Ai on Map 5-4 quite a different landscape appears. The narrow ridge at Ai broadens out into an open area, not unlike the Central Benjamin Plateau but much smaller in scale. Low hills in this plateau-like region (in Hebrew specifically called *HaEmeq* or *the valley*) afford good visibility toward Ai, toward the routes which approach it from the east and toward the hills behind Ai (to the west). Thus Joshua's decision to position himself *in the midst of the valley* on the eve of the battle (Joshua 8.13) allowed him to keep eye contact on troops coming from his camp north of the pass, on Ai and on the hills to the west where his ambush was hidden in one of the canyons southwest of Ai. (Biblically speaking directions are not pure compass readings but point to any angle of a general direction. In this case southwest is intended instead of due west. Above it was noted that *north of Ai* has actually a tactical meaning of *north of the canyon which is north of the Ai ridge*.)

READING

With these factors in mind it would be wise to read **Joshua 8** again, noting carefully specific geographical information and Joshua's strategy in this important opening campaign in the Hill Country. Such careful planning following the initial defeat and the severe punishment of Achan and his family (Joshua 7) reflect the seriousness of this moment in Israelite history, especially in light of promises given to the patriarchs, to Moses, to Joshua himself and to the nation.

DISCUSSION AND READING

In the Bible the site of Ai (*HaAi* in Hebrew which means *the ruin* or *the heap of stones*) is linked with Bethel. The most prominent ruin in the entire area east of the Bethel Plateau is called in Arabic *et-Tell* (where Map 5-4 locates Ai), at the junction of the two main natural routes from Jericho to the Hill Country (discussed above). The site of et-Tell has no equal in the region, both in terms of strategic importance and in terms of surface debris indicating an ancient city.

Excavations at et-Tell have revealed a large city from the Early Bronze Age in the   2-4
millennium prior to Joshua's conquest. A small village later than Joshua's conquest (later than both the early and the late dates for the conquest) does not provide the answer to the question of the lack of remains at et-Tell. Therefore, although the setting of et-Tell fits perfectly the detailed geographical information in Joshua 8 and 9, an archeological problem exists due to the lack of remains from the period of Joshua at the site.

Many scholars have attempted to solve this problem without success. Other relatively small sites in the region have been explored, but finds have been disappointing. Recently it has been proposed that Ai be identified with a small ruin a number of kilometers southwest of et-Tell. This would also mean that Bethel would have to be relocated. However, in the attempt to find adequate archeological proof, the main objective and basic strategy of this campaign (discussed above) are violated.

To date no major excavations have been done in the oldest part of Deir Dibwan, an affluent Arab village just below et-Tell/Ai on the edge of the beautiful plateau region southeast of the site. Future exploration may provide an answer to the archeological problems of et-Tell. However, more basic and reliable geographical factors locate the scene of this initial campaign of the Israelites in the region of et-Tell.

Having considered the problem of archeological evidence (or rather the lack of it), your study should return to the Biblical text itself for other possible solutions. You should recall that Joshua's spies initially persuaded him not to send many soldiers up to the battle since *there are just a few of them.* Since Ai is the first line of defense for Bethel, it may be that the site was used as more of a rallying point to meet Joshua's impending invasion. If so, *the king of Ai* may be a leader of the forces mobilizing for the battle rather than an actual city ruler (as the *king of Arad* in the Negev campaign in Numbers 21.1). Certainly other people in the Hill Country, especially around Bethel, must have joined forces to meet Joshua's attack. In any event, the very name itself (*the ruin*) would seem rather strange if the site were a city or village which actually existed at that time. Thus, it may be that this name preserves the very nature of the site itself, still today a landmark visible from various vantage points — the most prominent ruin in the entire district.

It is interesting to note again that this first victory in the Hill Country was in the region of Ai and Bethel, exactly where some of the most significant promises had been given to Abraham and Jacob hundreds of years earlier, (Maps 4-3 and 4-4; Genesis 13 and 28.10-22). In addition to the strategic nature of the region, these earlier promises may have played a part in Joshua's decision to begin his campaign precisely here. Joshua's bold move toward this part of the Hill Country may have been just what was needed to unify the Canaanites in the Bethel region. Up to this point they appear to have been in disarray in the face of the Israelite threat (Joshua 5.1). What better place to make their stand than here at the entrance to the strategic region of Bethel and the Central Benjamin Plateau?

4-3 b
4-4 a

5-5 a
The fall of the region of Ai to the Israelites must have caused deep concern among the people and leaders of Bethel, Gibeon and Jerusalem. This becomes clear by a careful review of routes on Map 5-4. The Gibeonites were the first to respond to Joshua's victory. **Joshua 9** recounts how they came to terms with Joshua and can be read in conjunction with this map. The implications will be discussed in your study of Map 5-5.

Sit back and review this map's work, comparing it with *SMA*. Recall the elevations mentioned, difficulties of travel and the natural routes leading up from Jericho to important crossroads in the Hill Country. Much time has been spent discussing this region since it serves as background for future map studies.

S M M   5 — 5

TITLE: JOSHUA'S CAMPAIGNS IN CENTRAL CANAAN

DATE: EARLY 14TH CENTURY B.C. (Many prefer a 13th century date.)

INTRODUCTION

Joshua's initial campaign (Map 5-4) introduced the eastern approach to central Canaan via Jericho, the *back door* of the region. His subsequent campaigns in the Hill Country and its Shephelah (Lowland) provide an introduction to the western approaches to this same region. These approaches can be termed the *front door* of the Hill Country from the International Coastal Highway.

MARKING
1. **Brown write-in:**
   a. In blue area at E side of map = SALT SEA (DEAD SEA).

   b. Center of the map, just E of Gedor = HILL COUNTRY (in one line between Gedor and the N-S route).

   c. NW of Bethel = HILL COUNTRY (in two lines).

   d. W center of the map, in open area between Libnah and Adullam = SHEPHELAH (LOWLAND) in two lines.

   e. NW part of the map, in the flat, open area just NE of the name Aijalon = AIJA-LON VALLEY (in very small caps on an angle just E of the wadi into which all other wadis flow).

   f. In the flat, open area just N of Adullam, where all wadis begin to join = ELAH VALLEY (in very small caps and in two lines on both sides of the N-S route).

   g. Find Timnah (NW of Azekah). Along the route between Timnah and Beth-shemesh = SOREK VALLEY (in very small caps written on an angle on the route).

   h. In the open area between Jerusalem and the Dead Sea = WILDERNESS.

   i. In the SW corner of the map, spread out E to W from the region of Arad, W to the map number = NEGEV.

2. **Small green square (solid green) on dot = Gilgal.** Add the green write-in JOSHUA'S CAMP just E of Gilgal.

3. **Yellow HL on name = Gilgal, Jerusalem, Gibeon, Ascent of Beth-horon and Azekah.**

4. **Orange on dot:** Gibeonite cities = **Gibeon, Beeroth, Chephirah and Kiriath-jearim.**

DISCUSSION AND MARKING
Review the northeast section of this map, identifying familiar features (W. Suweinit, W. Qilt, W. Makkuk, etc.) and various ascents studied on Map 5-4. Locate Jerusalem, Bethel and the natural route which links them along the watershed.

Note the plateau just east and north of Gibeon. This plateau is not perfectly flat, but its low hills and shallow valleys do not restrict travel between various parts of the plateau. In Chapter Three we called this region the *Central Benjamin Plateau* since the tribe of Benjamin inherited it. It would be helpful to **write the abbreviation C.B.P. (small brown caps)** in the small open area east of Gibeon (near the north-south route), leaving space for later marking and circling of the name Gibeon. (It was also marked on Map 5-4.) This plateau is about the same elevation as the region around Jerusalem (about 750 meters/2500 feet above sea level). To the north of the Central Benjamin

Plateau the watershed route climbs about 100 meters/330 feet to the important crossroads in the region of Bethel.

One of the most important features of the Central Benjamin Plateau is that the north-south and east-west routes intersect here (just east of Gibeon). The name of the site of this strategic crossroads is Ramah (not named on this map). You will remember that Jerusalem's security is inseparably linked to this plateau and the routes which traverse it. Unless one recognizes this fact, much of Jerusalem's history (as well as the knotty problems of the contemporary scene) cannot be understood.

READING

Joshua 10, the chapter under discussion on this map, opens with a most interesting statement concerning Jerusalem and its dependence on the plateau just north of it.

5-5 a   Recall that the Gibeonites had already forfeited their area in a trick played on Joshua in Joshua 9. With the background gained so far in the study of Maps 5-4 and 5-5 read

5-5 b   **Joshua 10.1-2.** Put yourself in the place of Adoni-zedek, king of Jerusalem, as he followed the deteriorating situation north and northeast of his city.

DISCUSSION (It is helpful to study Map 5-5 as someone reads this discussion.)

Our study now turns to the western slopes of the Hill Country and the connections to the Coastal Highway via the Shephelah. The western limit of the Hill Country can be seen on Map 5-5 (and especially on the *SMA*), starting just east of the Aijalon Valley and running south to just east of the Elah Valley and beyond. The route from the Aijalon Valley to the Elah Valley runs along a connecting trough between the cities of Aijalon and Keilah (a type of eroded chalk moat). On all subsequent maps this route serves as a reminder of the border between the Hill Country (uplifted and deeply eroded limestone) and the rolling hills and broad valleys of the Shephelah. Note carefully this route and these features on Map 5-5 and the *SMA* for future reference.

Beginning at Gibeon find the wadi or nahal which drains south, southwest and then west as it cuts a deep gorge through the Hill Country before reaching Beth-shemesh in the Sorek Valley. Here other wadis join it. This canyon is called Nahal Sorek. (The broken blue line in it is sometimes missing and can be filled in with a blue ballpoint pen.) Erosion has exploited this geologically weakened region. This has resulted in deep canyons and high ridges, some maintaining an elevation of up to 700 meters/ 2300 feet above sea level as far west as the region overlooking the chalk moat and the Shephelah. Here these limestone ridges descend rapidly, disappearing beneath the much lower region of the Shephelah.

The combination of high ridges and deeply eroded wadis produce serious obstacles to north-south traffic on the western side of the Hill Country. This underscores the convenience of the watershed route (Bethel-Jerusalem-Bethlehem-Hebron). Travel from this main watershed route in the Hill Country to the lower Shephelah is mainly restricted to continuous ridges running between the two regions. Note these ridge routes on Map 5-5 via the Ascent of Beth-horon and via the ridge between Kiriath-jearim and the Aijalon Valley. Similar routes descend from the Hill Country to the Elah Valley. The red line of the International Coastal Highway (northwest corner of the map) serves as a reminder of the importance of the Shephelah and these approaches to the Hill Country.

In terms of local priorities, you should recall the Gibeonite deception (Joshua 9) and   5-5 a
its implication for Israelite control of the Central Benjamin Plateau with connecting
routes. Note the strategic importance of the Gibeonite cities marked in orange on Map
5-5. They are mentioned in Joshua 9.17 specifically to make this point. It is no
surprise that *the entire community [of Israel] made complaints about the leaders* who
had been taken in by this Gibeonite trick! (Joshua 9.18)

In order to prepare for the main part of the story and to reinforce the above discussion, the main local routes on Map 5-5 will now be highlighted.

MARKING — Yellow HL of the following routes:
1. **North-south connections in the Hill Country and Shephelah:**
   a. The main watershed route in the Hill Country beginning on the N edge of the
      map and passing through Bethel, Jerusalem, Bethlehem, Hebron and Debir before
      descending into the Negev. (This route ascends from a canyon N of Bethel.)

   b. The route beginning in the Aijalon Valley (anywhere in the valley) and running S
      along the edge of the Hill Country (between it and the Shephelah) to the Elah
      Valley, Keilah and S to the junction.

   c. A branch of the route just highlighted which begins just NE of Beth-shemesh and
      runs SW through the valleys and low hills of the Shephelah and by the site of
      Azekah to Lachish.

2. **East-west connections:**
   a. The most direct route from Gilgal (by Jericho) to the Central Benjamin Plateau
      (via the W. Suweinit pass) and Gibeon, and then continuing W to the Aijalon
      Valley along two possible ridge routes (via the two Beth-horons and via Kiriath-
      jearim).

   b. The ridge route from Jerusalem to Azekah (near Jarmuth) in the Shephelah via
      Bethlehem and the Elah Valley.

   c. The two Lachish-Hebron routes, one of which passes near the probable site of
      Eglon (not the one off the map) as it leaves the Shephelah and climbs 500 meters/
      1650 feet to Hebron.

DISCUSSION
The impending Israelite advance into central Canaan not only threatened the king of   5-5 b
Jerusalem. It had serious reverberations throughout the country. These were carried
along important local routes which are seen highlighted on Map 5-5. If the Israelite
advance were not checked on the Central Benjamin Plateau, the security of the Hill
Country and Shephelah could not be insured. Thus, the king of Jerusalem sent urgent
messages to other key Canaanite centers.

READING AND MARKING
1. Read **Joshua 10.3-5.** With a blue pen circle Jerusalem and the names of the cities in
   league with her against Gibeon. (Note: Debir is the name of a king in this passage,
   not a city. Only circle the Eglon on the map, not the other one.) Put a **small blue
   box around the name of Gibeon** to indicate the siege by the five kings.

2. **Sweeping blue arrows**: Mobilization against Gibeon called by Jerusalem =
   a. From the region of Hebron to Jerusalem.

   b. From the region of Jarmuth E along the route already highlighted, connecting with the Hebron-Jerusalem arrow by Bethlehem.

   c. From Jerusalem to Gibeon.

3. When word of the siege reached Joshua, his response was immediate. It constitutes one of the most dramatic stories in the Bible, one which brings fame to some of the places and features mentioned above. Carefully read **Joshua 10.6-14**, noting the geographical features and routes studied thus far on Maps 5-4 and 5-5. Remember the elevation differences: Jericho at 260 meters/850 feet below sea level, Gibeon at 750 meters/2500 feet above sea level, and the Aijalon Valley at 200 meters/650 feet above sea level. After thinking through possible markings, complete the following instructions.

4. **Sweeping green arrow**: Joshua's advance by night = From Gilgal to a point just E of Gibeon.

5. **Red encircling:**
   a. Around the name **Gibeon** and its blue box.

   b. Around a long region on both sides of the route from the Ascent of Beth-horon through the Valley of Aijalon, extending SW to the region of Azekah including Jarmuth. (Make some attempts with the dry end of your pen before marking.) Although the battle did not extend N of the two Beth-horons, these names may be included inside the red circle indicating the priority placed upon them in Joshua 10.

6. **Flight (blue) and chase (green) arrows**: Canaanite retreat and Joshua's chase =
   a. From Gibeon to the Ascent of Beth-horon.

   b. From the Aijalon Valley to the region of Azekah.

DISCUSSION, MARKING AND READING

The only site in this passage which has not been located on Map 5-5 is Makkedah (Joshua 10.10). Scholars have searched for its location during the past century. According to your reading so far, where would you locate Makkedah — near Azekah or farther south? Attempts to locate it by Azekah have not succeeded. Earlier in this century a similar sounding Arabic name was noted at a site northeast of Eglon, the ruin of Beit Maqdum. Recently, for archeological reasons, the nearby ruin of el-Kum was suggested. Both sites are found at the edge of the Shephelah near the Hill Country, due west of Hebron in a southwest line from the Aijalon-Keilah route. The exact position of the ruin (Khirbet) of el-Kum can be found by referring to Map 1-1 (SW corner). The name **Makkedah?** can be **written in red** at this location on Map 5-5 and compared with the sequence in Joshua's later campaign found in **Joshua 10.16-39.** (The name Makkedah is also found in a list of sixteen cities in Joshua 15.37. It is not in the index to the *SMM*.)

5-5 c

MARKING

1. **Red on dot with a red number by each city**: Joshua's later campaign in the Shephelah and southern Hill Country = **Libnah** (with a small **1**), **Lachish** (with a small **2**), **Eglon** in a blue circle (with a small **3**), **Hebron** (with a small **4**) and **Debir** (with a small **5**).

2. **Green arrows**: Joshua's advance in the Shephelah and southern Hill Country = From Libnah to Lachish, from Lachish to Eglon, from Eglon to Hebron and from Hebron to Debir.

3. **Orange circle around name = Gezer.**

4. **Sweeping orange arrow**: Gezer's attempt to aid Lachish in Joshua 10.33 = From Gezer to Lachish.

DISCUSSION

A summary of Joshua's campaigns up to this point is given in Joshua 10.40.

So Joshua mounted attacks against the entire land: the Hill Country, the Negev, the Shephelah (Lowland) and the hillsides and against all their kings.

An isolated reading of Joshua 10 would lead one to believe that these campaigns resulted in the total destruction of the cities and their inhabitants. In light of a larger   6-1 c
Biblical context it is clear that the indigenous population of Canaan remained a strong influence in subsequent decades and centuries. Hebron and Debir had to be reconquered, while campaigns against Jerusalem and Bethel are recorded in Judges 1 (Map   6-3 b c
6-3). It would appear, therefore, that the language of Joshua 10 and other such   f g
passages must be interpreted in terms of the larger picture. Everything in Joshua's path may have been destroyed (but not necessarily burned). However, his campaigns did not result in the total destruction of all inhabitants of the land nor of all of its settlements.

LEGEND

Name circled in blue   = League mobilized by Jerusalem against Gibeon.
Red on dots and numbers = Joshua's campaign in the Shephelah and southern Hill Country.

S M M   6 − 1

INTRODUCTION

The marking of this map was completed in Chapter One. It is useful to review this work in the light of previous map studies and the special emphasis upon Judah in this chapter.

With Map 6-1 open locate the following routes and regions. (The regions are not marked in brown but can be reviewed by referring to Maps 5-3 and 5-5, if necessary.)

1. The main Coastal Highway and the Transjordanian Highway (printed in red).

2. The main north-south internal highway between Shechem and Beer-sheba, via Bethel, Jerusalem, Bethlehem and Hebron.

3. The east-west highway from Heshbon (on the Transjordanian Highway at the edge of the Medeba plateau) to Gezer (via Jericho, Ramah, Upper Beth-horon and the Aijalon Valley) or to Aphek (via Jericho, Bethel and Timnath-serah).

4. Regions in and around Judah: the Wilderness, Hill Country, Shephelah, Coastal Plain (Philistia), and the Negev.

6-1 c   The books of Joshua and Judges make it quite clear that Joshua's campaigns did not extend to all the cities or regions on Map 6-1. Some of the exceptions in and around Judah are listed here. They are represented by blue dots on Map 6-1.

6-3 f   *As to the Jebusites living around Jerusalem, the Benjaminites did not take over their territory, and to this day the Jebusites live with the Benjaminites.* (Judges 1.21)

6-1 c   *The Amorites were able to keep control [of the regions] of Har-heres [Beth-shemesh], Aijalon and Shaalbim. However, they were forced to do service [to Israel] when the House of Joseph became stronger.* (Judges 1.35)

They [the Ephraimites] did not take over the territory of the Canaanites living around Gezer, and to this day the Canaanites live [in the territory allotted to] Ephraim. However, they are forced to do service [to Ephraim].
(Joshua 16.10)

6-3 f
7-7 b   In spite of an early attempt by the tribe of Judah to dislodge them (Judges 1.8 and Joshua 15.63), the Jebusites remained in control of Jerusalem (just off the main internal watershed route) until the time of David (Map 7-7). [Some feel that the native population of Jerusalem was destroyed by the Israelites and that the Jebusites later settled the area, forming a buffer zone between Judah and Benjamin.] Amorite and Canaanite control also continued in the region of the Sorek and Aijalon Valleys (Har-heres/Beth-shemesh, Aijalon, Shaalbim and Gezer). This was a serious problem since the Aijalon Valley constitutes the *front door* to the Central Benjamin Plateau.
5-5 a   The Gibeonite cities along main routes to the Central Benjamin Plateau (via Gibeon and Kiriath-jearim) did not improve the situation.

These problems were compounded by a significant development on the Coastal Plain, a development which would change the course of local history — the arrival of the
6-1 b   Philistines. The Philistines appear to have originated from the region of the Aegean (between modern Greece and Turkey), perhaps from an area like the island of Crete. Deuteronomy 2.23 states that earlier the *Avvim had lived in villages as far as Gaza* but that they had been replaced by the *Caphtorim, who came from Caphtor (Crete).* The Caphtorim had destroyed the Avvim and *settled in their stead.* The prophet Jeremiah mentions *the Philistines, the remnant of the coastland of Caphtor* (47.4). Amos also speaks of *the Philistines from Caphtor* (9.7).

In the period of David and Solomon the terms *Cherethites* (Cretans) and *Pelethites* (Philistines) are often used in reference to the region of the Philistines or to the

Philistine mercenaries who constituted an important part of the king's personal army and bodyguard (1 Samuel 30.14; 2 Samuel 8.18; 15.14-18; 20.7, 23; 1 Kings 1.38-49). The strong words of later prophets also link the Cherethites with the Philistines (Zephaniah 2.4-5; Ezekiel 25.15-17).

The immediate significance of this new element on the Coastal Plain will be seen in Philistine political, economic and military expansion along the International Coastal Highway. This expansion to the north and south into the Negev resulted in a major threat to the unification of the Israelite tribes. Judges and kings struggled with this problem for centuries.

Philistine interests also included the domination of key valleys in the Shephelah and, when possible, political centers in the Hill Country. Samuel, Saul and Jonathan attempted to meet this challenge in different ways. However, it is David (whose entire life was closely intertwined with the Philistines) who turned the tables and checked Philistine domination and expansion. After the deaths of David and Solomon the control of the Shephelah was the all-important indicator of the relative strength of the Philistines and of the Israelites. The ebb and flow of history in this battleground has produced one of the most exciting chapters in the study of the country.

     7-3 b-d
     7-4 d

     7-5 c d
     7-6 a-d

S M M   6 − 2

DISCUSSION

This map was marked in Chapter Three. It has particular relevance to Judah since the book of Joshua gives more detail regarding the allotment to that tribe than to any other. This detail (Joshua 15) is one of the most important sources for scholars interested in the study of historical geography of the Old Testament.

     6-2 a

One has only to glance at the text for Map 6-2 (printed on the page preceding the map) to see that information on Judah occupies the first three columns of this page. Note the border descriptions and the names of cities in the eleven districts of the tribe. This coverage is also seen on Map 6-2 by the red numbers in the area of Judah. Also note the many names on the lists, which as yet are unidentified (those without numbers next to them on the page of text).

There is a striking lack of detailed information about the House of Joseph (Ephraim and Manasseh) in column four. This can also be seen by the lack of red numbers on the map itself.

The territory of tribes between Judah and Ephraim is given good coverage. Benjamin (columns four and five) is especially well-represented with a border description which compliments those of Ephraim and Judah. Benjamin also has a detailed city list. Dan's border description is missing, but the descriptions of Judah and Ephraim help to define the limit of the tribe. A city list for Dan is shown in column seven.

     6-2 b

The following comments are a few among many which could be made about the significance of the tribal allotments given in Joshua 15-19:

6-2 a   1. Judah dominates the entire list. The reason for this predominance is not stated. Some suggest that all original lists were as complete as Judah's but only those in and around Judah were preserved by those who kept records. Others feel that some of the lists (like that of Judah) were completed or even compiled in later periods. What is clear is that the lists we have today for the tribe of Judah represent an unparalleled source of information on settlement in the southern Hill Country. As such it is used as background on every map of the region in Section Six of the *SMM*.

6-7 c   2. The civil war in Benjamin seriously weakened the tribe. At the same time the move
6-4 a   of most of the Danites from their insecure and threatened position between Ephraim and Judah to a new region in the north left a vacuum in the region. This vacuum became a disputed region once Judah and Ephraim became strong enough to make their presence felt in places like Beth-shemesh (No. 43 on Map 6-2) and Gezer (No. 116).

            3. The study of Benjamin and Dan shows that some cities or regions assigned to these tribes are duplicated in Judah or Ephraim. This should be no surprise since these duplications may well represent areas shared or coveted by more than one tribe. Certainly, later Biblical records illustrate tensions in these areas (Bethel, Beth-shemesh, etc.).

S M M   6 − 3

TITLE: EARLY DEVELOPMENTS IN AND AROUND JUDAH

DATE: 13th − 11th Centuries B.C.

INTRODUCTION

On Maps 6-3 and 6-4 a variety of events are studied which are listed in the *SCS* for each map. An important use of these maps is to show local tribal territories (with background names from Map 6-2) and regional settlement problems (from Map 6-1).

A glance at the unmarked maps (6-3 and 6-4) show there is an overlap in the two maps (the western side of Map 6-3 and the eastern side of Map 6-4). For this reason some of the background marking (tribal territories and regional settlement problems) is common to both maps. This will be noted in the marking instructions below for Map 6-3.

This marking assignment is one of the most concentrated in the *Guide*. Its importance is reflected in the fact that over two-thirds of the history recorded in the Old Testament which can be marked on a map occurred in the regions covered by these two maps. As the marking proceeds, make a serious attempt to note features already studied in the *Guide*. These include wadi/nahal systems, internal and international routes and strategic regions such as the Central Benjamin Plateau and the Aijalon Valley. Also note the position of cities in strategic regions and at or near important road junctions. If proper attention is given to the topography and the features of the map while marking, this assignment will constitute one of the most important reviews in this chapter.

MARKING (On Map 6-3 unless otherwise specified.)

1. **Brown write-in:**

   a. In the Dead Sea area (be sure to leave room for the Legend) = SALT SEA (DEAD SEA) in two lines.

   b. In the region between En-gedi (the site on the W shore of the Dead Sea) and Jerusalem = WILDERNESS.

   c. In the center of the map just W of Peor = HILL COUNTRY.

   d. In the W center of the map, between Libnah and Mareshah = SHEPHELAH (LOWLAND) in two lines.

   e. In the SW of the map, spreading out E to W two letters above and three letters below Hormah = NEGEV.

   f. Some of the regions written in above are also found on Map 6-4. Compare the two maps and write in on Map 6-4 any corresponding regional names.

2. **Blue underlining:** Unconquered Canaanite centers (from Map 6-1) =

   a. **Jerusalem/Jebus** with JEBUSITES written in blue just E of Jebus. (Leave enough space by the name for a later red circle around Jerusalem/Jebus.)

   b. **Aijalon, Shaalbim, Gezer** and **Har-heres/Beth-shemesh.**

   c. Some of the cities underlined in blue above also appear on Map 6-4. If so, underline them in blue on Map 6-4.

3. **Blue box around name:** Philistine cities (from Map 6-1) =

   a. **Ekron, Gath, Ashkelon** and **Gaza.**

   b. Find these cities on Map 6-4 and draw a blue box around them on that map. Add a blue box around **Ashdod** on Map 6-4.

4. **Orange underlining on name:** Gibeonite cities (from Maps 5-3/5) =

   a. **Gibeon, Beeroth, Chephirah** and **Kiriath-jearim.**

   b. Also underline them in orange on Map 6-4.

5. **Orange on dot:** Cities or border sites of Benjamin (from Map 6-2) =

   a. **Jericho, Jerusalem/Jebus, Geba, Parah, Ramah, Mizpah, Zemaraim, Gibeon, Beeroth, Mozah** and **Chephirah.** (Gibeah and Kiriath are named in Benjamin's list in Joshua 18.28, but there is disagreement as to what sites or features are intended.)

   b. If any of these appear on Map 6-4, color their dot orange.

6. **Yellow on dot:** Cities or border sities of Dan (from Map 6-2) =

   a. **Aijalon, Shaalbim, Eshtaol, Zorah, Beth-shemesh, Timnah** and **Gibbethon.**

b. Find these same sites on Map 6-4 and color their dot yellow. Also color the dot yellow of the following cities of Dan on Map 6-4 = **Baalath** (W of Gibbethon), **Eltekeh, Jehud, Bene-berak, Gath-rimmon** and **Joppa.**

7. **Green border**: Northern border of Judah and the southern border of Ephraim. Draw this first with a green pencil. It is helpful for someone to read the instructions as you mark. Remember, the broken blue lines are the dry stream beds. Steep slopes are shaded, but the top of the ridge is lighter.
a. **On Map 6-3** draw the northern border of Judah from E to W =
   1) Beginning in the NE corner of the map, beneath the & of the title.

   2) Move W in the nahal and then on the ridge up to the *t* of Ascent.

   3) From the *i* of Adummim SW to the dot of En-shemesh.

   4) SW to the *r* of En-rogel and then NW to the dot of En-rogel.

   5) From En-rogel to Kiriath-jearim via the dot of Waters of Nephtoah, the *z* of Mozah, the *t* and *r* of Mt. Ephron and then NW to the dot of Kiriath-jearim.

   6) From Kiriath-jearim to the dot of Beth-shemesh via the ridge of Mt. Seir and S of Eshtaol and Zorah.

   7) NW passing S of Timnah but N of Ekron.

On Map 6-4 copy the relevant border from Map 6-4, from the Waters of Nephtoah westward. Note geographical features. (Name positions sometimes change!) Finish off the border on Map 6-4 extending it W via the dot of Shikkeron and then out to the sea along the nahal which runs W and then NW of Shikkeron, S of Baalath but N of Jabneel. With green pencil shade in the N side of the border on both Maps 6-4 and 6-3.

b. **On Map 6-3** draw in the southern border of Ephraim from E to W =
   1) Beginning in the NE corner of the map, beneath the third *e* of settlement.

   2) Through the *o* of Jericho, up the large ridge between the broken blue lines of the nahals, and S of Bethel and Ai.

   3) Curving SW between the dots of Zemaraim and Ataroth-addar to the ridge W of the *b* of Gibeon.

   4) W, via the name Shaalbim and then curving SW to the E and S of the name Gezer before turning back N to pass W of Gittaim.

On Map 6-4 copy the relevant border of Ephraim. Finish off the border on Map 6-4 to pass just E and N of Jehud and then NW to the swamps E of Gath-rimmon and out the river to the sea by Me-jarkon (Waters of Yarkon). With a green pencil shade in the S side of the border you have just drawn on both Maps 6-4 and 6-3.

    c. **On both Maps 6-3 and 6-4** draw a green border from the dot of Kiriath-jearim N to Ephraim's border (passing just below Baalah to the hills N of Kiriath-jearim).

8. **Green write-in:** Tribal names (to be marked on Map 6-3)

    a. In open area between Bethel and Upper Beth-horon = EPHRAIM enclosed in a green box indicating that it was one of the stronger tribes.

    b. In the open area S of Kiriath-jearim = JUDAH enclosed in a green box indicating that it was one of the stronger tribes.

    c. In the open area between Shaalbim and Timnah = DAN.

    d. In an E-W direction from Jericho to Beth-aven = BENJAMIN (keeping off the routes).

    e. In the SW corner of the map, by Beer-sheba = SIMEON.   6-3 d

    f. By the site of Arad in the eastern Negev = KENITES with a sweeping green arrow pointing to Arad from the SE (along the route coming from the shore of the Dead Sea). The Kenites were a group which joined the Israelites in the Wilderness and entered this region during the period of Israelite settlement.

    g. Transfer the tribal names EPHRAIM and JUDAH from Map 6-3 to the appropriate space on Map 6-4. Other green markings on Map 6-4 will be assigned later.

9. **Yellow HL on names:** Places mentioned in and around Judah in the period of Israelite settlement = **Bethel/Luz, Jerusalem, Hebron/Kiriath-arba, Debir/Kiriath-sepher, Arad** and **Hormah/Zephath** (in the Negev).

10. **Yellow HL on routes:**

    a. The main internal north-south route beginning just N of Bethel and running by Ramah, Bethlehem, Hebron and Debir to Beer-sheba.

    b. The Hebron-Arad connection and the route descending SE to the shore of the Dead Sea and from there to the S.

    c. The Arad-Beer-sheba connection and on to the W edge of the map.

11. **Red circle around names = Bethel/Luz, Jerusalem** and **Debir/Kiriath-sepher.**   6-3 f g

DISCUSSION

The marking just completed on Map 6-3 reveals a number of significant subjects for discussion. The main internal north-south route (Bethel to Beer-sheba via Hebron) runs across the map. For the most part it is on or near the watershed between eastern and western drainage. Since Judah controls most of this route, it has been called the *Judean Ridge Route.* In the southern Hill Country, Hebron is the main road center along this route, with important branches beginning there and running to Arad and to Beer-sheba in the Negev basin. (Negev always means the Biblical Negev introduced on Map 5-2.)

In order to appreciate the descent south of Hebron and the slope in the Negev basin itself (from east to west), it is interesting to note the following approximate elevations: the region around Hebron rises to over 1000 meters/3000 feet; Arad sits at 550 meters/ 1800 feet; Beer-sheba lies at 300 meters/985 feet. Hebron is situated at an interesting location. It serves as the main center in the southern Hill Country amidst rich and productive, terraced hills where vines predominate. It also is closely linked with the

4-3 e-g
4-4 e
5-2 c

strategic basin of the Negev farther south as was noted in the period of the patriarchs (Maps 4-3 and 4-4) and in the story of the spies sent by Moses from Kadesh-barnea (Map 5-2). The Bible alludes to Hebron's attractive character in the rather amusing dialogue between two of these spies who survived the wilderness wanderings and

6-3 b

remained good friends, Joshua and Caleb. Caleb received his inheritance from Joshua in the region of Hebron. He also had rights farther south around Debir, a city he

6-3 c

auctioned off with his daughter, Achsah. Othniel met Caleb's challenge and not only gained control of the important route between Hebron and Beer-sheba but also became directly related to the prominent family of Caleb at Hebron. Later Hebron's

7-6 a b

connections with the Negev appear again, especially in maps which deal with David's life and Judah's efforts to control routes and strategic centers in the Negev and beyond.

From the Shephelah in the west (at approximately 400 meters/1300 feet) routes climb up steep ridges to Hebron. There they meet other important routes from the north and the south. North of Hebron the important route via Beth-zur descends to the Elah Valley in the Shephelah.

The striking absence of routes from Hebron eastward is easily explained by the rugged topography and arid climate of the Wilderness of Judah and by the obvious difficulty of the Dead Sea lying at almost 400 meters/1300 feet below sea level. While less significant routes through these obstacles do exist (not shown on *SMM* maps), the region does not lend itself to common trade and travel. Therefore, for all practical purposes, the Hebron area is isolated from the Transjordanian Highway.

By comparison, the territories of Benjamin and Dan offer much more convenient routes from the Coastal Highway to Transjordan and to its International Highway. Benjamin was the key to expansion in the west (via the Gibeonite cities and the Aijalon Valley to the Coastal Highway) and in the east (via Jericho to the Transjordanian Highway). Benjamin's tendency to develop a highly skilled fighting force,

6-7 c

therefore, came naturally. During the civil war in Benjamin (Map 6-7) the Benjaminites mustered *seven hundred chosen men who were left-handed, each one of whom could sling a stone at a hair and not miss!* (Judges 20.16). Jacob's prophetic description of Benjamin is remarkably accurate.

> *Benjamin is a ferocious wolf; in the morning he is devouring the prey,*
> *and until nightfall he is dividing up the spoil.*   (Genesis 49.27)

READING

Read **Joshua 14.6-15 and Judges 1.8-26.** (The probable reading in Judges 1.18 is *did not take.*) Optional readings are listed in the *SCS* for Map 6-3.

LEGEND

Blue underlining and blue box	=	See blue dots and boxes on Map 6-1.
Orange dot	=	City in Benjamin tribal allotment.
Yellow dot	=	City in Dan tribal allotment.
Orange underlining	=	Gibeonite city.

S M M   6 – 4

TITLE: WESTERN CONFRONTATION: TRIBE OF DAN & SAMSON THE JUDGE

DATE: 13th – 11th Century B.C.

MARKING
Most marking has been completed in the assignments for Map 6-3 above. What remains to be done is listed below.

1. **Additional brown write-in:**
   a. In the NW corner = GREAT SEA, MEDITERRANEAN SEA in two lines.

   b. In the open area just E of Timnah = SOREK VALLEY (in two lines) with a small brown arrow pointing S to the broken blue line (stream bed) running between the dot of Har-heres/Beth-shemesh and Timnah.

   c. In the N of the map, in the area just SW of Aphek = YARQON RIVER (in two lines) with a small brown arrow pointing to the river which runs from Aphek to the sea.

2. **Additional green write-in:**
   a. In the open area between Eltekeh and Beth-dagon = DAN.

   b. In the open area between Gibeon and Chephirah, running E to W (avoiding the road), one letter under another = BEN. (an abbreviation for Benjamin).

3. **Yellow HL on route**: The International Coastal Highway (both branches) = Routes printed in red from SW to N.

DISCUSSION
Map 6-3 emphasizes the Hill Country of Judah and the location of the tribe of Benjamin. Map 6-4 centers on the Shephelah, the Coastal Plain and the territory allotted to the tribe of Dan. Background marking (just completed) allows the two maps to be used as a pair.

One does not have to look far for an explanation of Dan's difficulties in settling its   6-4 a
tribal allotment. The International Coastal Highway passed directly through its territory. This meant that any attempt to take control of the region automatically cut the main land link between Africa (Egypt) and Asia (Mesopotamia). Local centers and peoples in the area would be expected to resist any Danite offensive action. This is brought out vividly in the first chapter of the book of Judges, which in a few sentences accurately describes this region of valleys (Sorek and Aijalon) and nearby Hill Country (just east of the Aijalon-Eshtaol route).

> *The Amorites forced the Danites back up into the Hill Country, not*
> *allowing them to come down into the valley.*   (Judges 1.34-35)

Joshua 19.47 summarizes the option chosen by many Danites in light of this seemingly impossible situation. The comment immediately follows the description of the tribal territory outlined on Map 6-4.

> *However, the territory of the Danites was inaccessible. So the Danites went up and attacked Leshem, striking it down with the edge of the sword. They then took it over as theirs, settling it and calling it Dan instead of Leshem, according to the name of their ancestor.*   (Joshua 19.47)

Dan's choice is indicated in the north of the country on Map 6-2. The campaign no doubt took place in the century following the conquest (after the decline of Hazor) since *Jonathan [Moses' grandson] and his sons were priests to the tribe of the Danites in their newly acquired territory* (Judges 18.30). Perhaps the tribe's very name, which means *(God) judges*, was prophetic of its ultimate fate in the very region in which it at last felt secure (Maps 8-5 and 9-4). The story of the move is a very sad but enlightening commentary on the apostasy of the period. Six hundred armed Danites steal a graven image and a priest — who was overjoyed at the thought of a larger congregation!

8-5 a
9-4

READING
Read **Judges 17 and 18.**

DISCUSSION
Not all the Danites moved to the north. At least one clan (Hushim) joined Benjamin (Genesis 46.23 and 1 Chronicles 8.1, 8, 11-13). Others were still present in and around the Sorek Valley when the Philistines dominated the Shephelah and the Hill Country, in the days of Samson the judge.

6-4 b

MARKING
1. **Blue write-in and sweeping arrows**: Philistine settlement and expansion
   a. Between Ekron and Ashdod = PHILISTINES (large caps).

   b. Sweeping blue arrows out from this name N toward Jehud, E toward Timnah and S toward Ziklag.

2. **Yellow HL on names**: Places in Samson's life = **Zorah, Eshtaol, Timnah, Ashkelon, Gaza, Hebron** and **Etam** (E center).

DISCUSSION
Philistine ambitions came naturally. Their five cities (in blue boxes on Map 6-4) are located along the International Coastal Highway with important commercial connections in various directions. Their arrival was noted on Map 6-1 and signals the beginning of what will become Judah's and Benjamin's main *thorn in the flesh*.

6-1 b

The valleys of the Shephelah were the first step in Philistine penetration into the Hill Country. The territory of Benjamin (with all that the area now denotes) was one of the main objectives of the Philistines. Perhaps this was in order to prevent Judah or Ephraim from settling it and using it as a springboard to further expansion. It was certainly in Philistine interests to maintain a wedge between Judah and Ephraim, two of the strongest Israelite tribes. They also recognized the link Benjamin provided to Jericho and beyond to Transjordan.

Two lines in the story of Samson stand out above all others. One is a simple statement of fact in Judges 14.4. *At that time the Philistines had control of Israel.* The other is

6-4 b

a rhetorical question in Judges 15.11. It is posed to Samson by the men of Judah (!) after he had upset the delicate status quo and fragile conditions of Philistine occupation. His actions were certain to bring Philistine reprisals unless Samson surrendered. *Don't you realize that we're under the control of the Philistines?*

READING

Read **Judges 13.24-15.20** with Map 6-4 in view. If the story is unfamiliar, it would be helpful to skim over the entire account in Judges 13-16.

DISCUSSION

The two subjects discussed on Map 6-4 deal with the tribe of Dan and illustrate two basic problems facing the Israelites in the period of the Judges (Champions). One described a threat from the outside, in this case the Philistines. This threat was checked by Samson in his many exploits. The second was harder to define and much more difficult to solve. It was internal. The events in Judges 18.14-31 serve as a commentary on attitudes of the day: 1) the move of the tribe of Dan away from its allotted territory, 2) the use of force by one faction of Israelites against another in achieving selfish tribal interests, and 3) priestly apostasy in the house of Moses only a generation or two removed from Moses himself. All of this and more points to internal decay, both in relationships between men and with God.

6-4 b
6-4 a

In weighing the relative dangers of external threats and internal decay, these stories, and indeed the entire book of Judges, underscore the latter as the greater problem. This is seen in the concluding chapters (Judges 17-21) which culminate the message of the book itself. In them we read of the move of the tribe of Dan and the Benjaminite civil war. All is summed up in one phrase from a passage assigned for this map study. The phrase stands in stark contrast to the preaching of Moses, Joshua and subsequent reformers like Samuel, all of whom attempted to help Israel *recognize who God is*. The phrase is that of Micah, *a man from the Hill Country of Ephraim*.

You're taking away the very gods which I made . . . .
What do I have left?   (Judges 18.24)

LEGEND

The legend for this map is the same as the one for Map 6-3 with the addition of the following item:
Yellow on the name = Places in Samson's life.

S M M   6 – 6

INTRODUCTION

This map has been marked and discussed in Chapter Two of the *Guide*. Two additional aspects in the *SCS* for the map relate to the present study, the stories of Ehud and Jephthah. They are concerned with the growing pressure from the Ammonites and the Moabites along the Transjordanian Highway. Mounting tension on the Medeba Plateau (settled largely by the tribe of Reuben) and the resulting threat on Jericho (the eastern approach to Benjamin) were potentially as serious as the increasing Philistine pressure from the west.

6-6 a c

5-3 b   Map 6-2 shows Reuben's position on the Medeba Plateau. The plateau's importance
         stems from two basic facts. Firstly, it straddles the Transjordanian Highway. Secondly,
         it serves as a strategic staging ground for attacks on Jericho and the central Hill Country
         via the Plains of Moab and the Lower Jordan Valley. This is clearly seen in the Israelite
5-3 a   advances on Map 5-3. Moses, from the vantage point of Pisgah, had the foresight to
         warn the Israelites that the same campaign route which they were using could also
         serve other invaders if they forgot the Lord their God (Deuteronomy 8.17-20).

EHUD AND THE MOABITES

DISCUSSION AND READING

6-6 a   The story of Ehud is listed in the *SCS* for Map 6-6 since it has to do with eastern
6-7 a   confrontation. However, it was marked on Map 6-7 where the region of Jericho (in
         this case *the city of palms*) and Gilgal appear. The features which make the region
         especially important were introduced on Map 5-4. They include the oasis itself, the
         agricultural products of the region, east-west routes, ascents through the Wilderness
         into the Hill Country of Ephraim and Benjamin and the rugged territory just west of
         the oasis, a convenient region of refuge. All of these play a significant part in the
         study of this story, which has interesting parallels with Joshua's campaign (Map 5-4).
         Read **Judges 3.12-30** with Map 6-7 in view.

JEPHTHAH AND THE AMMONITES

DISCUSSION

6-6 c   The episode of Jephthah is another example of eastern confrontation. While Map 6-6
         lists the story and includes the marking, the larger context of the events is seen on
         Map 6-1, which should be used with Map 6-6. This same subject was introduced in
         Chapters One and Two. The Amorite threat in the east and the seriousness of the
         situation is summarized in Judges 10. The Ammonites had overcome the Israelites in
         Transjordan, and the invaders were poised for an attack west of the Jordan Valley (Map
         6-1).

> *In that year — and for eighteen more — they [the Ammonites] crushed and
> smashed the Israelites which were across the Jordan in the land of the Amorites
> in Gilead. The Ammonites even crossed [to the west of] the Jordan to mount
> military campaigns against Judah, Benjamin and the House of Ephraim, putting
> Israel in a real bind.*   (Judges 10.8-9)

A spiritual revival in Israel led to military action and the mobilization of the opposing
parties (Map 6-6).

> *Then the Ammonites were mobilized and set up camp in Gilead while Israel
> assembled [its forces] and camped at Mizpah [of Gilead]. The word going
> around among the people and leaders of Gilead was, 'Whoever is the first
> to fight against the Ammonites will be made the leader of all of those living
> in Gilead.'*   (Judges 10.17-18)

Jephthah, an outcast from his own family in Gilead, was called back from the land of
Tob to lead the Israelite forces. He first attempted to negotiate with the Ammonites
on the basis of Israel's prior claim to the disputed region (from Nahal Arnon to Nahal   5-3 a
Yarmuk). In defense of Israel's claim a lengthy historical review is presented (Judges
11.12-28). It is reflected in the marking on Map 5-3. This claim is underscored by
Jephthah's concluding question (Map 6-1).

> *For three hundred years Israel has been living in Heshbon and in its surrounding*
> *settlements, and in Aroer and in its surrounding settlements, and in all the*
> *cities which are around [Nahal] Arnon. Why didn't you take these back*
> *during this time? I've done nothing against you. It's you who are con-*
> *triving evil against me by starting a war with me. The Lord, who is the*
> *Judge, will pass judgment today between the people of Israel and the people*
> *of Ammon.*   (Judges 11.26-27)

Naturally, the Ammonites rejected Jephthah's reasoning. Negotiations broke down
and armed conflict ensued. Judges 11 summarizes the outcome (Maps 6-6 and 6-1).

> *So Jephthah crossed over to launch an attack on the Ammonites, and the*
> *Lord gave them into his hand. He struck them down from Aroer to the*
> *entrance of Minnith [location unknown], twenty cities up to Abel-keramim.*
> *It was a tremendous defeat, and the Ammonites were humiliated by the*
> *Israelites.*   (Judges 11.32-33)

As is so often the case, internal disputes broke out after the common enemy was
subdued. The main issue appears to be Jephthah's unilateral action in Transjordan.
However, a much more serious issue is apparent, a developing independence among
the tribes east of the Jordan. The conflict between the Ephraimites and the Gileadites
is a sad commentary on the lack of Israelite unity in this period. It no doubt provided some consolation for the defeated Ammonites. Following the actual encounter
in Gilead, a slight variation in the usage of two similar Hebrew consonants (*Shibboleth*
and *Sibboleth*) became a matter of life or death for the escaping Ephraimites. This
illustrates the fact that regional differences easily developed on either side of the
Jordan. Such differences underscore the potential for developing separate and independent political movements on either side of the Jordan. It is interesting to recall   6-6 b
here that in the same period and the same region Ephraimites had been called out late
in another battle to seize the fords of the Jordan, slaughtering the escaping Midianites
(Judges 7.24-25 and Map 6-6).

READING
The entire story of these events in Transjordan is found in Judges 10.6-12.7. The
matter of the *Shibboleth* makes interesting reading in **Judges 12.1-6.**

S M M   6 — 7

DISCUSSION

This map was thoroughly discussed in Chapter Three. Its relationship to Ephraim and to Judah is summarized here. Have the map in view while reading this short summary.

6-2 a
1. Both the House of Joseph (Ephraim and Manasseh) and the tribe of Judah were in positions of leadership among the other Israelite tribes. Ephraim's position of prominence embraced the territory of the tribe of Benjamin on her southern flank. From Bethel, Ephraim's influence extended along those routes highlighted on Map 6-7. The tribal territory of Benjamin was the key to Bethel's control of the region.

6-7 c
5-5 a
6-3 f
2. The tribe of Benjamin was seriously weakened by the civil war which resulted from the *Gibeah affair*. This, together with the four Gibeonite cities and the Jebusite enclave around Jerusalem, left the tribal territory in a vulnerable position.

6-7 c
3. Bethlehem served as the main city in the northern Hill Country of Judah. From it one could easily travel to Jerusalem and to the Central Benjamin Plateau around Ramah. Judges 19.7-15 relates how the Levite, his servant, his concubine and their donkeys loaded with supplies (no doubt including many gifts from the concubine's family) were able to leave Bethlehem late in the day and arrive at Gibeah the same evening. The convenient ridge route along which they traveled can be seen on Map 6-7. The importance of this connection (via the non-Israelite territory of the Jebusites) and the strategic nature of the Central Benjamin Plateau would sooner or later tempt a leader of Judah to claim the region for himself.

S M M   7 — 3

DISCUSSION

The preceding chapters have laid down a basic historical and geographical framework for studies in the second half of this chapter. Beginning with Section Seven of the *SMM*, studies in this chapter of the *Guide* build upon a certain chronological order given in the *SCS* of each map (with Biblical references). Thus your review of each *SCS* will help you to follow the rather complicated history of Judah.

Map 7-3 was marked and discussed in Chapter Three. Historically it opens the period of Samuel's ministry. This ministry served as a bridge between the period of the Judges and the establishment of the monarchy. Glance at Map 7-3 as you read the following paragraphs.

7-3 a
7-3 b
7-3 c
Samuel's early life was tied closely to Shiloh in the Hill Country of Ephraim. The battle of Aphek was a major military defeat for Israel in which Shiloh played a part. After the Israelite defeat the Philistines may have campaigned in the Hill Country and destroyed Shiloh. The Ark of the Covenant, captured at the battle of Aphek, was returned to the Israelites via Beth-shemesh (in the Shephelah/Lowland) and then was brought up to Kiriath-jearim in the Hill Country.

Samuel's ministry was concentrated between Ramah and Bethel in the important area between Ephraim and the Central Benjamin Plateau. It was to this region that Samuel summoned *all the house of Israel* during his renewal campaign (1 Samuel 7.5). At Mizpah he demonstrated God's deliverance from the Philistines, who earlier had overrun Israelite forces at Aphek. An Israelite victory on this strategic plateau must have provided an impressive object lesson for all Israel to see.   7-3 d

Samuel's preaching and the events portrayed on this map set the scene for the early   7-3 e
years of the monarchy. The great defeat at Aphek was seen in the light of religious and moral decadence. On the other hand, the stunning victory near Mizpah followed a ceremony in which Samuel had led the people of Israel to *recognize who God is*. This contrast must have made a deep impression on sensitive spirits like those of Jonathan and David. Both of these boys (one from Benjamin and another from Judah) would later come under the influence of Samuel's teaching during a period when Israel was ruled by a king.

S M M   7 — 4

INTRODUCTION

Part of this map was marked in Chapter Two and part in Chapter Three. The remaining marking will be completed in this chapter. It is concerned with relations between Saul (Israel's first king, a Benjaminite) and the Philistines in the region of the tribe of Benjamin.

DISCUSSION

Pressures on the Israelite tribes had mounted during the twelfth and eleventh centuries B.C. Internal problems between tribes were exploited by an expanding Philistine control along the country's main routes. This control even reached the Hill Country, as events in the lives of Samson and Samuel illustrate.

During the eleventh century there was a growing trend among the tribes to find a strong leader who could organize some type of Israelite defense force to cope with the situation. This trend culminated in the question put directly to Samuel by all of   7-4 a
Israel.

> *All the elders of Israel got together and made a trip to Ramah to [meet with]*
> *Samuel. 'Look,' they said to him, 'you are getting along in years, and your*
> *sons are not following in your footsteps [which means that they will be unfit*
> *to lead the nation]. Appoint a king for us now, someone to govern us as*
> *all the other nations have.' Samuel was not at all pleased when they said,*
> *'Give us a king to govern us.'*   (1 Samuel 8.4-6)

The events surrounding this turning point in Israelite history and the early years of   7-4 a-c
Saul's reign were discussed in Chapter Three. The initial success of Saul the Benjaminite was impressive. The deliverance brought to Jabesh-gilead in Transjordan was the type yearned for in the Hill Country west of the Jordan. This desire was probably expressed at Gilgal where Saul was confirmed as king. There, all opposition to Saul's rule was overcome (1 Samuel 11.12-15).

Philistine control in the Hill Country appears to have been concentrated in the region of the Central Benjamin Plateau for obvious reasons. This plateau was in effect *a land between* the two strongest Israelite tribes, Ephraim and Judah (Maps 6-3 and 6-7). The principle was simple: *Divide and conquer.* Command of this plateau was the most effective way for the Philistines to control the Israelites in the hills. The region, however, was also the home territory of Saul, the new king of Israel.

Given this situation it was only a matter of time before pressure would be put on Saul to do something. His family (which according to 1 Chronicles 8.29-33 came from Gibeon), his capital (established sometime during this period at Gibeah), Samuel's ministry (from Ramah), the approaches to Ephraim and to Judah (from the Central Benjamin Plateau) and the security of all of Israel were at stake — not to mention his own personal reputation. Only by considering these tribal and geographical issues can one appreciate the great burden on the shoulders of Saul, a person who had tried so hard to avoid the responsibility of the office.

7-4 d   The confrontation with the Philistines finally took place in and around the Central Benjamin Plateau. Since the story of this engagement is presented in great detail in 1 Samuel, it is worthwhile to take time to review the geographical nature of the region.

The area between Jericho and the Central Benjamin Plateau/Bethel Plateau was discussed earlier in this chapter on Map 5-4 (a detailed map of the region). In the region there exist two great obstacles, the Wadi Qilt and the Wadi Makkuk, two separate systems which drain eastward to the Jordan (Rift) Valley. They have both eroded through the chalk wilderness and into hard limestone to create canyons almost impossible to cross. Cutting into the limestone hills northeast and southeast of Bethel, these systems define a ridge route from Bethel to Jericho, the most direct and only continuous ridge route between these two sites.

Because of geographical factors, these two wadi systems are relatively easier to cross at two points. These points are called *passes* and can be seen on Map 5-4. Find them by starting on the Central Benjamin Plateau (east of Gibeon) and moving your finger east through the pass across Wadi Suweinit (part of the Wadi Qilt system). Then proceed north through a rather flat region of small valleys nestled among low hills which the Bible calls the *emeq* (plain or valley). To do this you must leave the road which leads toward Jericho and head due north to join the important Bethel-Jericho road. By some maneuvering you can reach another pass which crosses Wadi Makkuk to a ridge route leading to Jericho.

These two passes, the area of small valleys between them and the surrounding connections to Bethel and to Jericho are very important for our present study. Anyone who commands the Central Benjamin Plateau and the region between these two passes
5-3 c   has effective control of the entire central Hill Country. On Maps 5-4 and 5-5 Joshua's
5-5 b c   campaigns in this area (the opening battles of the Israelite conquest) demonstrated his understanding of this strategic region.

During the early Israelite period certain cities (not shown on Map 5-4) sprang up in this area. These cities are often located on higher chalky regions but surrounded by fields where good soil from harder limestones has formed. One such city is Ramah at the crossroads of the Central Benjamin Plateau. Another is Geba east of Ramah on the south side of the Wadi Suweinit. A third is Michmash, controlling the pass across the Wadi Suweinit and much of the strategic area between the two passes discussed above.

Finally, on Map 5-4 note the triangle of important routes from 1) the Central Benjamin Plateau to Bethel along the main north-south ridge route, 2) from Bethel toward the area of small valleys east of Ai, and 3) from this area of small valleys to the Central Benjamin Plateau via the pass across Wadi Suweinit. Find this same triangle of roads on Maps 6-3, 6-7 and 7-3. Note how Ephraim and Benjamin, as one would expect, share this important triangle. You should add this information to what you already know about the relationship between these two tribes.

On Map 7-4 find this same triangle of roads. Note how both Samuel (at Ramah) and Saul (at Gibeah) would have been well-acquainted with the region and its strategic importance.

READING AND DISCUSSION

With these geographical factors and the historical background in mind, read **1 Samuel**   7-4 d
13. Note the following points as you read locating places and routes on Map 7-4.

1. The chapter opens by noting the Philistine military post at Geba just east of Ramah. (Some believe that this Geba is the same location as is mentioned in 1 Samuel 10.5.) The Israelites were divided by this Philistine presence, part encamped with Saul *in Michmash and the Hill Country of Bethel* and part *with Jonathan at Gibeah.*

2. Jonathan brought things to a head by attacking and defeating the Philistines at Geba. Realizing that a severe Philistine reprisal was forthcoming, Saul summoned all Israel together as Samuel had done earlier at Mizpah. This time Saul took precautions by calling the meeting at Gilgal in an area removed from the scene of action. He may have believed that Gilgal's famous history and its reputation as a religious center (on Samuel's circuit) would bolster the people's confidence. Centuries before, Israelite forces had gone out from Joshua's camp at Gilgal to victories at the battles of Jericho, Ai, Gibeon and in the Shephelah (Maps 5-3, 5-4, and 5-5). Saul also needed a recommitment by the people who earlier had declared him king at Gilgal. Such a recommitment here could be important at this crucial hour. Saul's choice of Gilgal and his reactions there reflect above all his own insecurity. In the situation in which he found himself, the most difficult he had yet faced, Saul like Joshua was called upon to *recognize who God is.* A quick reading of **Joshua 1** is necessary here to place this last statement in its proper context.

3. The Philistine response to the Israelite rebellion was massive. Even if the numbers are understood in terms of *units*, it still represents the greatest concentration of Philistine forces in the Hill Country known to us. Some think that these forces came up by the shortest and easiest route, via Beth-horon. Others believe they took the longer Aphek-Bethel approach. The important thing to note is that they were not content to remain on the Central Benjamin Plateau or at Bethel. They established their camp at Michmash. In the small valleys north of the city they found ample space for such a concentration of troops and equipment.

4. The remaining part of the chapter is easily understood. Only two items need to be underscored here. First is the fact that from this strategic region north of Michmash the Philistines were in a position to send out units to plunder in all directions:

1) to the north (toward Ophrah), 2) to the west (toward Beth-horon via the Michmash pass, perhaps to keep a supply line open to Philistia), and 3) to the east (toward the wilderness overlooking Gilgal). Thus the wedge between Judah and Ephraim was made complete.

Secondly, the Israelites, in contrast to the Philistines, had no arms with which to fight. This is brought out at the very end of 1 Samuel 13, after Saul and his few remaining followers returned to the Hill Country and to Gibeah with little hope of success. The desperate situation in which Israel found herself is underscored by noting the military equipment in Israelite hands at that time. This discouraging chapter closes with the statement, *And a Philistine outpost was set up [overlooking] the Michmash pass* (1 Samuel 13.23).

MARKING

The following marking shows the situation as it stood at the end of 1 Samuel 13.

1. **Blue box around dot**: Philistine camp = **Michmash.**

2. **Green box around dot**: Jonathan's camp = **Geba.**

3. **Yellow HL on name** = **Michmash** and **Geba.**

4. **Sweeping blue arrows**: Philistine raids =
   a. From Michmash toward Ophrah taking into consideration the pass across Wadi Makkuk.

   b. From Michmash toward Upper Beth-horon, running along the north of the route and skipping over HL names.

   c. From Michmash to the Wilderness, running about 2 cm./1 in. E of Michmash.

5. **Large red circle**: Area of confrontation with the Philistines = Around the triangle of roads discussed above including the names Bethel, Gibeon, Gibeah and Michmash. (Red on a red name makes it difficult to read.)

DISCUSSION

1 Samuel 13 ended on a pessimistic note. In the opening verses of 1 Samuel 14 we find that Saul stationed his remaining forces at Gibeah where, at a safe distance, he had a panoramic view of the entire region. He could see Geba and Michmash beyond and had no difficulty imagining the Philistine camp hidden just behind the ridge of Michmash.

Jonathan, on the other hand, was at Geba, much closer to the Philistines. He had more to fear than his father, although the Wadi Suweinit separated him from the Philistines. He could easily see the Philistine outpost which had been set up to keep an eye on the pass. The best location for this type of outpost was on a ridge rising southeast of Michmash. It afforded a sweeping view in all directions, especially west toward Geba and Gibeah and northwest down into the pass itself.

Although the names of Michmash, Geba and Gibeah do not appear on Map 5-4, it is the best map on which to see the region. On it note that all the tributaries to the Wadi Suweinit northwest of the pass form one canyon, just below the word *Suweinit* (printed in blue). For geological reasons (erosion through a small anticline) a deep ravine was formed at this point. Wadi Suweinit runs through this canyon. Where the canyon begins, large layers of limestone emerge (by the *S* of Suweinit). It is no doubt here that one can locate a *tooth (point, precipice or cliff)* on each side of the canyon, as described in 1 Samuel 14.4 and 5. One was called *Bozez* and the other *Seneh*. As the canyon deepens to the southeast, its sides rise some 250 meters/800 feet above the rocky and dry stream bed below. It then enters the greater Wadi Qilt system. In the region there are many caverns and hiding places to which the Philistines refer in the story.

READING AND DISCUSSION
You are now ready to read **1 Samuel 14.1-46**, one of the Bible's most dramatic accounts. In the midst of the geographical dynamic and city names, note Jonathan's response to the impossible situation described in 1 Samuel 13. Unlike his father, the crown prince *recognized who God is* and acted accordingly. The message of Joshua 1 had penetrated his spirit. Also note Saul's response once victory was assured. The difference between the father and the son is clear in Jonathan's remark to the young man accompanying him.

> *Come on, let's go across to the outpost of these uncircumcised [Philistines].*
> *The Lord might well do something to help us out. After all, nothing stops*
> *the Lord from winning, be it by many or by few.*   (1 Samuel 14.6)

After finishing the reading consider what the capture of Philistine arms meant to the Israelites. The distribution of this new equipment and the training of troops must have occupied Saul's officers for some time. This defeat also gave the Philistines cause to worry — and to prepare for the next encounter. It is not surprising that this chapter ends with these words:

> *There was fierce fighting with the Philistines throughout Saul's life.*
> *Therefore, whenever Saul ran across any brave man or any courageous*
> *fellow, he recruited him into his [army].*   (1 Samuel 14.52)

Such a person would cross Saul's path during the next episode with the Philistines in the Shephelah/Lowland of Judah. His recruitment by Saul would alter the history of the region, relations between Judah and Benjamin, and, as a result, relations between Judah and Ephraim. The young man's name was David.

MARKING (Map 7-4)
1. **Yellow HL on route** = From Michmash to Gezer via Beth-horon.

2. **Flight (blue) and chase (green) arrows** = Two sets of such arrows indicating chase to Gezer and drawn along the route HL above.

DISCUSSION AND READING
In spite of Saul's personal failures, the Bible gives him credit for some very important accomplishments. These may have begun with the equipping and the training of an efficient Israelite army. Another accomplishment basic to Saul's success was Israel's ability to keep the Philistines out of the Hill Country. Only after the death of Saul do we again hear of a new Philistine offensive into the hills (as a result of David's move   7-7 b c
from Hebron to Jerusalem near the Central Benjamin Plateau).

In addition to these accomplishments, Saul campaigned in the Negev and in Trans-jordan where he claimed territory from those who had been oppressing Israel. Some of these events and their place in Saul's overall policy will be considered in your marking of Map 7-5 (*SCS* 7-4 e and f; *SCS* 7-5 a to d). In the meantime read **1 Samuel 14.47, 48** and complete the marking below on Map 7-4.

MARKING

1. **Brown write-in**: On the plateau E of the Dead Sea on the E edge of the map below the red and black lines in the legend = MEDEBA PLATEAU.

2. **Blue write-in**:
   a. In the SE corner of the map, near the edge of the map, E of the Dead Sea = MOAB (with black arrow pointing S).

   b. In the Dead Sea, on the S edge of the map near the W shore = EDOM (with a black arrow pointing SE).

   c. In the open area between Hebron and Tekoa = AMALEKITES (with a black arrow pointing S).

3. **Sweeping (but broken) green arrows**: Saul's campaigns =
   a. From the plain in the Jordan (Rift) Valley just NE of the Dead Sea toward Ammon and toward Moab (two arrows).

   b. From the region of Bethlehem toward Edom and toward the Amalekites (two arrows pointing off the map).

LEGEND
Blue dot   =   Same as Map 6-1
Broken green arrows   =   Saul's accomplishments (1 Samuel 14.47, 48)
Small black letters in circles may be added in the appropriate places on this map to indicate locations of *SCS* 7-4 **c, d, e** and **h**.

S M M   7 − 5

TITLE: **DAVID AND SAUL**

DATE: **LATE 11th CENTURY B.C.**

INTRODUCTION

Map 7-5 provides the setting for some of the best loved stories in Biblical history. In order to understand them within the geopolitical context of this period it is necessary to outline briefly Saul's overall objectives. These were touched on in your study of Map 7-4 but are here made explicit before you begin to mark Map 7-5. Keep Map 7-4 open before you for reference in the following paragraphs.

SAUL'S OVERALL STRATEGY

DISCUSSION

Becoming king of Israel at this crucial moment in Israelite history, Saul was faced with multiple difficulties of a very complex nature. Although he appeared not to covet the position, once officially in it he was forced to give a great deal of thought to overall strategy. His basic goals must have included Israel's security and her control of sufficient territory to insure that security. An important factor related to territorial expansion in this *Land Between* was the control of trade routes and the resulting economic growth for Israel.

Security and economic growth, as important as they are, did not overshadow another basic issue, that of tribal support for Saul's Benjamin-based monarchy. Without this support Saul's very existence was threatened. What you know already about strained tribal relations and the insecure nature of the country in which these tribes lived (*SMM* 6-1 and 6-2) helps you appreciate the predicament in which Saul found himself.

The greatest immediate threat to Saul's Benjamin-based kingdom came from the Philistines. However, before Saul could develop his strategy to meet this enemy on the west, he was called upon to lead a rescue operation to Jabesh-gilead in Transjordan (1 Samuel 11), a city which had a strong tie to Benjamin since the period of the Judges (Judges 21). Saul's initial success in Gilead was complemented by later campaigns in Transjordan against Moab and Ammon. These campaigns were probably on the Medeba Plateau, an important region on the Transjordanian Highway, which Moab and Ammon could use as a staging area for attacking Jericho and the Hill Country west of the Jordan. Saul realized that Israelites had used this same plateau in their conquest of the land (*SMM* 5-3).   7-4 c

The battle at Michmash gave Saul the prestige he needed. A major Philistine offensive   7-4 d which culminated many decades of pressure on Israel had been checked. At last these invaders had been routed from the Hill Country. Benjamin, Ephraim and Judah could breathe a sigh of relief, and Saul could begin to solve internal organizational problems and deal with pressing matters beyond the Hill Country. It appears that Saul had no difficulty in appropriating this victory which was due to his son's courage based upon a simple trust in God.

Once the Philistine threat in the Hill Country was eased, Saul took logical steps to insure the security of regions outside the Hill Country. To the south of Judah he   7-5 a campaigned in the Negev against the Amalekites. To the west of Judah he attempted to stop the Philistine advance in the Shephelah/Lowlands. Finally, to the north of   7-5 c Ephraim/Manasseh in the Jezreel Valley he mobilized Israelite forces in an effort to   7-4 h break the Philistine hold on international routes, a hold which divided the Israelite tribes and threatened both tribal and national interests. In this last campaign both Saul and his son Jonathan lost their lives.

SAUL'S CAMPAIGN AGAINST AMALEK

DISCUSSION

7-4 a   Since Saul came from Benjamin, he no doubt had substantial support from the House of Joseph, especially from Ephraim. However, we read little of Judah's attitude toward the Benjamin-based monarchy. It would seem reasonable, if not imperative, that Saul's political and military strategy included campaigns which would gain Judah's backing of his monarchy.

7-5 a   This concern forms the background for Saul's campaign against the Amalekites in the Negev, that strategic region south of the Hill Country of Judah. In the Negev basin, and along the natural routes which approached it from Egypt and from the southern Wilderness, the Amalekites appear to have made substantial inroads, threatening Judah's southern flank. There was also an *account to settle* with the Amalekites, who in the days of Moses and Joshua had attacked Israel on her way through the Wilderness. Any connection established between these two respected leaders and Saul would certainly not hurt his cause. Given all of these factors Saul was wise to follow the directive from Samuel. He also may have seen this as an opportunity to prove himself after disappointing Samuel at Gilgal during the campaign of the Philistines from Michmash.

The general geographical perspectives of the Negev were discussed earlier in this chapter (Map 4-3). On the *SMA* (north and south sheets joined) the region can be seen as a valley (a plain or basin) between higher hills north and south of it. Part of the southern Hill Country of Judah and the Eastern Negev basin is drained by a central system known today as *Nahal Beer Sheva*. (*Beer Sheva* is the Hebrew pronunciation of *Beersheba* in English. The same difference is maintained between the Hebrew *Negev* and the English *Negeb*.) In the west, Nahal Beer Sheva joins the great Nahal Besor, which flows through the Western Negev before emptying into the Mediterranean Sea just south of Gaza.

Approaches to the Negev from all directions can be seen on Map 7-2. In the west the International Coastal Highway and the important city of Gaza are very accessible. In the south natural passes connect the Negev to the main highway between the southern Transjordan (Edom) and Egypt (a route printed in red on Map 7-2). Beyond the Wilderness lies the Red Sea port of Elath, which provided an added incentive for anyone interested in trade. Other links to the Transjordanian Highway run eastward from Arad in the Eastern Negev (Maps 6-3 and 7-2). The centers of Beer-sheba and Arad were also closely tied to Hebron in the Hill Country north of the Negev as Map

6-3 b c   6-3 shows. In their dependence on Judah, settlements in the Negev looked first of all to Hebron. This ancient city served as a natural power base in southern Judah. Its prominence was enhanced by strong attachments to the patriarchs and by the fact that Caleb, Joshua's friend, had settled there.

The importance of the Negev and the natural routes connecting it to surrounding regions and nations meant that Judah needed to control the region for her own security and economic well-being. In preparing for his campaign, Saul must have considered Judah's need.

Prior to Saul there is archeological and Biblical evidence that the Negev was already settled. Unfortified cities of the early Israelite period have been unearthed in several

places in the Negev (Iron Age I sites on Map 2-5). They appear to have supported a   2-5
sizable population. Early in the period of Israelite settlement two groups had occupied the region (Map 6-3). One was the tribe of Simeon, which took over a part   6-3 d
of Judah's inheritance, the region around Beer-sheba. Another group, the Kenites, had
entered the land together with the Israelites. They settled in the Eastern Negev in the
region of Arad. Israelite populations in the Negev were served by the sons of Samuel,
who *were judges in Beer-sheba* (1 Samuel 8.2).

This background helps to explain Saul's decision to proceed with the military action
against the Amalekites in and around the Negev. Success in this region would satisfy
a number of demands placed upon his Benjamin-based monarchy. In addition to his
political, economic and military goals, Saul's actions had religious overtones. The
operation was carried out in the context of Judah itself, whose spiritual leadership
rivaled that of Ephraim. Names like Moses, Joshua and Caleb were associated with
this southern region of the country, especially in the area of Kadesh-barnea (Map 5-2).

Putting all of this together, Saul must have felt that this was the moment he had been
waiting for, an opportunity to prove his abilities both on the battlefield and in response to Samuel's stern words at Gilgal (1 Samuel 13.8-14).

Although he led his troops to a stunning victory, Saul had not yet learned the lessons
of Gilgal. Saul's inward commitment did not measure up to what most saw as apparent
success.

READING AND DISCUSSION

In reading **1 Samuel 15** carefully note cities mentioned and routes implied in the text.   7-5 a
The marking which follows may be done before or after this reading.

As you read, note that the first half of the chapter deals with Saul's great victory in
the south. This victory, however, is outweighed by the sad dialogue in the second half
of the chapter. It is a dialogue between Saul, Israel's first king, who wanted so much
to succeed, and Samuel, the prophet of Israel, who was requiring the leader of the
nation *to recognize who God is.* This message is echoed often in the Bible when man's
attempts to placate God without simple faith make a mockery of His commandments.

This time Saul and Samuel returned from Gilgal in much the same mood as recorded
during the Michmash Affair (1 Samuel 13.13-15). Their homes on the Central Benjamin Plateau (Gibeah and Ramah) were just minutes apart. However, we read that *To
the day of his death Samuel did not see Saul again* (1 Samuel 15.35).

MARKING
   1. **Green write-in:**
      a. In the center of map in the open area N of Beth-zur and W of Hushah = JUDAH
      (in large caps).

      b. In N of map, between Mizpah and Gibeon = BEN. (for Benjamin).

      c. In S of map in the open area between Ramoth of the Negev and the nearest
      Arad = KENITES.

2. **Brown write-in:**
   a. In the open area just E of Beth-zur and Hebron = HILL COUNTRY.

   b. In W of the map in the open area between Keilah and Mareshah = SHEPHELAH (LOWLAND) in two lines.

   c. Between Bethlehem and the Dead Sea = WILDERNESS.

   d. Between Carmel (by Ziph) and the Dead Sea = WILDERNESS.

   e. Vertically (from E to W) and running just left of the route between Arad (by Kabzeel) and Beer-sheba = NEGEV.

3. **Blue write-in:** Between the two Arads, written from N to S = AMALEKITES (in large caps).

4. **Yellow HL on route** = Route from Gibeah (Saul's capital) to the eastern Arad via Bethlehem, Hebron, Ziph and Carmel.

5. **Large red circle** = Around the word Amalekites.

6. **Large green broken arrow:** Saul's campaign = From Ziph to red circle.

7. **Flight (blue) and chase (green) arrows** = From red circle to S (via route by Aroer) and to W via Hormah (toward Egypt).

8. **Yellow HL on name** = **Carmel** and **Gilgal**.

SAMUEL ANOINTS DAVID AS KING OF ISRAEL

DISCUSSION

7-5 b   Chapter 16 of the book of 1 Samuel serves as the watershed of your current study in this book. In this chapter there is a definite shift in emphasis from the Benjamin-based monarchy (always overshadowed by Ephraim) to a Judah-based monarchy.

In a certain sense a geographical reorientation can also be detected. Previous studies have stressed the importance of the route north of Ramah connecting it to Bethel in the Hill Country of Ephraim and to sites farther north like Shiloh, prominent in the early chapters of 1 Samuel. In chapter 16 of the book, Samuel is told to travel south of Ramah to the House of Jesse in Bethlehem of Judah to anoint a new king of Israel.

6-7 c   It was along this same route that the Levite traveled to negotiate the return of his concubine, later killed in the *Gibeah affair* (Map 6-7). As noted in that story, the convenient route between Ramah and Bethlehem passed by Gibeah and the Jebusite enclave at Jerusalem. Samuel was well-acquainted with this route and also knew of Saul's threatened and deteriorating personality. This gave him reason to think twice before leaving on his special mission to Bethlehem. His response to his orders should not be surprising: *How on earth can I go [from Ramah to Bethlehem on this assignment]? Saul will hear about it and kill me!* (1 Samuel 16.2).

The geographical setting of Bethlehem serves as the background for this and other stories on this map. It may be true that Bethlehem's significance is overshadowed by Hebron, the important center in Judah's southern Hill Country with its Calebite   6-3 b c leadership and connections with the clans of the Negev. However, work on this map demonstrates the strategic value of Bethlehem in northern Judah with routes connecting it to the Shephelah and to Moab (via the Wilderness) as well as to the Central Benjamin Plateau and to Hebron.

MARKING

1. **Yellow HL on name** = Sites along the main N-S ridge route from Ephraim to Judah via Benjamin = **Bethel, Gibeah, Bethlehem, Beth-zur** and **Hebron.**

2. **Blue write-in:**

   a. In the SE corner of the map on the piece of land sticking out into the Dead Sea from Transjordan (called the *tongue, Lisan* in Arabic and *Lashon* in Hebrew) = MOAB. Add a small black arrow pointing SE of this word.

   b. In the W edge of the map, just W of the names Ekron and Gath = PHILISTINES.

3. **Yellow HL on route:**

   a. From Bethlehem to Moab via En-gedi.

   b. From Bethlehem to Gath of the Philistines via Hushah, the Valley of Elah, Socoh and Azekah.

   c. From Hebron to Socoh via Beth-zur, Adullam and the Valley of Elah.

4. **Blue on dot = Jerusalem.**

5. **Black write-in:** Under the word Wilderness E of Bethlehem = DAVID THE SHEPHERD (in small caps).

DISCUSSION

The importance of Bethlehem is now clearly seen on Map 7-5. It is located in northern Judah in the midst of hills covered with grapevines and orchards of olives, almonds and pomegranates. The city itself is actually situated on a promontory just east of the main north-south ridge route and overlooks the Wilderness to the east. Between the Wilderness proper and the city, areas of easily plowed soil and sufficient winter rainfall combine to allow the cultivation of grains. Some feel that this explains one possible meaning of the name Beth-lehem, *House/place of Bread/food.* Others understand *lehem* as a form of the Hebrew word *to wage war* or as the name of a local god.

READING AND DISCUSSION

It was in this setting, east of Bethlehem, that the story of Ruth the Moabitess and   6-1 f Boaz, a leader of Bethlehem, took place. Since these two figures were the grandparents of Jesse (David's father), now is an appropriate moment to skim the book of **Ruth.** The four short chapters of this book not only provide information on David's family background. They also create an atmosphere for the region you are now studying, the grain fields to the east and below Bethlehem. Especially take note of the references to the grain harvest in this area, which takes place during the month of May.

The story also refers to travel and religious/ethnic exchange between Moab and the people of Bethlehem. This could have taken place via the En-gedi route or through the Gilgal/Jericho region. The story has its temporal setting at the end of the period of the Judges, a period when Moab posed a threat to Benjamin and surrounding tribes. This makes the story even more meaningful.

DISCUSSION
Farther east the Wilderness forms the home of the shepherd. In the summer after the grain harvest, his herds may be brought up to eat the stubble in the fields. The chalk hills of the Wilderness normally receive enough rain each winter to produce a light covering of grass. Northern slopes shaded from the winter sun turn a beautiful green for a few short months. In the spring, the grass turns brown during the first weeks of hot, dry weather. The region remains dry and dusty until the following winter.

It is the job of the shepherd to find food and water for his herds in this Wilderness and to protect them from the heat of the day and from wild animals which prey upon them at night. Since herds of sheep and goats represent an important investment (sometimes the only investment for the bedouin), tending the herd is a very serious task which takes constant care and wise planning. For instance, if water is not available at the right time, an entire herd may perish.

In addition to the bedouin, who may gain their entire livelihood from their sheep and goats, farmers around Bethlehem (or any other city which borders on the Wilderness) also keep herds. A lesser member of the family, old enough to be trusted, or a hired servant tends the farmer's herds, taking them out into the Wilderness to pasture for days or weeks at a time. Alone in the Wilderness the shepherd must take full responsibility for the herd with nowhere to turn for help.

While the shepherd must always be vigilant, there is also time to reflect on recent events or on life in general. To pass the time of day many shepherds improvise a simple musical instrument to play and to keep them company in the lonely surroundings. Some become versatile at playing such instruments, especially on a form of flute which is easy to carry.

READING AND DISCUSSION
The setting of the Wilderness serves as the background for many of the Psalms attributed to David the shepherd. The most beloved of all of these songs of the shepherd is Psalm 23. Others use the imagery of a threshing floor (for grain) which the shepherd from Bethlehem would have passed often on his way to and from the Wilderness. References to grass, paths (especially level paths), sure-footing, heat, thirst and many other perspectives of the shepherd's Wilderness appear often in the Psalms.

7-5 b

With the setting of Bethlehem in mind read **1 Samuel 16.** In your reading remember Samuel's concern in making a trip to Bethlehem in order to anoint a new king. Also recall how Saul kept his eye out for *any brave man or any courageous fellow* who could be added to the ranks of his growing army (1 Samuel 14.52). Note how Samuel himself had to be reminded that *the Lord looks on the heart* (1 Samuel 16.7).

Two trips from Bethlehem to the Central Benjamin Plateau are recorded in this chapter. One is Samuel's return trip to Ramah after anointing David the shepherd as king of Israel (1 Samuel 16.13). He must have had many questions as he walked along the ridge route between the canyons of the Wilderness and the nahals draining to Philistia. The other trip was David's. He went from Bethlehem to Gibeah at the request of Saul, who knew nothing of Samuel's earlier mission. David, like the Levite and his concubine before him, had a donkey loaded with presents. Like the Levite, at Gibeah he found a self-centered attitude, one which showed less and less respect for both God and man. As Saul's armor-bearer David had opportunity to know the king's deep-seated insecurities. Later in the Wilderness during a period when the king was trying to kill David, David himself drew back from killing the king when he had the chance. Perhaps part of the reason for David's hesitancy is to be found in his sensitivity to Saul's threatened personality, an understanding he gained while serving Saul at Gibeah and in his shepherding responsibilities to his father Jesse in Bethlehem.

DAVID DEFEATS GOLIATH IN THE VALLEY OF ELAH

DISCUSSION

Saul (with his son Jonathan) was able to meet the Philistine campaign in the Central Benjamin Plateau and at Michmash (Map 7-4). The Philistines, however, were still a threat to Judah's western flank, the Shephelah. Occupying these lowlands is the natural first step to an invasion of the Hill Country.   7-4 d

7-5 c

Control of the main valleys of the Shephelah was always a Philistine priority. In the north the Aijalon Valley served as the strategic approach to the Central Benjamin Plateau via Lower and Upper Beth-horon (Maps 5-5, 7-1 and 7-4). Gezer was the key site in this valley. Nearby was the crossroads of local and international routes.

The second valley (north to south) in the Shephelah was the Sorek Valley (Maps 6-3 and 7-4). Beth-shemesh and Timnah were the most important cities in this area. In the Hill Country due east of the Sorek Valley, the *Sorek System* of nahals draining the hills made a direct approach to the area of Jerusalem very difficult.

Farther south the Valley of Elah (Map 7-5) provided access both to Bethlehem (via the Hushah ridge) and to Hebron (via the Beth-zur ridge). Anyone who commanded the Valley of Elah was in the best possible position to attack northern and southern Judah from the west. Map 6-4 shows Judah's official territory in the Shephelah south of what was to have been Dan.

The following marking prepares the *playing board* for the confrontation between Israel and the Philistines in the strategic Valley of Elah.

MARKING

1. **Green border**: Symbolic frontier between the Israelites and the Philistines = From the W edge of the map below Lachish, NE through the hyphen of Moresheth-gath, bending around to the north between Azekah and Socoh (leaving an empty space on both sides of the highlighted road), N between the names Shaaraim and Beth-shemesh and continuing N off the map. Shade in (green pencil) the E side of this border.

2. **Yellow HL on name = Valley of Elah, Socoh, Azekah, Gath, Ekron and Shaaraim.**

3. **Blue square**: Philistine camp (possible location) = At the crossroads just E of the name Azekah.

4. **Additional roads and yellow HL**: Drawn in with a normal pencil and then HL in yellow =

   a. From the Philistine camp NW via the nahal just N of Azekah and continuing NW to Ekron along the most convenient path.

   b. A small stretch of road from the Philistine camp W via the z of Azekah and then joining the route from Azekah to Gath already highlighted.

5. **Large blue arrow**: Philistine mobilization = Three arrows (one from Ekron, one from Gath and one in the middle) joining into one large point pointing toward the dot of Azekah.

6. **Green square**: Saul's camp (possible location) = At the edge of the Hill Country just E of the *V* in Valley of Elah.

7. **Sweeping green arrow**: Israelite mobilization =
   a. From Beth-zur to the Israelite camp.

   b. From Hushah to the Israelite camp, running along the ridge just E of the camp.

8. **Red confrontation mark**: Possible location of Goliath's challenge to the Israelites and to David = ❋ Between the dot of Socoh and the *E* in the word Elah.

9. **Flight (blue) and chase (green) arrow** =
   a. Along the route from the Philistine camp to Ekron (running N of the route).

   b. Along the route from the Philistine camp to Gath (running S of the route).

DISCUSSION

The Bible does not state specifically what events led up to this particular Philistine-Israelite confrontation in the Shephelah. From what you already know about this period it should not be difficult to understand the perspectives with which each side came to the battle.

The Philistines, barred from the Hill Country and no doubt still angry from their defeats near Mizpah and at Michmash, wisely chose the Valley of Elah for their next advance on Israel. The end of the ridge on which the impressive site of Azekah is located gave them a good view of much of the valley and the surrounding hills. (This ridge between Azekah and Moresheth-Gath is not seen clearly in the relief of your map.) Socoh and its ridge gave them a fine forward camp. The location of their main camp (Ephesdammim) is not known, but the blue box gives a possible location *between Socoh and Azekah* (1 Samuel 17.1). Here in this convenient valley of the Shephelah the Philistine army had a perfect staging area for their campaign against Judah. It was so impressive that they felt simple scare tactics would be enough to force Israel's capitulation before any battle broke out.

The Israelites, on the other hand, would not have ventured out into the valley or onto the rolling hills of the Shephelah. This would have exposed them to ambush or encirclement by the Philistines. The most probable place for their camp was at the edge of the Hill Country just east of the Valley of Elah, an area of canyons and terraces in which the Philistines appear to have been reluctant to fight.

We are not told of Saul's attitude in this crisis. His great expectation, of course, was that a victory on this important western flank of Judah would establish his popularity in that tribe once and for all. Things did not go as planned, if indeed Saul was making an offensive rather than a defensive move. The daily Philistine challenge with no effective Israelite response was dishonoring to the people, to the king and to the God of Israel. What pride was left from the battles of Mizpah and Michmash had disappeared. Although details on events leading up to this mobilization are not available, the same gloomy mood must have prevailed in the Israelite camp as presented in 1 Samuel 13 prior to the battle of Michmash.

During this campaign David, Saul's armor-bearer, appears to have been busy with his father's sheep in the Wilderness. Jesse's concern, however, was centered on his three older sons who had been conscripted by Saul. One wonders just what Jesse had in mind in sending gifts to the commander of his sons' unit.

READING AND DISCUSSION

The stage is set for one of the most well known stories in the Bible, the battle of David   7-5 c
and Goliath. While many details of the episode could be discussed here, it is more rewarding to discover them for yourself. The account is found in **1 Samuel 17**. Also read **1 Samuel 18.1-16, 30**, skimming the rest of this chapter if you desire. As you read, carefully note the setting of the story on Map 7-5. Remember the place that the Valley of Elah plays in the defense of Judah. You may want to reflect on Saul's deep disappointment at the turn of events, both prior to the battle, when Goliath's threats went unanswered, and then after the battle, when a home town boy, David from Bethlehem in Judah, usurped Saul's claim to fame. For Saul the outcome of the battle could be summed up in the proverbial *good news and bad news*.

In contrast to Saul's fear and disappointment, David's simple faith during this crisis highlights a theme which has been evident throughout Samuel's ministry: *Fix your heart firmly on the Lord, worshiping Him alone, and He will deliver you from Philistine domination* (1 Samuel 7.3). As you follow this theme through the story, try to recall earlier episodes in the book of Judges and in the book of Samuel when people were called upon *to recognize who God is* in times of crisis. In this sense the story of David and Goliath culminates a long series of contests between the *champions* and their opponents.

During subsequent years of Saul's reign David often challenged Philistine authority on the field of battle. Unfortunately, no details of these battles are given except that in each of them *David was able to achieve more through his good sense [on the battlefield] than Saul's entire army* (1 Samuel 18.30). As a result David's popularity increased among the people and the leaders of Israel until *all Israel [including the House of Joseph and the northern tribes which followed it] and Judah loved David* (1 Samuel 18.16). It was this acceptance which Saul had sought from the first day of his reign. The strained relationship between Saul and David which resulted from these developments forms the background for the remaining chapters of the book of 1 Samuel.

DAVID'S FLIGHT IN JUDAH FROM SAUL

DISCUSSION

Accomplishments during Saul's reign, with the aid of Samuel, Jonathan and David, were impressive. To the east across the Jordan, pressures from the Ammonites and the   7-4 c

7-4 d   Moabites had diminished. In the Hill Country Philistine domination had ceased. To
7-5 a   the south the Negev and its approaches were free from the Amalekites. In the west the
7-5 c   Philistine incursion in the Shephelah was checked. Only in the north, especially in the
         Jezreel Valley, was there a need to limit, or better yet, to eliminate Philistine control
7-3 b   of main routes which had developed after the Israelite defeat at Aphek (Maps 7-3 and
         7-4).

MARKING, DISCUSSION AND READING

7-5 d   Saul's energy, however, was diverted to an internal matter, that of controlling the
rising star of Judah, David, the son of Jesse. This subject receives special attention in
1 Samuel 18-26. Geographical detail in these chapters abounds. Not all of the events
can be thoroughly discussed here. The following paragraphs summarize the main
themes and supplement each reading. Marking, discussion and reading are all inte-
grated to facilitate your study. While it would be good to read all of these chapters,
you may want to skim them, only concentrating on geographical information in them.
On Map 7-5 **the number of each of the locations,** with the number of the section
below, should be written in by the dot of the city or in the place indicated. **This
number should be in orange. The dot of each city listed below should also be colored
in orange.**

1. Gibeah: 1 Samuel 18.1-19.17
(Orange on dot and the number 1 written in by the dot)
The events at Gibeah explain the background of Saul's negative attitude toward
David and can be reviewed by skimming this chapter.

2. Ramah: 1 Samuel 19.18-24
The trip to Ramah from Gibeah took David only a matter of minutes. When he
arrived, he and Samuel moved on to what is called the *naioth in Ramah*. This is
probably not a proper name but simply means *dwellings* somewhere near the city.
It may have been a gathering place outside the city in a more secluded area (like
on the slopes overlooking Wadi Suweinit northeast of Ramah) where Samuel could
retire with his disciples. Saul had no trouble finding David but did encounter
other difficulties on the way.

From Ramah David returned to Jonathan at Gibeah or nearby. The events of
1 Samuel 20 all happened in the region around the city. In these moments the
depth of Jonathan's commitment to David (that of the crown prince himself)
far outweighed Saul's fixation on *kingdom-building*. David's reciprocal commitment is a theme that is felt throughout the remaining chapters of 1 Samuel and on
into the early reign of David.

3. Nob: 1 Samuel 21.1-9; 22.6-19
Nob is located somewhere in the vicinity of the Mount of Olives, east of Jerusalem.
There in a small sanctuary David received supplies and the sword of Goliath, which
served him well in the coming months. When an Edomite, the head of Saul's herdsmen, informed Saul of what had happened at Nob, Saul reacted in a similar way to
6-7 c   those *men of Gibeah* on Map 6-7, who lacked all respect for God and for man.
In his frustrated quest for power and fame nothing stood in Saul's way. **Underline Nob in red** to indicate the violent massacre which took place there (1 Samuel
22.19).

4. **Gath: 1 Samuel 21.10-15**
David could think of no better place to escape from Saul than in Philistine territory. When he found that he was in potential trouble, quick thinking allowed him to leave without a fight.

5. **Adullam: 1 Samuel 22.1-2**
Somewhere in the vicinity of Adullam in the Shephelah of Judah, David made an important decision. This decision may have come out of his experiences with Saul and with the Philstines at Gath. Knowing that it was no longer possible to serve his people in Israel's defense force and that with him gone it was only a matter of time before the Philistines again invaded Judah and Benjamin, he organized his own 7-5 e private army. It was a *mixed bag* of volunteers, something like Robin Hood's band. In training them David's wisdom and patience no doubt were taxed at times. However, they served him well. A list of these *mighty men* and their home towns is given in 2 Samuel 23.8-39.

6. **Moab: 1 Samuel 22.3-4**
David's concern for his mother and his father, Jesse, meant that a trip from Bethlehem to Moab was necessary. Since his great-grandmother was Ruth the Moabitess and since in his service to Saul he had not been involved in any military action against Moab, he could be assured of Moabite cooperation at this time. Although the route to Moab is not specified, it seems likely that the safest route was via the Wilderness (that David knew well) and En-gedi. From there he could follow the shore of the Dead Sea, below the large and isolated rock platform known as *the Stronghold* (probably today's Masada) and to a place where he could cross to Moab.

7. **The Stronghold: 1 Samuel 22.4-5**
Returning from Moab David went to the *Stronghold* or *fortress* (in Hebrew *Metsudah*). The name is perserved in first century A.D. writings of Josephus Flavius in the form *Masada*. Here Herod the Great created a magnificent stronghold 12-2 e palace used later by Jewish rebels in their last stand against the might of Rome. Perhaps the description of this Jewish historian, although slightly exaggerated at times, gives an idea of the character of this *Stronghold*.

This rock, of no small circumference [about 1300 m./4200 ft. at its summit] and very high [400 m./1300 ft. above the Dead Sea], is surrounded by ravines so deep that [standing at the edge of the summit] one cannot see its base. Its sides are so steep that it is impossible for any living creature to scale them — except at two places where the rock allows some type of ascent. One of these ways leads from the Lake Asphaltitis [Dead Sea] on the east. The other, from the west, offers an easier ascent. The first is called the Snake [Path]. Narrow and constantly twisting, it resembles this animal. At places sheer cliffs obstruct the path. Often there are switchbacks. Then, with great difficulty, it slowly lengthens out again. Anyone who [dares] use this path must advance by placing one foot carefully after the other. The chasms and cliffs on all sides are so terrifying that even the bravest are tempted to give up. After navigating this way . . . one arrives at the summit which turns out to be an open area instead of a pointed peak.

(*Wars* 7.280-84/8.3)

The natural defenses of this Stronghold gave David the imagery which he and others would later incorporate into many of the Psalms (Psalms 18, 31, 71, 91 and 144). After his departure from the Stronghold, David *went into the forest of Hereth*, an area which as yet cannot be identified.

8. Keilah: 1 Samuel 23.1-13

The word which David received from the Shephelah of Judah confirmed his fears — the Philistines were beginning to move again. His vigilant defense force was ready. It was late spring, and the grain of the valleys in the Shephelah was being harvested and processed at the many threshing floors in the area. The Philistines advanced beyond Socoh to the southern end of the Valley of Elah and to the region of Keilah. In spite of the danger of being intercepted by Saul, David knew he would have to move fast. He needed all of the leadership ability he could muster to convince his followers to cross over the Hill Country of Judah and to descend into the Shephelah. If caught, many of the men would face criminal charges due to their backgrounds, plus suffer the consequences of following the rebel leader, David.

9. Wilderness of Ziph: 1 Samuel 23.14-29

(Orange number 9 just west of the word Wilderness which is written in to the east of Ziph, Carmel and Maon)

It is not possible to pinpoint the location of David and his men during this period. The Wilderness of Ziph is somewhere east of the city of Ziph, an area which is today the home of various bedouin tribes. The men of Ziph, although from Judah, may have recalled Saul's campaign against the Amalekites and the force which accompanied him on that expedition. There was always the monument which Saul had erected at Carmel to remind them of this operation. Either out of respect or out of fear, the men of Ziph informed Saul of David's whereabouts. David had to move again, this time farther east into the badlands above the Dead Sea. This is what the Bible may mean by the term *Jeshimon*, an area which the shepherd and his herds of goats do not frequent.

7-5 a

In spite of the rough terrain Saul finally cornered David and his men. Only a Philistine raid (perhaps again in the Shephelah of Judah) saved David. Saul's attention again returned to his duties as king. This raid confirmed the increasing Philistine threat to the west of Judah.

10. En-gedi: 1 Samuel 24

The most beautiful and refreshing place along the dry and inhospitable western shore of the Dead Sea is En-gedi. Springs in a number of places provide fresh water and allow greenery of interesting sorts to grow in the warm climate of almost 400 meters/1300 feet below sea level. Just south of En-gedi the great Nahal Arugot emerges from the Wilderness. Its canyon walls rise to elevations just above sea level, and in it flows a stream fed by a strong spring. The entire region (including some of the areas discussed in number nine above) can be seen better on Map 13-4 (from the Late Roman Period) or on the *SMA*.

Nahal Arugot divides the Wilderness east of Bethlehem from the Wilderness east of Ziph and Maon. Running just north of this major nahal is a natural route from Bethlehem and Tekoa to En-Gedi. Just north of En-gedi itself is a good sized spring (blue dot on Map 7-5) which gushes forth in a small nahal known today as

Nahal David. Indeed it may be to this canyon and spring that David and his men retired after barely escaping Saul's troops.

When Saul returned from his defensive operation against the Philistines and heard that David was in En-gedi, he picked an elite corps of men for what he felt would be the final action against David. He would have had to pass Bethlehem, David's home town, on his way to En-gedi, traveling on the same route along which David may have led his elderly father, Jesse, in his escape to Moab. In this episode at En-gedi David's respect and concern for Saul are clearly demonstrated.

11. The Stronghold: 1 Samuel 24.22

Leaving En-gedi David and his men again climbed *the Stronghold*. The combination of the massive cliffs and the deeply-eroded canyons by which he and his men passed must have left a lasting impression upon his sensitive spirit. The striking view of the steep Transjordanian slopes (rising 1200 meters/4000 feet in the east) and the challenge which faced him may have made young David recall Joshua's early days of leading Israel and the impossible odds against him. It should not be surprising that **Psalms 27 and 37** contain some of the same themes as Joshua 1 since both of these young men looked to the God of Israel for courage and strength. This was especially true at this moment in David's life when he received word that Samuel, his counsellor and the spiritual father of Israel, had died in Ramah (1 Samuel 25.1). One wonders at Saul's reaction to the same news.

12. Wilderness of Paran/Maon: 1 Samuel 25

(Orange number **12** southeast of Maon)

David and his men now moved closer to the villages of southeastern Judah. The location of the Wilderness of Paran (or Maan/Maon as some manuscripts read) would have to be somewhere east or southeast of Maon and Carmel on Map 7-5. An area by the same name in the book of Genesis is known to have existed much farther south.

This interesting episode in David's wanderings demonstrated that not all in Judah supported David. The combination of sheep and agricultural products listed in the chapter illustrate the region well. David's discipline over his men was such that they refrained from the normal practice of desert raiders and instead protected the farmers and herdsmen of the region. Finally, the effective use of words to dishonor one's family and to discredit one's actions is clearly seen in Nabal's remarks. Abigail, who appears to have respected David, acted quickly and saved the young leader from discrediting himself in the eyes of all Judah — particularly Nabal's prominent clan of the Calebites from Hebron.

13. Wilderness of Ziph: 1 Samuel 26

(Orange number **13** east of Ziph by the word Wilderness)

Again the men of Ziph reported David's whereabouts to Saul, and the Wilderness and the Jeshimon served as the geographical context of Saul's pursuit and David's flight. And yet again David allowed Saul to escape harm. Another conversation is recorded between Saul and David from either side of one of the deep canyons in the region. This time Saul appeared to be convinced to give up his chase. At the end of the chapter the two separate, never to meet again.

The story of David and Saul and their separate activities continues on Map 7-6 and Map 7-4. Before you put aside Map 7-5 two additional numbers should be added to it. One is a second number by Gath of the Philistines where David finally returned to seek employment (number **14** in orange). The other is by Ziklag (number **15**), the city which the king of Gath assigned to David. (With **orange color the arrow** pointing off the map to the city).

Glance over Map 7-5 and note where the action has taken place. The chapters you have read have taken you across the changing geographical landscapes of the country, from the valleys of the Shephelah through the Hill Country into the Wilderness along the edge of the Dead Sea and to Moab beyond. They have also reached from the Central Benjamin Plateau to the Negev in the south. These stories, more than any other part of the Bible, illustrate Judah and the regions which surrounded her.

LEGEND

Orange numbers and orange dot   = Sites or regions in David's flight from Saul
(Gibeah to Ziklag)

S M M   7 − 6

TITLE: DAVID WORKS FOR THE PHILISTINES AT ZIKLAG

DATE: LATE 11TH CENTURY B.C.

INTRODUCTION

The life of Saul is outlined in the *SCS* for Map 7-4. Some of the subjects (7-4 e and f) were studied on Map 7-5. (Under *Primary sources* for *SCS* 7-4 f, a misprint of 7-8 should read 7-5 in the first edition of the *SMM*.) The map you will now study portrays events during the 16 months that David lived in Philistia at Ziklag (7-4 g).

In the closing years of Saul's reign and in the final chapters of the book of 1 Samuel activity centers around two regions. One is in the south, in the Western Negev where David operated from Ziklag, a city assigned to him by Achish, king of Gath. There David of Judah carried out operations under the pretext of serving Philistine interests. The other region was in the north in the Jezreel Valley where Saul, the head of a Benjamin-based monarchy, organized a major offensive against the Philistines. Had it been successful, it would have restricted Philistine control on major highways and linked the House of Joseph with the Israelite tribes in Galilee. The objective of the study on this map is to interrelate events in these two regions.

DAVID'S PROTECTION OF PHILISTIA'S SOUTHERN FLANK

DISCUSSION

7-6 a   Once the immediate threat from Saul had passed, David had second thoughts about staying in the Wilderness. He had the choice of moving to Moab in Transjordan where he had taken his family or of joining forces with the Philistines on the Coastal Plain.

David must have given careful thought to this important decision. Although Moab straddled the Transjordanian Highway, it was completely isolated from Judah and offered David little political opportunity. If escaping from Saul had been his only concern, he could have crossed over to Moab at any time during his flight. It is clear that David had more in mind than his daily security.

The Philistines were an expanding force. Their position west of Judah and north of the House of Joseph (Map 7-4) put them into direct contact (and conflict) with Israel. In their expansion along the highways of the north they could not forget their southern flank which bordered on the Negev. The constant threat of an attack from the Amalekites had to be considered. This threat was even more serious now that Saul's concerns had shifted to the north. Achish, the king of Gath, had a special interest in this southern flank since his inland territory extended south to Ziklag on the northern edge of the Negev (Map 6-1).

David, using his good sense which had served him well in military exploits, now used it to obtain what he needed, a base of operations near Judah. Protected from Saul in southern Philistia, he could develop good relations with the Israelites and the clans of the Negev. His move can be summed up in a common saying in the Middle East, *Make a friend before you need him.*

MARKING

1. **Yellow HL on name** = **Gath, Aphek, Ziklag** and **Hebron.**

2. **Yellow HL on route** =
   a. The two branches of the International Coastal Highway (printed in red), one from Ekron to Gath and SW off the W edge of the map, and the other nearer the coast by Ashdod and Ashkelon.

   b. The route through the Hill Country from the N edge of the map (by Jerusalem) via Bethlehem to Hebron.

   c. The triangle of routes between Hebron, Beer-sheba and Arad and back to Hebron, the route E of Arad and the route W of Beer-sheba (to the edges of the map).

   d. The route SW of Beer-sheba to the SW edge of the map.

3. **Brown write-in:**
   a. Between Bethlehem and Beth-zur = HILL COUNTRY OF JUDAH (In three lines and along the highlighted route).

   b. Between Socoh and Adullam = SHEPHELAH.

   c. From the crossroads at Arad to just W of Hormah (The dot between the question mark and the broken blue line of the nahal is missing in the first printing of the *SMM*) = NEGEV (written vertically along the highlighted route).

4. **Blue border:** Symbolic limit of the Philistines = From the N edge of the map (just W of Beth-shemesh) running S (just above Azekah), turning SW via the hyphen of Moresheth-gath, passing NW of Lachish and just E of T. Nagila to about 1 cm./ ½ in. E of the question mark of Ziklag; continue W to the edge of the map with only a broken blue line. Shade in the W side of this border with your blue pencil.

5. **Blue write-in:** Between Ashdod and Gath but not too close to Gath = PHILISTINES (CHERETHITES) in two lines.

6. **Green write-in:**
   a. W of Hushah (W of Bethlehem) = JUDAH (large caps).

   b. S of Hebron = CALEBITES.

   c. By the eastern Arad (the one at the crossroads) = KENITES.

   d. Between the other Arad and Aroer = JERAHMEELITES.

   e. Just E of Beer-sheba = JUDAH-SIMEON (in two lines).

DISCUSSION

The northwestern corner of Map 7-6 (between Gath and Ashdod) appears to be the same type of region as the rest of the Coastal Plain to the southwest around Ziklag. However, there are important differences.

Ziklag, according to the probable location represented in the *SMM*, is situated in the Western Negev. The site stands on the edge of a small spring-fed nahal which flows westward into the great Nahal Besor. Geographically the region belongs to the Negev, an area of fine loess (wind blown) soil which covers most of the Negev basin.

To the north between Ziklag and Ashdod, a slightly higher area separates Ziklag from what could be termed the *Philistine alluvial plain* (a broad basin between Gath and Ashdod which has been filled with rich soils washed down from the Hill Country of Judah). The edges of this basin were exploited by the Philistines, three of whose five main cities were located around this plain (Ashdod, Gath and Ekron). This should not be surprising since the area offered agricultural potential not found farther south. This also provides one of the reasons for locating Gath of the Philistines relatively close to Ekron, both of which take advantage of the rich soils to the east of the plain.

7-6 a

Another point to be considered in locating Gath and Ziklag (a question widely discussed over the past half century) is an understanding of the chapter you are about to read. Had Ziklag and Gath been adjacent to each other, the king of Gath would have had no reason to ask David's assistance in protecting his southern flank. By the same token, had there not been considerable distance between Gath and Ziklag, David never could have tricked the king into believing that his exploits were directed against his own people. (The word *today* in 1 Samuel 27.10 does not necessarily mean within one twenty-four hour period.)

READING AND DISCUSSION

The background of how David arrived at Ziklag is recounted in the opening verses of **1 Samuel 27**. This chapter also explains David's cunning in his dealings with both Achish of Gath and with the people of the Negev. Achish considered David to be rather foolish for the operations he claimed to have carried out in the Negev. At the same time the people of the Negev grew to appreciate David's protection. This was particularly true now that Saul's attention was turned to the north and the Amalekite threat in the south again became real. In this context David's ability to take advantage of every situation can be seen clearly. His dealings represent *bluff tactics* which those who live in the Middle East fully appreciate.

In order to maintain continuity in the story, you might want to turn back to Map 7-4   7-4 h
and read **1 Samuel 28** after reading 1 Samuel 27. The conversation between David and Achish in the opening verses is especially amusing. To maintain credibility David's bluff had to extend to Achish's demand for assistance in the battle against Saul. While David must have regreted this, he no doubt knew that the other Philistine leaders would reject such help.

DAVID'S HELP REJECTED BY THE PHILISTINES AT APHEK

DISCUSSION
As can be seen in Map 4-5, 7-3 and 7-4, Aphek is the natural gathering point on the Coastal Highway for any forces which would head north. It was here that the leaders of the Philistine cities mobilized their forces for the final battle with Saul and his army (Map 7-3). David, with his contingent of troops must have had mixed feelings as he marched to Aphek with the army of Achish. After all, it was near Aphek that the   7-3 b
Philistines had earlier destroyed an Israelite force, killing Eli's two sons in the battle and capturing the Ark of the Lord.

In spite of his inward feelings David had to maintain an outward appearance of support for the cause. Otherwise all would have been lost. Again, a most amusing   7-6 b
conversation between David and Achish of Gath adds the finishing touches to David's effective bluff in **1 Samuel 29.**

MARKING
1. **Sweeping blue arrow**: Philistine mobilization =
   a. Along the W branch of the Coastal Highway from the name Ashkelon via Ashdod, pointing NE off the map.

   b. Along the E branch of the Coastal Highway from the area of Gath and pointing N off the map (with the arrow running W of this route).

2. **Sweeping green arrow**: David's contingent of troops marching with those of Gath = Beginning W of T. el-Areini, pointing NE and attached to the end of the blue arrow just drawn. (Read the next two instructions before marking.)

3. **Green write-in**: Above the green arrow just drawn = DAVID'S MEN.

4. **Black write-in**: Below the green arrow just drawn = (See 7-4).

AMALEKITE RAID ON ZIKLAG AND THE NEGEV

DISCUSSION
While David was at Aphek, the worst happened. The Amalekites, who no doubt knew   7-6 c
of Saul's preoccupation in the north and kept track of David's whereabouts, made a major raid on the Negev and into the southern Hill Country of Judah. Ziklag, the city of their chief opponent, was not exempted from their fury.

This tragedy, happening as it did while both Saul and the Philistines were in the north, gave David an unparalleled opportunity to demonstrate his commitment to the people of Judah and those living in the Negev. The *headlines* of those days would have covered both fronts, the Amalekite attack on the south and the coming showdown with the Philistines in the north. All of Israel was waiting to see what the outcome would be and what effect all of this would have on their future.

David's pursuit of the Amalekites carried him beyond the Nahal Besor (Brook Besor), the natural southern boundary of the country, and deep into Northern Sinai. There he finally caught up with the Amalekites, dealing them a serious blow and recovering all the spoil from their raid in Judah.

The generosity exhibited by David upon his return to the Negev and southern Judah was not without an ulterior motive. He knew all too well the strength of the Philistine force which had left Aphek for Shunem in the north. He also knew that Saul's army was no match for these forces. Saul would undoubtedly be captured or killed. At best the future of the Benjamin-based monarchy was questionable. Samuel had anointed David king, and Jonathan, the crown prince, had sworn allegiance to him. It is clear that David knew his hour was at hand. Thus there was all the more reason to cultivate friends in the influential region of Hebron and southern Judah.

David, however, had no cause to rejoice, either over his successful retaliatory campaign against the Amalekites or over the prospect of becoming king of Israel. Jonathan his friend was also in the north with Saul. These must have been days of mixed emotions within David's sensitive spirit, days when he recalled the songs of trust in God composed in the Wilderness when he was a simple shepherd.

MARKING

1. **One large red circle** (not necessarily round): Amalekite raid in the Negev and southern Judah = Encircling the triangle of highlighted routes in the center of the map, all green names around this triangle and extending out to include Ziklag but not T. Beit Mirsim nor Eglon.

2. **Small red circle** = **Ziklag** (burned with fire).

3. **Orange write-in and blue circle**: SW of the large red circle (S of Beer-sheba) = AMALEKITES (large caps) with a circle around the name.

4. **Sweeping orange arrow**: Amalekite raid =
   a. From the blue circle just drawn pointing NE toward the Negev.

   b. From the center of the triangle of highlighted routes (by Eshtemoa) and curving W to Ziklag.

   c. From Ziklag S and curving SW toward the SW corner of the map.

5. **Orange and black write-in**: Above the last orange arrow drawn = AMALEKITES (orange) TAKE SPOIL (black).

6. **Yellow HL on name** = Brook Besor.

7. **Sweeping green arrow** =
   a. Pointing to Ziklag from the north (about 5 cm./2 in. long).

   b. From Ziklag pointing S and running parallel with the orange arrow previously drawn (with at least 1 cm./½ in. between the two arrows).

8. **Green and black write-in:**
   a. Above and below the green arrow pointing to Ziklag = DAVID (green) RETURNS FROM APHEK (black).

   b. Above the green arrow S of Ziklag = DAVID'S (green) PURSUIT (black).

READING AND DISCUSSION

Read carefully **1 Samuel 30**. You may want to skim 1 Samuel 31 and 2 Samuel 1   7-6 c
to finish the sequence of events which brings Saul's reign to a close. Do not neglect to   7-4 h
read David's lament in **2 Samuel 1.17-27**. In it David's inner feelings are exposed. No   7-6 d
mention of his successes is heard. There in Philistia his distressed spirit had to tolerate
the shouts of victory and Philistine pride after this their final triumph over the first
king of Israel.

David also recalled his relationship with Jonathan at Gibeah and how they had shared
experiences of earlier battles with the Philistines, both at Michmash and in the Valley
of Elah. In his own way each of them knew what Samuel meant when he said, *Fix
your heart on the Lord, worshiping Him alone, and He will deliver you from the Philistines* (1 Samuel 7.3). This, more than any other thing, had drawn their spirits together in that late eleventh century, decades which brought to an end the period of the
Judges and Philistine domination over Israel. Now at Ziklag in southern Philistia
there was the news of Jonathan's death at the hand of the Philistines on the slopes
of Mt. Gilboa.

During these years of varied and unpredictable experiences, David had grown to manhood. At times he no doubt questioned how his anointing by Samuel at Bethlehem
would ever be realized. He was pursued by the recognized king of Israel, subject to
the Philistines, his nation's archenemy, and exposed to Saul by members of his own
tribe, Judah.

However, the events of this period in David's life, perhaps more than any other, proved
his patience and real trust in God. They also served to train a simple shepherd boy in
the important regional and political realities of the country he was about to govern. It
was this period of testing and training — when David learned the dynamic of the
Negev, the Shephelah and the Hill Country as well as the mentality of Amalekites, the
Philistines and his own people — which best prepared him for his future place of
leadership.

S M M   7 – 7

TITLE: DAVID'S REIGN

DATE: LATE 11TH AND EARLY 10TH CENTURY B.C.

INTRODUCTION

A full discussion of the reign of David is beyond the scope of this limited *Guide*. Only main geopolitical themes will be covered in the paragraphs below. The *SCS* for this map provides an outline which can be used for your personal study of this gifted and sensitive leader. Read over the list of subjects in the *SCS* to acquaint your-self with the topical outline of this important period in the history of Israel and Judah.

Up to this point in your study of maps in *SMM* Section Seven, readings have been restricted to the books of 1 and 2 Samuel. From here on (and throughout Sections Eight and Nine) readings in 2 Samuel and in 1 and 2 Kings are paralleled by passages in 1 and 2 Chronicles. A listing of these parallels is given under *Primary Sources* in the *SCS* for each map after each specific subject.

MARKING

1. **Green write-in:**

    a. Between Hebron and Bethlehem = JUDAH (large caps inside a green box).

    b. In the triangle of routes NW of Bethel = EPHRAIM (large caps inside a green box).

    c. W of Shechem = MANASSEH (large caps).

    d. Between the dot of Jericho and name Michmash (written vertically and between the routes = BENJAMIN (small caps).

    e. In Transjordan E of Penuel = GILEAD (large caps).

2. **Blue on dot = Megiddo, Taanach, Ibleam** and **Beth-shan.**

3. **Blue write-in:**

    a. S of Megiddo = CANAANITE CENTERS.

    b. On the very SW edge of the map in the open area N of the map number = PHILIS-TINES.

    c. On the very N edge of the map (written vertically) between the Transjordanian Highway and the Dead Sea = MOAB.

    d. In the Dead Sea on the S edge of the map = EDOM (with a black arrow pointing SE).

    e. In the Transjordan W of Rabbah/Rabbath-ammon leaving enough space for a later circle to be drawn around the city name = AMMON.

f. In the NE corner of the map on the E edge beneath the & of the title = TOB (with a black arrow pointing E off the map).

g. In the NE corner of the map, 2.5 cm./1 in. from the E edge of the map = ARAM-ZOBAH (with a black arrow pointing N off the map).

3. **Yellow HL on name** =
   a. In Transjordan = **Rabbah, Medeba** and **Mahanaim** (only the one by Penuel).

   b. W of the Jordan = **Hebron, Jerusalem, Gibeon** and **Gezer**. (In the first printing of the *SMM* the arrow points the wrong way.)

4. **Yellow HL on route** =
   a. The Transjordanian Highway (printed in red) from Moab on the S edge of the map N via Ammon and Gilead running NE off the map.

   b. From Heshbon on the Transjordanian Highway W to the Coastal Highway (just off the W edge of the map) via Jericho, Bethel (HL both routes from Jericho to Bethel), Timnath-serah and NW off the map. In normal pencil add and HL a connection from Medeba to the ridge route descending to Jericho from Heshbon.

   c. From Rabbah to Jericho (the route running to the N of the Heshbon-Jericho route).

   d. From Gezer to just beyond Michmash including both the ascent via Beth-horon and the Aijalon—Kiriath-jearim—Gibeon route.

   e. From Hebron to Bethel.

   f. From Bethlehem W to Socoh in the Shephelah and off the W edge of the map.

   g. From Jerusalem to Jericho.

   h. From Aijalon to Shaaraim in the Shephelah.

5. **Green border and write-in:** Judah's northern border = From the mouth of the Jordan River emptying into the Dead Sea N and NW to Beth-arabah, W and SW (keeping S of the Jericho-Jerusalem route) to the *h* of Bahurim, to the *n* of En-rogel, beginning again below the *h* of Rephaim to the *h* of elohim, W to the dot of Kiriath-jearim, beginning again by the *h* of Baalah and SW down the ridge to the dot of Beth-shemesh. Shade in the S side of this border and write in (black and small caps) JUDAH'S NORTHERN BORDER in the Wilderness just W of the Dead Sea with a green arrow pointing to the border just drawn.

6. In the SW corner of the map correct *T. Beit Mirsim* (in the first edition of the *SMM*) to read *Debir*. Corrections can also be made in the *Index of Main Names*.

DAVID BECOMES KING OF JUDAH AND THEN OF *ALL ISRAEL* AT HEBRON

DISCUSSION

The death of Saul of Benjamin with his three older sons on Mt. Gilboa and the earlier   7-4 h
death of Samuel at Ramah left a serious vacuum among the Israelite tribes. The

question of who would now rule Israel was no doubt on everyone's mind. Old tribal rivalries had not died out, and competition between Judah and Ephraim was still a very live issue.

The Philistine victory in the Jezreel Valley added another reality. The open character of the region of Manasseh (Samaria as it is called in Chapter Three) allowed Philistine penetration into this area. Nothing is mentioned of Philistine control, but the fact that Ish-bosheth (Saul's son who was not at the battle of Gilboa) was brought to Mahanaim in Gilead and crowned king there gives a strong hint that conditions did not permit a new government to be established west of the Jordan. One wonders why this event did not take place in Benjamin itself. Perhaps pressures from Judah or from the Philistines had something to do with it. Mahanaim, inside the deep Nahal Jabbok
1-11   which drains much of the Dome of Gilead, offered the type of security needed at this hour when conditions were chaotic and anything could happen. In Mahanaim Abner, the late king's commanding general, appears to have directed the affairs of state, although Ish-bosheth was king. The name of the new monarch was actually Esh-baal (*man of Baal* or *Baal exists*), but most Biblical writers called him Ish-bosheth (*man of shame*).

During these days of uncertainty the leadership of Hebron in southern Judah was quick to sieze the opportunity of changing the status quo. They had put up with the Benjamin-based monarchy (under the influence of Ephraim) long enough. It appears that no one consulted with the rest of the tribes of Israel when the people of Hebron
7-7 a   made David *king over the House of Judah*. After all, in David they had a popular candidate whom they thought no one could oppose.

David (king of Judah at Hebron) and Abner with Ish-bosheth (Saul's son, king in Mahanaim) set the stage for two difficult years of political intrigue, war and bitter personal feuds. Through it all, with his usual good sense and charisma, David remained on good terms with everyone and emerged as king *over Israel and over Judah, from Dan to Beer-sheba.*

READING AND DISCUSSION

With this background and with Map 7-7 in view, read **2 Samuel 2.1-5.5**. Note how Abner is first able to talk the northern tribes into maintaining the Benjamin-based monarchy over which he appears to have a certain control. However, during subsequent months we read that *David was gaining strength all the time, while the House of Saul kept losing its influence* (2 Samuel 3.1). This frustrating period climaxed in a quarrel between Ish-bosheth and Abner, after which Abner made a complete reversal of policy. He had little difficulty persuading the north (including Benjamin!) to transfer their allegiance over to David. Through the misguided actions of Joab (David's commanding general) and two of David's over-enthusiastic supporters from Benjamin, both Abner and Ish-bosheth were removed from the scene. Thus the Benjamin-based monarchy, exiled in Mahanaim, comes to an end. Only Jonathan's young crippled son, Mephibosheth, still remained alive.

A NEW POLITICAL CAPITAL AT JERUSALEM

DISCUSSION

David reigned at Hebron for seven and a half years. The first two years were difficult. Nothing is known about the other five years in southern Judah. However, it is possible to imagine some of David's thoughts during those silent years of organization and planning in Hebron.

Hebron was a celebrated city. Its connections with the patriarchs placed it on a par with Shechem and Bethel (Maps 4-3 and 4-4). The area had been the first and the last visited by the spies from Kadesh (Map 5-2). In Joshua's early campaigns in the land, he returned to this city which he had visited earlier as a spy (Map 5-5). The city's connections with the Negev, Judah's southern flank, and the clans which had settled there made it strategically important.

5-2 c

5-5 c

The geographical setting of Hebron was briefly discussed earlier in this chapter on Map 6-3. By glancing at this map you will recall that Hebron is located in the southern Hill Country of Judah, on a high plateau (1000 meters/3300 feet) made up of valleys and rolling, terraced hills. Both sides of this plateau are deeply eroded. This isolates it from surrounding regions except for a few natural approaches via ridge routes. To the south a dryer landscape finally falls off into the eastern and western Negev basin. To the north a ridge route links the Hebron plateau with Bethlehem, Jerusalem and the Central Benjamin Plateau. To the east of Hebron the Wilderness, the cliffs above the shores of the Dead Sea and the Dead Sea itself create a serious barrier to travel. Although it is a beautiful place to live (good soil, sufficient rainfall, near an area for herds and secure within the Hill Country), the region's opportunities for a larger role in the political leadership of the country do not compare to those of Shechem, nor even to those of the Central Benjamin and Bethel plateaus.

Again on Map 7-7 note the advantages of travel, trade and expansion from the territory of Benjamin seen by the highlighted routes. This factor was fully discussed in Chapter Three. Here it has been reviewed since it provides an important clue to David's next move on the local *playing board*, the establishment of a new capital in Jerusalem.

7-7 b

This move constitutes the best example of David's good geopolitical sense. He realized that Hebron offered none of the advantages of the Central Benjamin Plateau. From this plateau he could easily reach the International Coastal Highway (via the Aijalon Valley and Gezer) and the Transjordanian Highway (via Jericho).

READING
Fortunately for David there was a natural first step to taking the Central Benjamin Plateau, the conquest of the Jebusite enclave at Jerusalem, which no one had yet occupied. This local episode is interesting in its own right. Placed in its larger context of Map 7-7 David's action can be seen as an absolute necessity if his kingdom was to be more than an appendix to that of Saul. Read the account of David's move in **2 Samuel 5.5-10.**

PHILISTINE ATTEMPTS TO CRUSH DAVID'S UNITED KINGDOM

DISCUSSION
Up to this point the Philistines do not appear to see David's kingdom as a threat. Since the death of Saul they had enjoyed the control of the country's main routes. As far as is known, their activities went unchallenged, and there was no need to confront David as long as he was simply the king of Judah in Hebron.

Everything changed, however, when David became king over Israel and Judah and captured Jerusalem, making it *crown property*. The Philistines, who had had much experience in the region just north of Jerusalem, could not tolerate the prospect of a king of Israel and Judah again extending his control over the Central Benjamin Plateau and its approaches. Just as the region had served the Philistines well in their domination of the tribes in the hills, in the same way it could serve David as a springboard to expansion in all directions. Since it appeared that Ephraim was in no position to stop David or did not wish to because of his popularity, the Philistines knew that they had to move now or never.

7-7 c   Philistine troops were sent at least twice into the region south of Jerusalem to weaken or destroy what has been termed David's *United Kingdom*. Both operations began by the setting up of a camp in the Valley of Rephaim, a beautiful sloping valley southwest of Jerusalem, draining into the Nahal Rephaim which runs west to join the Sorek System, a region of canyons between Jerusalem and Beth-shemesh. To approach the Valley of Rephaim from the west and to avoid ambush by the Israelites, the Philistines probably used a ridge route between the Valley of Elah (by Socoh on Map 7-7) and Hushah. From there it was possible to descend northeast into the Valley of Rephaim. Control of this valley enabled the Philistines to cut off Judah (Bethlehem and Hebron) from David's new capital at Jerusalem.

In the first encounter David repulsed the Philistines in a frontal attack. In the second round David used the canyons east of the main north-south ridge route (an area he knew well as a Bethlehemite) in order to circle around the Philistine camp and attack them from behind (from the south).

The difficult nature of the Hill Country west of Jerusalem (the Sorek System with no natural and continuous ridge routes to the Shephelah) meant that the Philistines had no convenient escape route to the west. With David south of them the only way out of the hills was north to the Central Benjamin Plateau and then west by Gibeon to the Aijalon Valley and Gezer.

This flight of the Philistines followed the same route along which Joshua had pursued
5-5 b   the Canaanites in the first and most famous battle recorded in the region (Map 5-5).
7-3 d   Subsequently Samuel's revival meeting at Mizpah ended with a Philistine retreat along this route (Map 7-3). Jonathan and Saul chased the Philistines along the same route
7-4 d   *from Michmash to Aijalon*, following the Philistines's major offensive in the hills (Map 7-4).

7-7 c   David's pursuit of the Philistines through this same region (Map 7-7) not only demonstrated the fact that God's blessing was on him. It also showed the people living in the territory of Benjamin (and Ephraim nearby) that the Central Benjamin Plateau was now under his control and that his new capital at Jerusalem was there to stay. Any hope for reestablishing a Benjamin-based monarchy was gone for good.

MARKING

1. **Green box around dot**: David's new capital = **Jerusalem.**

2. **Sweeping blue arrow**: Philistine advances into the Valley of Rephaim = From Socoh to Baal-perazim via Hushah.

3. **Red confrontation mark**: On the route half way between Bethlehem and Jerusalem = ✳ .

4. **Flight (blue) and chase (green) arrow**: Philistine retreat and David's chase in the second encounter = From Gibeon to Shaalbim by Gezer via Beth-horon.

READING
Read **1 Chronicles 14.8-16**. Follow these developments on Map 7-7 as you read.

JERUSALEM BECOMES THE RELIGIOUS CAPITAL OF THE UNITED KINGDOM

DISCUSSION AND OPTIONAL READING
With the passing of Samuel an era had ended. It was now possible to create a religious center which would be one and the same as the political capital of the country. David took advantage of this opportunity by bringing the Ark to Jerusalem from Kiriath-jearim (Baale-judah/Baalah) where it had been kept since the Philistines returned it to the Israelites (Map 7-3). The most convenient route from Kiriath-jearim was via Gibeon and the Central Benjamin Plateau. If this is the route taken by David and the Ark, then it may explain part of David's enthusiasm as he danced along the way on the route through Benjamin. **2 Samuel 6** describes this procession to which at least one person from Benjamin took exception, David's wife Michal, the daughter of Saul.

7-7 d

ADMINISTRATION AND EXPANSION OF DAVID'S KINGDOM

DISCUSSION
David's administrative policies are now discussed here. Biblical passages relating to them can be found on the *SCS* for this map. You may note that certain Philistines were among David's personal body guard (Cherethites and perhaps also the Pelethites). In the midst of the political intrigue of the day these outsiders appear to be trusted more than the locals.

7-7 e

David's use of Jerusalem and the Central Benjamin Plateau for the purpose of extending his control to the west, east and north is an important theme of Map 7-7. A glance at the map reveals the strategic importance of the plateau and its approaches in David's overall planning. What the Philistines had feared most had actually happened. Once David was established in his new political and religious capital, there was no peace on the Transjordanian Highway, along the Coastal Highway near Joppa or along northern highways until David's control of the country was complete.

Some of David's campaigns in this period are explained in great detail, like the battle for Rabbah in Ammonite territory on the Transjordanian Highway. Others are hinted at in single verses or short passages. Still others, like the take-over of the Canaanite centers in the Jezreel Valley, are not mentioned at all. It appears that David understood the dynamics of the *Land Between*. His push into Transjordan and then to the north far beyond the limits of Map 7-7 isolated the Canaanite centers in the Jezreel Valley. Once that was accomplished, control was extended south to Edom via the Transjordanian Highway or via the Negev. In the west his main objective was Joppa, Jerusalem's nearest port on the Mediterranean Sea. In reaching Joppa David automatically cut the International Coastal Highway, making all who used it dependent upon him.

All of this could only have happened in a period when an international vacuum existed in this *Land Between*. This same type of local control of the country was impossible once Assyrian power developed. While it would take three centuries to make itself felt directly in Judah, Tiglath-pileser I had already crossed the Euphrates far to the north and had boasted of victories *as far as the Great Sea*, the Mediterranean Sea. Fortunately for David, Assyria had already retreated back into her territory proper on the Tigris River. Egypt also had entered a lull in her history. In one sense this period could be summed up by the phrase used of the *Son of David* in the New Testament, *In the fullness of time* . . . (Galatians 4.4).

MARKING

1. **Red circle around names** = Rabbah/Rabbath-ammon, Medeba and Gezer. (Correct the arrow of Gezer if not done already.)

2. **Sweeping green arrow**: David's expanding kingdom =
   a. Two short arrows starting just N of the green box around the dot of Jerusalem, one branching E in the direction of Jericho, another branching W in the direction of Gezer. Skip over names which are in the way.

   b. One arrow beginning E of Jericho and splitting into three arrows, each with a separate point: One pointing to Rabbah, another to Medeba and a third curving around and pointing N along the Transjordanian Highway E of the word Gilead.

   c. From Medeba S toward Moab.

   d. From the word Judah S and SE off the map toward Edom (actually via the Negev which is off the map to the S).

   e. From the word Judah W toward Socoh or Adullam in the Shephelah.

   f. From the word Gilead NE toward the word Tob.

3. **Red write-in**: In the NE corner of the map, on the E edge just N of the word Tob = **Helam** with a black arrow pointing E toward the location of this city off the map.

4. **Green border with green write-in**: Symbolic limit of Israelite settlement = From the E shore of the Dead Sea on the S edge of the map, running E up the canyon (Nahal Aroer), curving to the NE (beyond Aroer) to the E edge of the map, continuing N but bending below the word Ammon and back out to the E edge of the map, N until it is just below the *a* in Monarchy (of the printed map title), then curving NW between the word Aram-zobah and Rogelim to the N edge of the map. Shade in the W side of this border and write in (green) LIMIT OF ISRAELITE SETTLEMENT along the W side of this line near Rogelim to the region of Ammon. David's control, however, reached far beyond this limit.

5. **Black write-in**: Under the blue word Canaanite centers = APPARENTLY TAKEN BY DAVID (See 6-1) in small caps.

READING

7-7 e   Read the **passages listed in the** *SCS* **7-7** e under western, eastern and southern expansion. Most of them are short but say much about David's geopolitical objectives.

You may want to add your own notes (Biblical references) on the map in small letters in the appropriate location for future reference. The story of David and Bathsheba is included under eastern expansion. In connection with the death of Uriah, Bathsheba's husband, read **Psalm 51**. In the midst of geopolitical priorities it illustrates that David's sensitive spirit was not lost.

SELECTED EPISODES DURING DAVID'S REIGN

DISCUSSION

Most of these topics (*SCS* 7-7 f) are left for your optional reading. Only two are represented by marking on Map 7-7. One is the *Southern Revolt* under Absalom (iv). The other is the *Northern Revolt* under Sheba, son of Bichri (v). These two revolts demonstrate that there were constant undercurrents throughout David's reign, both in Judah (Hebron) and in Israel (among the northern tribes). Leaders in these areas felt that David's administration had gone too far and that such governmental (and probably religious) centrality had seriously reduced their status and influence. This, however, was the price which had to be paid for the expansion which had come with David. In the southern revolt Mahanaim in Transjordan again became a place of retreat and refuge, this time for David.

7-7 f

MARKING

1. **Sweeping but broken green arrows and green write-in**:
   a. David's flight from Absalom = From Jericho across the Jordan and N to Mahanaim passing just SE of Succoth. Write in DAVID (small caps) along this arrow.

   b. From Jokmeam (center of the map) to a point just N of Succoth. Write in ABSALOM (small caps) along this arrow.

2. **Red confrontation mark**: Just N of Succoth = ✸ .

3. **Brown write-in**: In the hills N of Succoth = FOREST OF EPHRAIM (in three lines).

4. **Yellow HL on name**: On the N edge of the map = **Abel-beth-maachah.**

5. **Orange arrow and write-in**: From Shechem NE (via Tirzah and Beth-shan) to the N edge of the map (below the name Abel-beth-maachah). Write in SHEBA'S (orange) REBELLION PUT DOWN (black).

6. **Long green chase arrow**: Joab's pursuit of Sheba = From N of Bethel to the end of the orange arrow (by Shechem) just drawn.

READING

Skim the Biblical texts given for each of these rebellions: **2 Samuel 15.1-20.22**. Take special note of geographical information. Strong words between the men of Judah and the men of Israel during David's return to Jerusalem (by Gilgal) in 2 Samuel 19.41-20.2 underscore the tension which continued to exist between the northern tribes (Israel) and Judah. It is interesting that Sheba, who initiated the northern rebellion, was a man from the tribe of Benjamin.

7-7 f
iv, v

DAVID'S REIGN: CONCLUSIONS AND READINGS

Any attempt to summarize David's life and reign or to explain its relevance upon later Old and New Testament history falls short. As shepherd or as king he is unique in the annals of Israel.

David's life illustrates the unexpected, when the weak and the insignificant rise to overpower the strong. As a simple shepherd in the Wilderness (the youngest son of Jesse), or as a youth before Goliath in the Shephelah, it was difficult to recognize in David the future king of Israel. Even the prophet Samuel had to be prepared before he met him that first time in Bethlehem (1 Samuel 16.4-13).

From these weak beginnings (as man sees weakness) David developed into a military genius, an astute politician and a respected leader. It was a big step from the dry Wilderness of Judah to the Brook (Nahal) of Egypt or the Euphrates River in northern Mesopotamia. As with few in such position, popularity and success did not alter his sensitive spirit or simple trust in God. A comparison of David and Saul in this respect can be an interesting study.

The expansion of David's kingdom to the edge of Mesopotamia and the frontier of Egypt remains the theme of later prophets. One prime example is found in **Isaiah 11**. There the prophet states that both international and local problems during one of Judah's most difficult periods are finally to be resolved by *a shoot from the stump of Jesse.*

Within the context of the Israelite tribes and the nations which surrounded them, **Psalm 108** represents one of the best statements on David's accomplishments. This shout of exultation (attributed to David) should be balanced by the reading of **Psalm 32**.

12-4 The rise of David of Bethlehem during the late eleventh century B.C. has parallels with developments surrounding the coming of Jesus, *the Son of David*, in the first century B.C. when Jerusalem was again the political and religious center of the country for its Jewish inhabitants. It was in those days, when King Herod ruled under the shadow of Rome, that Joseph and Mary returned to Bethlehem of Judah. As they traveled along the route north of Bethlehem, they must have asked questions similar to those of Samuel the prophet after he had fulfilled his strange mission in Bethlehem: *How can all of this work out?*

12-5 When Jesus was born in Bethlehem in the city of David, there were still shepherds in the regions east of the city. Like Samuel, it appears that the wise men who came months later had also been prepared to recognize the new king, the Son of David, still in a simple setting of weakness compared to the palaces and fortresses of Herod in Jerusalem and at
12-2 e the Herodium, only an hour's walk from Bethlehem.

Years later, after his own wanderings in the Wilderness, which David knew so well, another prophet, John, pointed to Joshua (Jesus' name in Hebrew) and said, *Look, there goes the Lamb of God!* This happened after His temptation in the Wilderness and in the same
5-3 c vicinity as an earlier Joshua had crossed the Jordan with the children of Israel to celebrate the first Passover in the land.

Later in His ministry this same first century Joshua, the Son of David, would announce in Jerusalem, *I am the good shepherd; the good shepherd lays down his life for the sheep* (John 10.11), no doubt recalling David's bravery and his commitment to his father's charge (1 Samuel 17.32-37). Following His resurrection, the Good Shepherd gave explicit instructions to His chief disciple, *Feed my sheep* (John 21.15-17). We later hear that the Good Shepherd and the Lamb are actually one and the same providing both security and well-being (Revelation 7.15-17).

All of this imagery, and more, permeates the pages of the New Testament. Much of it comes from the same setting in which David was taught the lessons of life and trust in God. The Apostle Paul, who knew this background well, summed up the lives of Samuel, David, Jonathan, Joseph, Mary and even that of Joshua (Jesus) of Nazareth in his letter to the Corinthians.

> *For God's stupidity is wiser than men,*
> *and God's weakness is stronger than men.*
>
> *Think about your own call, brothers.*
>
>> *Not many are wise judged by human standards.*
>> *Not many have established power bases [in the community].*
>> *Not many come out of influential backgrounds.*
>
> *[In fact, it is quite the opposite.]*
>
>> *God has picked out the world's know-nothings to humiliate the wise;*
>> *God has picked out the world's weak to humiliate the strong;*
>> *God has picked out the world's lower class, those the world*
>>> *looks down on [like the shepherd in ancient Israel],*
>>> *yes, even that which does not exist at all [in the world's*
>>> *eyes], in order to abolish that which does exist.*
>
> *[All this] so that no human being (flesh) might glory in the*
>> *presence of God [but might recognize who He is].*   (1 Corinthians 1.25-29)

This same theme appears in **Psalm 78** which summarizes the history of Israel and the long-standing competition between Ephraim (of the House of Joseph) and Judah. In this Psalm (which should be read in its entirety) Ephraim's impressive record on the battlefield could not be substituted for a heart that recognized who God is, demonstrated by what He had done for Israel in the past. The threat to Israel's existence expressed in verses 60-64 (Philistine domination?) found its answer in the simple words of a young shepherd boy before Goliath (1 Samuel 17.41-47). The closing verses of Psalm 78 highlight the apparent surprise of God's choice of David as a leader for His people in those difficult days.

> *[The Lord] rejected the tent [House] of Joseph*
>> *By not choosing the tribe of Ephraim.*
> *Instead He chose the tribe of Judah,*
>> *Even Zion's mount which he loves . . . .*
> *He chose David who served (worshipped/recognized) Him,*
>> *Taking him from the [lowly and smelly] pens of sheep,*
> *From the care of ewes who nursed their young He brought him*
>> *To tend the flock of Jacob His people, of Israel His possession —*
> *And he tended them with a heart of integrity;*
>> *With a hand of discernment he lead them.*   (Psalm 78.67-72)

Finally, any discussion of David, the shepherd and the king, would not be complete without a quiet reading of the song which best reflects his deep-rooted belief and unshaken confidence in the God of Israel — **Psalm 23** echoed in verses 52 through 55 of Psalm 78.

S M M   7 — 1/2

INTRODUCTION

This set of maps (facing each other in the *SMM*) shows the kingdom which Solomon received from his father David. Northern perspectives on Map 7-1 were marked and discussed in Chapter One and in Chapter Two. These discussions can be reviewed if necessary. On Map 7-2 your study will concentrate on Judah's priorities in the south (in the Negev and beyond to the Red Sea) and in Transjordan. The title and date of Map 7-1 can serve for Map 7-2, or you can write it in again on Map 7-2.

MARKING (Map 7-2)

1. **Blue write-in:** Nations or peoples surrounding Judah =
   a. In the NW corner of the map, N of Ziklag = PHILISTINES.

   b. In Transjordan, E of the Dead Sea, on the plateau just E of the Transjordanian Highway = MOAB (see Map 7-1).

   c. In Transjordan on the plateau SE of Bozrah and NE of Teman, between the two highways = EDOM.

   d. On the W edge of the map, S of the International Coastal Highway, between the two routes printed in black = EGYPT with a black arrow pointing to the W.

   e. On the W edge of the map, in the SW corner of the map, N of the map number = EGYPT with a black arrow pointing to the W.

2. **Yellow HL on name = Beer-sheba, Arad** (only the eastern Arad), **Tamar** (SE of Arad), **Elath** and **Ezion-geber** (both on the Red Sea).

3. **Black write-in:** Two names and dots to be added to this map from locations on Map 9-2 = **Kadesh-barnea** and **Kir of Moab**.

4. **Yellow HL on route:** Note geographical features and obstacles, as these routes are traced. Also find where each one would pass on the *SMA*, southern sheet =
   a. From Elath to Jerusalem (off the map) via Tamar, Arad and Hebron.

   b. From Arad W to the Coastal Highway via Beer-sheba.

   c. From Hebron to Ezion-geber and Elath via Beer-sheba and Kadesh-barnea.

   d. From Ezion-geber W to Egypt (route printed in red).

   e. From Tamar W to Egypt (route printed in red).

   f. The connections to Egypt (routes printed in black N and S of Kadesh-barnea).

5. **Green write-in**: Between Beth-zur and Tekoa on the N edge of the map = JUDAH.

6. **Brown write-in**:
   a. In the same position as on Map 7-6 = NEGEV.

   b. In the Rift Valley SE of Tamar, west of the route to Elath = ARAVAH.

   c. Between the Aravah and Kadesh-barnea = WILDERNESS.

DISCUSSION

Except for the Biblical Negev, the south of the country has not yet been discussed. This larger area is seen both on Map 7-2 and on the *SMA* (northern and southern sheets joined).

As noted earlier in this chapter, the general term *Negev* is used today for all of the regions south of the Hill Country of Judah, almost to the southern edge of Map 7-2, the southern part of the modern State of Israel. However, when the same term occurs in the Bible, it refers only to the northern part of today's Negev, the region of Arad and Beer-sheba and to the west toward Gaza. This *Guide* uses the term *Negev* in this restricted sense and not in the modern sense of the word. The area south of this Negev is referred to as the *Wilderness,* although not all of it could be classified as badlands. The Rift Valley south of the Dead Sea is sometimes termed the *Arabah* (*Aravah* in modern usage).

Rainfall in Hebron is sufficient for vines and orchards but decreases rapidly south of the Hill Country of Judah. Trees and vines disappear, and even grain crops in the Negev are in constant danger from drought. Farther southeast, in the region of the Aravah, rainfall is almost non-existent except for short and heavy downpours which cause flash floods. In the Wilderness south of the Tamar—Kadesh-barnea route, up-lifted hills rise again to over 800 meters/2700 feet. On the northwest slopes of this area (east of Kadesh-barnea) some grains can still be grown.

With this bleak perspective it is not difficult to understand that most of the area of Map 7-2 is not the land of the farmer or even of the sower. During most periods of history this region, together with Northern Sinai farther west, was used only by the bedouin and by desert raiders such as the Amalekites. Only when a strong central government in the Hill Country or in Transjordan (Edom or later Nabatea) was able to insure security and trade did the area become settled with forts and some cities. One of the first such periods is the one you are now studying, the end of David's reign and the beginning of Solomon's rule.

The routes highlighted on Map 7-2 represented some of Judah's priorities in the south. The International Coastal Highway and the Transjordanian Highway were not highlighted although they were very high priorities for David and later for Solomon. This is because your present concern is with Judah's push to Ezion-geber, Elath and the Red Sea.

It is clear on Map 7-2 that Judah's control of these southern routes (highlighted) automatically cut off Egyptian-Edomite trade. Map 7-1 showed that commerce on the International Coastal Highway was also controlled by David and Solomon. Campaigns

7-7 e   aimed to take command of the Transjordanian Highway were seen on Map 7-7. Capturing a port on the Red Sea and the routes reaching it were final moves in Judah's overall plan.   While Solomon receives much of the credit for this, it was actually David who masterminded the plan, leaving the south of the country to Solomon as part of his inheritance.

It was during this period that many of the southern forts and cities were established. While the dating of many of the smaller outposts is still a matter of debate, it appears that only a few were built on previous settlements. Thus during the reign of David and Solomon the region south of Judah began to flourish, both in the Negev proper and in regions farther south. David's experience of guarding this region before he became king had impressed upon him the importance of now securing these routes for Judah.

Control of such a resource of trade was a major contribution to the affluency of Solomon's reign. Egypt, who was in no position to challenge Jerusalem, had to be content with alliances supported by marriage ties (Solomon and pharaoh's daughter). Edom, which was only beginning to get on her feet, felt that Judah had usurped her right to Transjordanian trade and income from commerce through the Red Sea ports.

All of this was dependent upon a strong and a united Israelite nation. The rumblings of rebellion heard in David's time (Map 7-7) are not audible during Solomon's rule. However, the explosion following his death proved that dissident voices were only contained during his lifetime. Nothing had been solved, only postponed.

A few hints of coming problems are mentioned in 1 Kings 11. There we hear of certain *adversaries* like Rezon of Damascus (Map 7-1). There were also Hadad of Edom and Jeroboam, Solomon's gifted Ephraimite labor leader. Both of these had to flee to Egypt for safety. There, the pharaoh encouraged their desire for independence and prepared for the day when Solomon would be gone. The *united* kingdom dominated by Jerusalem would again be divided and weakened by internal dissension and external threats from surrounding *liberated* nations. Only then was there hope that the routes of the south and those of the Coastal Plain would return to Egypt's control.

MARKING

7-1/2 b   1. **Green circle around name:** Southern limit of David's census = **Beer-sheba**.

2. **Green box around name:** Jerusalem's control on surrounding nations = **Moab, Edom** and **Philistines**.   (The Philistines were contained if not controlled by Jerusalem.)

3. **Green write-in:**
Archeological evidence of settlements south of the Negev: To be written in starting approximately 5 cm./2 in. E of the Kadesh-barnea and Hazar-addar forts, over the highlighted route in five lines = ISRAELITE AGRICULTURAL SETTLEMENTS AND FORTRESSES. These are along this highlighted route and also along other local routes just south of it.

4. **Black write-in:** By the Arad which has been highlighted = (FORT) in small caps.

5. **Sweeping green arrow**: Solomon's income from tribute and trade =
   a. From Ezion-geber toward Tamar (skipping over the word Aravah).

   b. From the box of Edom to Tamar.

   c. From Tamar to Arad.

   d. From Ezion-geber toward Kadesh-barnea.

   e. From Kadesh-barnea (from the SW) and from Egypt (from the W) two green lines joining into one arrow along the highlighted route and pointing toward Beer-sheba.

   f. Along the International Coastal Highway pointing NE of Gaza.

   g. From Moab pointing N along the Transjordanian Highway (note Map 7-1).

6. **Black write-in and red underlining**: Solomon's adversaries.
   a. By the box of Edom = HADAD (with red underlining) and 1 Kings 11.14-22 (in two lines).

   b. By the word Egypt (N of Kadesh-barnea) = JEROBOAM (with red underlining) and 1 Kings 11.26-40 (in two lines).

DISCUSSION

Sit back and look over Maps 7-1 and 7-2. They represent one of the highest points in all the history of Israel and Judah. Affluency and security went hand in hand, summarized by Jesus' own words, *Even Solomon in all of his glory* . . . (Matthew 6.29). Much of the glory, however, was simply a reflection of David's careful planning and preparation before his death. It was only the bloom at the end of the sturdy stem.   7-7
                                                                             f vii

On Map 7-2 the strategic importance of the Negev, especially the sites of Arad and Beer-sheba, is clear. Archeological remains at both sites add evidence to this fact. In later centuries, when the rest of the country cut itself off from Judah, the Negev took on even greater importance as her southern and main flank.

READING

Most of the readings for this section in the *SCS* for Maps 7-1/2 are optional. The following are especially important to read with these maps in view: **2 Samuel 24.1-9, 1 Kings 4, 9 and 11.**

S M M   8 – 3

TITLE: JUDAH UNDER REHOBOAM AND SHISHAK'S CAMPAIGN

DATE: LATE 10TH CENTURY B.C.

INTRODUCTION

Section Eight of the *SMM* opens the period which has been called the Divided Kingdom. It is a period when all the seeds of tribal animosity discussed in previous sections of the *SMM* grew into two full-fledged and independent Israelite kingdoms, *Israel* and *Judah*. Your previous study prepared you for this moment, since you know that the division was not something that happened one day in Shechem but had existed for centuries. It had been contained only by the strong arm and wise actions of David and later maintained by his son Solomon.

With the death of Solomon (930 B.C.) an era had passed. Soon the world which David had so carefully constructed would be in ruins. Tribal bitterness quickly developed into civil war which continued for two decades. No doubt even the pharaoh of Egypt had not counted on such a rapid deterioration in Solomon's kingdom. During this period he appeared on the scene with what Egyptian military might he could muster to destroy Judah's and Israel's control over major highways in the country. The background of these years was covered on Map 8-2 in Chapter Two and in Chapter Three. Take time to review these discussions now with Map 8-2 before you.

MARKING (Map 8-3)
   1. **Green write-in:** In the open area between Hebron and Etam = JUDAH.

   2. **Yellow HL on name and green box around it:** Judah's capital = **Jerusalem.**

   3. **Orange write-in:** On N side of the map, N of Mt. Zemaraim = ISRAEL.

   4. **Blue write-in:**
      a. In the open area just W of Ekron and Gath = PHILISTINES.

      b. In Transjordan on the E edge of the map just SE of Kir of Moab = MOAB.

      c. In Transjordan SE of Bozrah = EDOM.

      d. On the W edge of the map between Kadesh-barnea and Yurza = EGYPT with a black arrow pointing W off the map.

   5. **Brown write-in:** Between Arad (Rabba) and Beer-sheba, on the S side of the route written vertically = NEGEV.

   6. **Yellow HL on route =**
      a. The International Coastal Highway from below Gaza to north of Aphek via Ashdod and Joppa. Also the link (printed in black) to Gittaim and on to Aphek.

      b. The Gittaim-Gibeon routes (via Upper and Lower Beth-horon and via Kiriath-jearim) and on to Mizpah, Bethel and N off the map (printed in black).

      c. The road which comes on the center of the W edge of the map heads due E to Beer-sheba and on to both Arads and descends E and S to Tamar.

      d. The Transjordanian Highway through Moab and Edom (printed in red) and its connection to Egypt via Tamar and Kadesh-barnea.

      e. The connection between the route just highlighted and the Negev via Baalath-beer and Aroer.

f. The route from Tamar E (already highlighted) and then S in the Rift Valley (to Ezion-geber off the map).

7. **Blue border**: Limit of Philistines = From T. Qudadi (N of Joppa) running SE between Gittaim and Gibbethon, curving around E of Timnah and S under the name Moresheth-gath, SW between Gath and Lachish, SW via T. el-Areini and between T. el-Hesi and T. Nagila, SW between Gerar and Yurza to the W edge of the map. Shade in the W side of this border.

8. **Broken green border**: Northern border of Judah/Benjamin in a broken line indicating its unsettled state. Copy this border from Map 8-4 using the city dots, routes and nahals for reference. Note Map 8-1 for the E part of this border. Shade in the S side of this border.

9. **Red on dot**: Sites included in Pharaoh Shishak's list of conquered cities (although some are questioned) = **Sharuhen** (color arrow), **Yurza** (which should be printed in red), **Gaza, Gezer, Rabbah/Rubute, Aijalon, Lower and Upper Beth-horon, Kiriath-jearim, Gibeon, Zemaraim, Arad (Rabba/Great)** and **Arad (of Jerahmeel)**.

10. **Blue write-in inside a large red circle**: In between Kadesh-barnea and Baalath-beer (see Map 7-2 for reference) = SHISHAK'S DESTRUCTION OF SETTLEMENTS AND FORTS (in five or six lines). Add red circle around this phrase and in small black caps add **(see Map 7-2)**.

11. **Red write-in with black arrow**: On the S edge of the map along the route from Tamar to Ezion-geber (see Map 9-2 for location) = EZION-GEBER (red in small caps) with a black arrow pointing S off the map.

12. **Sweeping blue arrow**: Shishak's possible advance on Jerusalem and in the Negev =
a. From Gaza to Gibbethon (pointing to Gezer).

b. From Aijalon to Gibeon.

c. From the W edge of the map E to Beer-sheba.

d. From Beer-sheba to Arad (Rabba) on the N side of the route.

e. From Aroer to the large red circle.

f. From Tamar toward Ezion-geber (off the S edge of the map).

13. **Blue write-in**: On the Gaza-Gibbethon arrow = PHARAOH SHISHAK OF EGYPT.

DISCUSSION

There were three regions which Shishak had to attack in order to weaken Judah. The first was along the International Coastal Highway via Philistia to Gezer and the Aijalon Valley. This would reestablish an Egyptian presence on the coast and crush any hope that Jerusalem had of restoring or maintaining Joppa as her port. The earlier alliance between Solomon and the pharaoh, sealed by Solomon's marriage to his daughter, should be seen in light of this attack. Such agreements were necessary when Egypt could not cope with Israel's relative might. However, that day had passed, and in modern terminology these agreements were no more than *scraps of paper*.

8-3 b

7-1 c

The second priority was the Central Benjamin Plateau, Judah's newly acquired northern flank (from the time of David). While Solomon had administratively kept this region in a separate district, it was nevertheless incorporated in Jerusalem's northern line of defense.

Like the Philistines of the eleventh century (Maps 7-3 and 7-4), the Egyptians realized all too well the strategic value of the Central Benjamin Plateau. Their operation in this region and its western approaches is represented by a series of six names from Shishak's inscription on the walls of a temple in Karnak on the Nile in Upper Egypt: **Gezer** (probable reading of the inscription), **Rubuti, Aijalon, Kiriath-jearim** (from probable reading of *Kiriathaim*), **Beth-horon** and **Gibeon.** If all of these readings are correct, Shishak conquered three of the sites Solomon had earlier fortified (names here in bold and highlighted on Map 7-1). Jerusalem does not appear in this inscription, unless it has been lost in one of the damaged sections, which seems unlikely.

Once at Gibeon the Egyptians were in a position to demand *the treasures of the house of the Lord and the treasures of the king's house,* (1 Kings 14.26) which Rehoboam's father (Solomon) and grandfather (David) had stored up. Egyptian presence on the plateau, even for a limited time, also created a vacuum and threw the area again *up for grabs.* Old rivalries between Ephraim and Judah were revived, which on Map 8-4 develop into full scale war.

The third region of Egyptian interest was the Negev and its links to the south and to Ezion-geber. There are seventy or so names in this part of Shishak's list, which constitutes the largest and most important collection of names known for the south of the country. However, there is difficulty attaching these names to actual sites since most local names in the south have not been preserved due to the lack of a permanent settled population in the region.

In spite of the fact that few identifications have been made, enough is known to state that this southern thrust was one of Shishak's highest priorities in his entire campaign, if not his highest. His chief goal was to break Judah's monopoly on trade in the south which had been developed throughout the tenth century by David and Solomon (Map 7-2). The Egyptian army effectively destroyed forts and settlements from the Negev to Ezion-geber, leaving Judah's southern flank in shambles.

One important name on Shishak's list which has been identified is that of Arad, which appears twice. One Arad is qualified in the inscription as the forts of the *great Arad.* This is the well-known Arad in the eastern Negev basin mentioned in connection with the Kenites (Map 6-3). There David and Solomon had constructed a fortress (Map 7-2) on the acropolis of an Early Bronze city that had disappeared 1300 years before. Some feel that this fortification is mentioned in Shishak's inscription itself.

6-3 d

Shishak's inscription also lists a second Arad, the *Arad of the House of Yeroham,* called the *Arad of Jerahmeel* in Map 8-3. It is located at another important center in the eastern Negev basin. A discussion of other possible site identifications in Shishak's southern campaign is beyond the scope of your present study and is summarized in the phrase encircled in red on Map 8-3 and the blue arrow pointing toward Ezion-geber.

DISCUSSION AND READING

A comparison of Maps 7-1/2 and Map 8-3 reveals that Judah's greatest moment had
passed away shortly after the death of Solomon, *in the fifth year of King Rehoboam.*
The rather brief mention of this disaster in the Bible should be read in **1 Kings 14.25-**   8-3 b
26. Beyond these verses and the Bible's general remarks on Rehoboam's reign, the list
of cities and fortresses destroyed by Jerusalem's former *ally*, Shishak, stands as a silent
witness on the southern wall of the great temple at Karnak above the Nile. Within
Judah itself there was little reason for rejoicing. Yet, in this *Land Between*, there may
have been those who realized the truth contained in **Psalm 62**, a psalm which tradi-
tionally has been assigned to David.

S M M   8 – 4

INTRODUCTION

With the division of Solomon's kingdom and the loss of the north, Judah had to
consider carefully her next step. Threats from Israel and from Egypt meant that
Rehoboam was forced to give serious thought to preserving the nation's security and
indeed its very independence. The development of a definite policy and Judah's
ability to implement that policy on all fronts is the subject of your present study.

The events on Maps 8-2, 8-3 and 8-4 represent a half century of military and political
activity (930-880 B.C.). In this half century three kings of Judah and seven kings of
Israel (representing five different families in the north) ruled in the country. To keep
all of them straight in your mind is not an easy task, nor one that this study requires.
However, during the rest of this chapter it may be helpful to color each king's name
on the *SCS* with the proper colored pencil (green for Judah and orange for Israel).
You may also want to note main dates in the left hand margin of the *SCS* and to refer
often to the charts in Appendix II at the end of the *Guide*.

REHOBOAM: DEFENSE STRATEGY IN JUDAH

DISCUSSION

Maps 8-2 and 8-3 have summarized events which happened in the first two decades
of the Divided Kingdom (930-912 B.C.). Since Rehoboam came to power in 930
B.C., Shishak's campaign *in the fifth year of King Rehoboam* must have occurred
around 924 B.C. In this chapter the main topic discussed on Map 8-4 is that of Reho-   8-4 a
boam's fortresses in Judah. The dating of this important defense project is not given
in the Bible, although it appears in the Biblical text before Shishak's campaign. If you
note Solomon's fortifications on Map 7-1 and compare them with Rehoboam's for-   7-1 c
tresses on Map 8-4, it appears that the latter simply supplement the former. Econom-
ically, Judah could have best undertaken such a project prior to Egypt's invasion and
appropriation of Jerusalem's treasures. Recent archeological evidence from Lachish
also suggests that Shishak's campaign included this site which had already been fortified by Rehoboam. All of this points to a date for Rehoboam's fortifications prior to
Shishak's campaign. If, however, Rehoboam's fortifications were created after
Shishak's campaign, they represent an area in which he could reasonably hope to
maintain control after this disaster.

READING AND MARKING

1. **Brown write-in:**
    a. In the open area S of Mozah (left center of map) = HILL COUNTRY.

    b. In the open area S of Azekah = SHEPHELAH.

    c. On the SW edge of the map, written vertically from the eastern Arad to Beer-
       sheba = NEGEV.

2. Open to **2 Chronicles 11.5-12** and take out your **green pen**. Starting with verse six
   put a **small green box** around the dot of each city mentioned in this text. For Gath
   in verse eight mark Moresheth-gath, not the Gath of the Philistines. Note any
   geographical order which you may find in this list.

3. With careful attention to regional perspectives (ridge routes in the Hill Country,
   valley routes in the Shephelah, strategic crossroads and approaches from the east,
   south and west), **highlight in yellow** the following natural routes:
    a. From Bethlehem to En-gedi on the shores of the Dead Sea via Tekoa. (A drop
       into a canyon can be avoided by slightly rerouting the road with a normal pen-
       cil.)

    b. From Bethlehem to Arad (the eastern Arad in the Negev at the crossroads) via
       Hebron and Ziph.

    c. From Hebron to Lachish via Adoraim.

    d. From Halhul by Beth-zur to Gath of the Philistines via Adullam, Socoh and
       Azekah.

    e. From Bethlehem to Socoh.

    f. The diagonal route from Lachish to Aijalon and the small stretch of road SW of
       Lachish.

    g. From Beth-shemesh to Ekron.

    h. From Hebron to Beer-sheba in the Negev.

DISCUSSION

What you have just produced on Map 8-4 from 2 Chronicles 11.5-12 is the best single
statement on the defense of the Hill Country of Judah and its Shephelah to the west.
The central core of Judah was the Hill Country and the main ridge route from
Jerusalem to Hebron. From this route, side ridge routes radiate out to the Shephelah,
the Negev and even eastward to the Dead Sea.

In the west these ridges lead to the valleys of the Shephelah and beyond to Philistia
on the Coastal Plain. Passing through side valleys of the Shephelah from Aijalon to
Lachish, a diagonal route links major valleys and main sites which control these
valleys discussed below. As you read the following paragraph, compare Map 8-4 with
other maps listed and with the *SMA*. Find the main sites in each valley and also
approach routes into key centers in the hills. Try to understand Rehoboam's strategy
in creating supply depots and military installations at certain points.

In the north the great Aijalon Valley with its approaches to the Central Benjamin
Plateau has been a common theme in your studies (Maps 5-5, 7-3, 7-4, 7-1, 8-2 and

8-3). The Sorek Valley, while lacking a direct link to Jerusalem, nevertheless appeared in various events (Maps 5-5, 6-4 and 7-3). The Elah Valley is one of the Shephelah's main staging areas for attacks into the hills (Maps 5-5 and 7-5). In later studies the important area of Moresheth-gath, Mareshah and Lachish will be illustrated by Assyrian and Babylonian campaigns. Rehoboam chose this area as his southern flank in the Shephelah.

On the east and the south of Judah Rehoboam was satisfied with fortifications in the hills overlooking the Wilderness and guarding main approaches from the Negev. In the north no specific information on fortified sites is given in the Bible. This should not be surprising since the *battle for Benjamin* was still being waged. Both Shishak's campaign on the Central Benjamin Plateau and the mounting pressure from Israel to the north may have had something to do with this silence.

In summary, Judah was now entering a period when an organized government in Jerusalem had to take responsibility for security in the separate Kingdom of Judah. This meant careful consideration of approaches from all directions. Except for the Central Benjamin Plateau the Hill Country was secure. However, the Shephelah remained a source of deep concern for Rehoboam and for all later kings of Judah.

ABIJAH: JUDAH'S MILITARY THRUST INTO SOUTHERN ISRAEL VIA BETHEL

DISCUSSION AND REVIEW

Abijah's campaign into southern Israel should be reviewed on Map 8-4 in Chapter   8-4 b
Three. This operation was only possible because Judah maintained control of the Central Benjamin Plateau and its approaches from the Aijalon Valley. Considering her overall losses in Shishak's campaign, the natural direction for Judah to expand was to the north. This advance into southern Ephraim was a type of preemptive strike since Abijah knew that it was only a matter of time until Israel applied pressure on her from the same direction. However, Israel had other plans along the Coastal Highway which could have changed this situation.

ASA: JUDAH MEETS THE THREAT OF ZERAH THE ETHIOPIAN NEAR MARESHAH

DISCUSSION AND READING

At least two threats from the west of Judah concerned **Asa** during his reign. One was   8-4 d
a campaign by Israel, presumably against the Philistines at Gibbethon — near the Aijalon Valley. However, victory there not only would have strengthened Israel's hand along the Coastal Highway but also would have placed her in a better position to invade Judah via the Aijalon Valley and the Central Benjamin Plateau with all that this implies. This tactic is well-known to you from earlier campaigns by the Philistines and by Shishak of Egypt.

Fortunately for Judah the assassination of King Nadab, Jeroboam's son, by Baasha at Gibbethon (909 B.C.) took the pressure off Asa in Jerusalem. It would be years before Israel's new government organized another expedition in this northwest approach to the Shephelah.

The second threat to Judah came from the southwest corner of the Shephelah. It was   8-4 c
led by Zerah the Ethiopian. The origin of this Zerah is debated. Some feel that he is a pharaoh of the Twenty-second Libyan Dynasty in Egypt, while others are convinced

that he was the leader of a large bedouin force from southern Arabia. Whatever the choice the threat was the same — Judah's hold on the Shephelah was challenged. (The word *million* or *a thousand thousand* in the text should perhaps be translated *a thousand units* of fighting men.)

This time Asa had to organize a defense line near Mareshah and trust God to deliver Judah. The outcome of this confrontation can be read in **2 Chronicles 14.9-15**. The background of this story and of Asa's rule is found in the texts listed in the *SCS*. Gerar, an important site in the western Negev (not too far from Ziklag), can be seen by referring to Map 8-3.

MARKING

1. **Blue write-in**: On the W edge of the map, NW of Lachish = ZERAH THE ETHIO-PIAN (in two lines).

2. **Blue arrow**: Zerah's advance = From SW to the word Zerah.

3. **Green arrow**: Asa's defense = W from the box of Mareshah (½ cm./¼ in. long and pointing W).

4. **Red confrontation mark**: Just W of the green arrow just drawn = ✳

5. **Yellow HL with red circle around name** = Gerar.

6. **Flight (blue) and chase (green) arrows** = From the red confrontation mark in the general direction of Gerar (off the map).

REVIEW AND SUMMARY OF EVENTS TO 880 B. C.

The *battle for Benjamin* actively resumed a few years later. The final chapter in this conflict was discussed in Chapter Three. The sequence of events from this point on to the end of Asa's reign in Judah and Baasha's rule in Israel can be reviewed by rereading the last pages of Map 8-4 in Chapter Three and opening pages of Map 8-5 in Chapters Two and Three.

The half century from 930 B.C. to 880 B.C. drew to a close with Judah and Israel at a tie. Neither had gained much from the other, except that Judah had been able to hold the Central Benjamin Plateau while Israel appears to have incorporated Jericho into her southern flank. Diplomatic and military maneuvering had been hectic, and time was ripe for a reevaluation of the situation by both sides. With a new family ruling a united Northern Kingdom from 880 B.C. (the House of Omri), Judah decided to *bury the hatchet*. By the time Jehoshaphat came to the throne in Judah (872 B.C.), the way was paved for cooperation without unification. Thus Israel and Judah entered a new era of political and military collaboration which lasted for almost another half century, until the entire region fell apart in that fateful year, 841 B.C.

S M M   8 − 6

TITLE: ISRAEL'S AND JUDAH'S RELATIONS WITH MOAB AND EDOM

DATE: MID-9TH CENTURY B.C.

INTRODUCTION

The two decades before 841 B.C. were a rare period of cooperation between Israel and Judah. Alliances were sealed by marriages, and in military campaigns the kings of the two nations rode side by side. One of the benefits of this cooperation was that it allowed the two kingdoms to expand to the east and southeast into Transjordan. Israel controlled Gilead and Moab, while Judah dominated Edom and the Red Sea port of Ezion-geber.

The rising power of Damascus (the Arameans) could not tolerate this situation in Transjordan. Throughout the period there is growing confrontation between Israel/ Judah and Aram to the east and northeast of Beth-shan (Map 8-5). The Arameans also appear with the Moabites (and later with the Edomites) in some Biblical texts. It was only natural that Damascus encouraged rebellion in those areas. Anything that weakened Israel's and Judah's control along the Transjordanian Highway could only strengthen the position of Damascus and bring her closer to the realization of her expansionist policy.

The threat of Assyria in northern Mesopotamia shocked these local competing nations into a unified front in 853 B.C. (the Battle of Qarqar). In the months that followed, however, wars broke out again, ending in the death of Ahab, king of Israel. These events were discussed in Chapter Two. Rebellion in Moab and Edom developed during this period, coming to a head in the decade prior to 841 B.C.

MARKING

1. **Green border:** Judah's northern frontier = Copy this border from Map 8-3, but in a solid line (skipping over names). Shade in the S side of this line in green.

2. **Green write-in:** In the open area N of Beth-zur = JUDAH.

3. **Orange write-in:** In the open area E of Jericho = ISRAEL.

4. **Blue write-in:**
   a. In NE corner just W of Rabbath-ammon = AMMON.

   b. 2.5 cm./1 in. SE of Kir of Moab = MOAB with a blue box around it.

   c. 2.5 cm./1 in. E of Borzah = EDOM.

   d. On the W edge of the map, W of Adoraim = PHILISTINES with a black arrow pointing W.

5. **Brown write-in:**
   a. Between Tekoa and En-gedi = WILDERNESS.

   b. In the same position as on Map 8-1 = NAHAL ARNON (with arrow).

c. Just W of the word Edom = (MT. SEIR).

6. **Yellow HL on names = Jerusalem, Bethel, Jericho, En-gedi, Kir-hareseth, Dibon** (N of Nahal Arnon) and **Medeba.**

7. **Green box around name:** Capital city = **Jerusalem.**

8. **Blue box around name = Dibon.**

9. **Sweeping orange arrow** = From Bethel to Jericho.

AHAB: JERICHO REBUILT BY HIEL OF BETHEL

DISCUSSION AND READING

8-6 a The first hint of Israel's move toward Moab in Transjordan is in 1 Kings 16.34, *In his [Ahab's] days Hiel of Bethel built Jericho.* The importance of Jericho as a link to Moab from Bethel is indicated on Map 8-6. On Map 8-1 the greater context of this link between the Coastal Highway and the Transjordanian Highway can be seen, the Aphek-Bethel-Jericho-Medeba route. With the Central Benjamin Plateau in Judah's hands, this connection would have been Israel's main east-west trade route on her southern front. Other connections through the Rift (Jordan) Valley and Beth-shan were also important.

JEHOSHAPHAT: RULE AND EXPANSION

DISCUSSION AND READING

8-6 b The cooperation between Judah and Israel in the days of **Jehoshaphat** and **Ahab** allowed both men to develop the resources in their respective kingdoms. The afflu-
8-5 c ency of Israel has already been discussed in Chapter Two. A parallel high period in Judah in the decades prior to 841 B.C. is reflected in **2 Chronicles 17.1-18.1.**

The opening verses of 2 Chronicles 17 sound a note of caution, however, and recall
8-4 e the *battle of Benjamin* which raged earlier in that century. Jehoshaphat's alliance with Israel could not allow him to relax his hold on what had belonged to Ephraim before the reign of David. In this time of relative peace and prosperity Jehoshaphat did not want to lose what his father Asa had gained through a very expensive diplomatic maneuver.

> *Jehoshaphat . . . strengthened his position in regard to Israel. He stationed troops in all the fortified cities of Judah and established military camps both in the land of Judah proper and in the cities of Ephraim which his father Asa had siezed [on the Central Benjamin Plateau and along its northern approaches via Mizpah and Geba].*
> (2 Chronicles 17.1-2)

This short statement reflects much of what you studied under *Ephraim's Southern Flank* in Chapter Three (Map 6-7). Benjamin, which earlier had nearly been assimilated into Ephraim, was now in danger of being slowly absorbed into Judah. It continued to play its role as a local *Land Between.*

MESHA, KING OF MOAB, REVOLTS AGAINST ISRAEL

DISCUSSION

The wars between Damascus and Samaria sapped the strength of Israel. This was a 8-5 f h
signal to Moab that the time had come to make her move, no doubt with the encouragement of Damascus. The exact timing of this revolt is debated. The Bible simply 8-6 e
states in 2 Kings 1.1 that *following the death of Ahab, Moab rebelled against Israel.*
2 Kings 3.5 uses almost the same phrase. The inscription of Mesha, king of Moab
(The Moabite Stone), claims that Ahab was still alive when the rebellion was in progress. The question is how each writer defined a rebellion. Certainly there were
already undercurrents or even actions before Ahab died. The wars in Gilead between
Israel and Damascus would have given Moab a good reason to announce a liberation
movement. The death of Ahab just added fuel to the fire. After the death of Ahab,
Moab was finally lost to Israel.

The natural northern border of Moab was Nahal Arnon. North of it, beyond the
smaller plateau of Dibon, was the strategic Medeba Plateau. It was an area coveted by
Israel, Ammon and Moab. In addition to its important position on the Transjordanian Highway, it had been a natural staging area for Israel's original entry into the country and could serve the same purpose for Ammon and Moab (Maps 5-2, 5-3, 6-1 and
6-7). Earlier in this chapter Jephthah contended with Ammon over the region both 6-6 c
in debates and in actions. Dibon served as Moab's forward position, a natural springboard for an advance on to the Medeba Plateau.

Most of the detailed geographical information about this revolt comes from the 8-6 c
famous *Moabite Stone* found near Dibon in 1878. This information will be represented by the following marking. If a copy of *ANET* or *ANE* is available, the pages
on which it can be found are noted in *SCS* 8-6 c under *Primary Sources*. (A biblio-
graphical note on these works appears in the opening pages of the *SMM*.)

MARKING

1. **Red on dot**: Names mentioned on the Moabite Stone as having been captured,
   destroyed or rebuilt by Mesha, king of Moab =
   a. All red names N of Nahal Arnon.

   b. **Hauronen/Horonaim** (SW of Kir-hareseth).

2. **Yellow HL on route** = From Kir-hareseth to Medeba.

3. **Sweeping blue arrow** =
   a. From the blue box around Moab N to Aroer (one point) plus a branch from near
      Aroer to Jahaz (another point).

   b. From Dibon to Medeba.

   c. From Medeba to Nebo, to Beth-baal-meon and to Bezer (three arrows).

4. **Blue border**: Moab's new border = From the NE corner of the Dead Sea NE and
   then E to the E edge of the map (passing just N of Nebo and Bezer). Shade in the S
   side of this line.

5. **Orange border**: Israel's E border = From N of Bezer (Moab's border) N to the N edge of the map running under the word Ammon. Shade in the W side of this line.

6. **Sweeping orange arrow**: Possible Israelite counter-attack alluded to in the Moabite Stone = From the word Israel to Jahaz (passing just SW of Bezer).

ISRAEL AND JUDAH JOIN IN A CAMPAIGN AGAINST MOAB

DISCUSSION AND READING

The gory details of Moab's rebellion are provided by the Moabite Stone. At Nebo (in the vicinity where Moses earlier had warned the Israelites of such attacks), *seven thousand men, boys, women, girls and maid-servants* were killed or offered to Chemosh, the god of Moab. These terrible events are summed up by Mesha's statement, *I have triumphed over him [the king of Israel] and over his house, while Israel has perished forever!*

8-6 d   Around 850 B.C. Israel and Judah jointly responded to Moab's rebellion. Their campaign is described in detail in **2 Kings 3.4-27** with only a brief mention of the revolt itself. Try to work out this campaign on Map 8-6 before doing the marking below. (The forces of Israel and Judah approached Moab from its *back door*, probably via Arad in the Negev, the *way which leads to Edom* mentioned in 2 Kings 3.20).

MARKING

1. **Yellow HL on route** = From Jerusalem to Kir-hareseth via Hebron, Arad, Zoar and near Hauronen/Horonaim (where Mesha claimed a later victory). The *Wilderness of Edom* mentioned in 2 Kings 3.9 may mean the area south of the Dead Sea or simply the Wilderness which is on the way to Edom.

2. **Sweeping orange and green parallel arrows and write-in**: Israel/Judah march to Moab =
   a. E of the Ziph-Arad route and curving SE with room to write in JEHOSHAPHAT (in green on green arrow) and J(EH)ORAM (in orange on orange arrow).

   b. From just NE of Zoar curving around via Hauronen and pointing N to Kir-hareseth (with no write-in).

3. **Sweeping blue arrow**: Edom's contingent which apparently was forced by Judah to join against Moab = From Edom N and then parallel with the orange and green arrows pointing to Kir-hareseth.

4. **Red circle around name** = Kir-hareseth/Kir of Moab.

MOAB'S CAMPAIGN AGAINST JUDAH VIA EN-GEDI

DISCUSSION

8-6 d   Judah's decision to march with Israel against Moab must have tested Israel-Judah relations. Jehoshaphat, after all, was a descendant of Ruth the Moabitess. His hesitancy is reflected in the straightforward question put to him by **Jehoram**, king of Israel, in 2 Kings 3.6. To show his support Jehoshaphat even pressed Edom into the battle, probably against her will. Together, Israel, Judah and Edom conquered the territory of Moab but withdrew after their siege of Kir-hareseth failed.

Moab's response to what she regarded as Judah's treachery came quickly. Probably in the same year (850 B.C.), she mobilized her allies in Transjordan and attacked Judah. The people listed as her allies are interesting. First were the Ammonites with whom Moab now had a common border. With Israel's decline in Transjordan their hopes were raised for better times. An attack on part of the Israel-Judah alliance would serve them well.   8-6 e

To this Moabite/Ammonite force, 2 Chronicles 20.1 adds *some of the Meunites* (This reading from the Greek version is preferred to avoid a repetition of the word *Ammonites* in the original Hebrew. A simple correction in the Hebrew allows this reading.) It is thought that the Meunites came from the area of Maan on the eastern edge of Edom. (Maan can be seen on Map 13.2, southeast of Petra.) These Meunite troops may represent the men from *Mt. Seir* (a general name for the high plateau of Edom) rather than actual Edomites (2 Chronicles 20.10, 22 and 23). There is also the possibility that some Edomites actually did join this Moabite expedition since a few years later, shortly after the death of Jehoshaphat, an Edomite revolt liberated them from Judah.   8-6 f

The attack on Judah designed by Moab is another example of Judah's preparing for battle and then trusting God. Although it was Israel who had initiated the original operation against Moab, she did not come to Judah's aid now. Jehoshaphat was left to his own resources.   8-6 e

In this operation Moab and her allies employed the same tactics which Israel and Judah had used earlier. They came by a *back door* via En-gedi on the shores of the Dead Sea and the edge of the Wilderness. There by the same springs which David had enjoyed in his flight from Saul, Moabites, Ammonites and men from Mt. Seir organized their next step. It appears that the discussion turned into a war of words and finally turned into armed conflict. The forces which had been mobilized to attack Judah spent themselves fighting with each other, a phenomenon not uncommon in the Middle East. When the fight was over, Judah was left with abundant booty without even having engaged the enemy.

The road from En-gedi to Tekoa and Bethlehem (on which the captured spoil was carried) is not difficult except for the lack of water in the Wilderness and the initial ascent above En-gedi itself, called in this story *The Ascent of Ziz.* It climbs over 550 meters/1800 feet in less than one kilometer/one half mile. This steep ascent is due to a major geological fault which runs along the western side of the Dead Sea. Once above this escarpment the route levels off, leading northwest above the great Nahal Arugot to the Wilderness of Tekoa and on to Bethlehem and the ridge route to Jerusalem. These features can be seen on Maps 1-14 and 13-4 as well as on the *SMA.*

READING
With this background in mind read **2 Chronicles 20.1-30.** The marking below helps to create the setting of this unusual *back door* attack on Judah.

MARKING
1. **Yellow HL on route** = From Bethlehem to Kir-hareseth via En-gedi and crossing the narrowest part of the Dead Sea (very shallow or even dry at times).

2. **Sweeping blue arrow and write-in**: The advance of the Moabite campaign = From Kir-hareseth along highlighted route to En-gedi. On this arrow write in MOAB, AMMON, MEN OF MT. SEIR.

3. **Sweeping green arrow and write-in**: Jehoshaphat's defense forces with *choir* in front = From Jerusalem to En-gedi. On this arrow write in JEHOSHAPHAT.

4. **Red circle around name**: Transjordanian *summit meeting* which ended in self-destruction = **En-gedi.**

JEHORAM: RULE AND EDOMITE REVOLT

DISCUSSION

Jehoshaphat died in 848 B.C. after a short co-regency with his son **Jehoram**. The ascension of Jehoram meant that the king of Israel and the king of Judah in this brief period had the same name. (Jehoram and Joram are the same name in two different forms.) The two kings were also related by a marriage arranged earlier between Ahab and Jehoshaphat. Jehoram of Judah was married to Ahab's daughter (or adopted daughter) Athaliah.

8-6 f   Jehoram of Judah added to the confusion and in-fighting of this decade prior to 841 B.C. His actions and those of Athaliah, his wife, brought intense strife into the royal family and apostasy to Jerusalem. The writer of 2 Chronicles 21.6 sums it up when he says that *he [Jehoram of Judah] followed the paths of the kings of Israel, just as the House of Ahab had done, for the daughter of Ahab [Athaliah] was his wife.* The situation was so bad that the Biblical writer uses it to point out God's faithfulness to the House of David in spite of Jehoram's actions (2 Chronicles 21.7). Following the momentous events of 841 B.C. this same Athaliah, as queen of Judah, attempted to establish the worship of Baal in Jerusalem itself as her mother Jezebel had done in Israel earlier in that century. This, however, is the subject of Map 9-1.

The internal strife in Jerusalem and the successful revolt of Moab from Israel were not the final chapters in the story of these decades prior to 841 B.C. Sometime after Jehoram took full responsibility for Judah (after 848 B.C., the date when Jehoshaphat died), Edom rebelled. About the same time Libnah on the edge of Philistia also revolted. These revolts were followed by Jehoram's campaign against Edom (which failed) and by campaigns against Judah from the southeast (Edom), from the west (the Philistines) and from the south (*the Arabs near Ethiopia*). The latter were probably bedouin tribes like the Amalekites. It is difficult to imagine that only a decade or so after Jehoshaphat had received *presents and tribute in silver* from the Philistines and *seven thousand seven hundred rams and seven thousand seven hundred male goats* from the Arabians, Judah was again under siege by these same forces.

MARKING

1. **Red confrontation mark**: Between Zoar (Zair?) S of the Dead Sea and Feifa = ✳

2. **Sweeping green arrow and green write-in**: Judah's campaign to recover control of Edom = From a point 5 cm./1 in. SE of Ramoth of the Negev, curving along the S side of the highlighted route to the confrontation mark just drawn. Along this arrow write (green) J(EH)ORAM.

3. **Sweeping blue arrow**: Edom's advance to meet Judah = From the region of Bozrah W along the S edge of the map and curving around to the N and on to the red confrontation mark.

4. **Black write-in**: By red confrontation mark = 2 KINGS 8.20-22 (small caps).

READING
Read both **2 Kings 8.16-22** and **2 Chronicles 21** noting geographical information discussed above and marked on Map 8-6.

CONCLUDING DISCUSSION OF EVENTS UP TO 841 B.C.

The period between 853 and 841 B.C. saw the decline of Israel's and Judah's power which had characterized Ahab's and Jehoshaphat's rules. See-saw battles between Moab and Israel/Judah had ended in a draw — except that Moab maintained its independence, and Israel lost one of its main sources of trade along the Transjordanian Highway.

For her part Judah's rapid decline cost her the important region of Edom (with the Red Sea port of Ezion-geber) and parts of the Shephelah. It appears that she was able to hold on to the Negev, but her southern flank came under great pressure from the Arabians. At one point an invasion reached Jerusalem itself (2 Chronicles 21.16-17).

The worst, however, was yet to come. Israel's losses left a certain military strongman and his troops very discontent. All he needed was the blessing of *one of the sons of the prophets* to push him into action. In an over-reaction to his times, he destroyed kings, administrative officials and international alliances. What was left was no match for the new strongman on the throne of Damascus who had waited for this moment. Thus began the reigns of **Jehu** of Israel and Hazael of Damascus, amidst threats from Shalmaneser III of Assyria. These events can be reviewed by rereading *SCS* 8-7 d in Chapter Two.   8-7 d

Athaliah, daughter of Ahab and Jezebel and wife of the late king Jehoram (killed by Jehu), came to the throne in Judah in that same year, 841 B.C.

S M M   9 – 1/2

TITLE: INTERNAL POLITICS AND WARS PRIOR TO MAJOR ASSYRIAN INVASIONS (NORTH) on 9-1 and (SOUTH) on 9-2. (On Map 9-1 do not write in the top left corner above the section number.)

DATE   841-734 B.C.

INTRODUCTION
The dates above and the topics listed in *SCS* 9-1/2 reveal that these maps serve as a *catch-all* for more than a century of history. The two maps complement each other since Map 9-1 presents the north of the country and 9-2 the south.

While the events of this century are important in your study, none of them contains enough geographical detail to merit a separate map in the *SMM*. Therefore, the objectives of the paragraphs below are to sort out this century's events, establish priorites of the various nations represented and complete selected marking on the maps themselves.

A convenient and simplified division of the *SCS* topics covered on this map are as follows:

840-800 B.C. Aramean (Syrian) oppression under Hazael   9-1 c-e

800-740 B.C. The revival and decline of Israel and Judah   9-1/2 e-i

740-734 B.C. The league between Aram (Syria) and Israel   9-1 j
                  against Judah

The *players* for this century of change will now be put on the *board*.

MARKING (On Map 9-1)
1. **Yellow HL on routes:**
    a. The International Coastal Highway and northern approach from Damascus (route printed in red) = From the SW corner of the map, both branches of the highway printed in red, and then N via Aphek, Megiddo, Hazor, Dan and to the NE corner of the map, plus the small section N of Abel-beth-maachah. Also HL the Megiddo-Hannathon-Hazor route around Gath-hepher. (This connection is printed in black).

    b. The Megiddo—Beth-shan connection (via Ophrah) and then to the E off the map (via Lo-debar and Beth-arbel) and also NE from Lo-debar toward Karnaim passing near (Lower) Aphek.

    c. The Transjordanian Highway (printed in red) from the S edge of the map (by Kir-hareseth) N off the map (via Medeba and Rabbath-ammon).

    d. From Heshbon near Medeba on the Transjordanian Highway to Gittaim on the International Coastal Highway via Jericho, Ramah, Gibeon, Beth-horon and Gezer.

    e. From Gath of the Philistines to Jericho via Azekah, Bethlehem and Jerusalem (on the E to Jericho from Jerusalem).

    f. Connecting route from Jerusalem to Ramah.

    g. From Azekah to Gibeon via Beth-shemesh and the Aijalon-Gibeon route.

2. **Yellow HL on name = Jerusalem, Rabbath-ammon, Damascus, Tyre** and **Samaria.**

3. **Red write-in on yellow background:** Just E of Dan = **Lebo-hamath** with black arrow pointing N off the map. HL first and then write in the name (not in caps) with a red ball point pen.

4. **Green write-in with green box:** Between Bethlehem and Hebron = JUDAH (with green box around it).

5. **Orange write-in with orange box** S of Samaria = ISRAEL.

6. **Blue write-in with blue box around each name**:

   a. In the SW corner of the map by map number = EGYPT (with black arrow to SW).

   b. S of Ashdod = PHILISTINES.

   c. Between Tyre and Achzib on a straight line with part written in the sea area = PHOENICIANS.

   d. S of Damascus and W of Karnaim = ARAM.

   e. Just W of Rabbath-ammon = AMMON.

   f. Spread across the Nahal Arnon in the open area between Dibon and Madmen = MOAB.

7. **Brown write-in**:

   a. In the same location as on Map 8-1 = NAHAL ARNON (with arrow), NAHAL YARMUK (with arrow) and GILEAD.

   b. On the E edge of the map, just below the *B* in the printed map title = BASHAN with black arrow pointing NE.

840-800 B.C.: ARAMEAN (SYRIAN) OPPRESSION UNDER HAZAEL

DISCUSSION AND READING

The background of events in the north during this difficult period was discussed in Chapter Two and in Chapter Three. If necessary, these discussions should be reviewed now by consulting the *Index* at the end of the *Guide*. 8-7 d e 9-1 d

Temporary relief from Assyria meant that Hazael of Damascus could take advantage of Israel's weak position. Jehu, who may have been concerned about the lack of leadership in the nation during Moab's earlier revolt, lived to see the Israel he ruled invaded and overrun.

Meanwhile civil strife in Jerusalem (due to Athaliah's takeover and demise) was also having its effect on Judah's ability to resist threats from the outside. Details on this period in Judah (840-800 B.C.) should now be skimmed in **2 Kings 11 and 12**. At the end of this passage note Hazael's attack on Gath, either Gath of the Philistines or Gittaim (meaning *two Gaths*) to the north. Once one of these two positions west of Jerusalem was controlled by Hazael, the city was open to him, either by way of the Aijalon Valley and the Central Benjamin Plateau or via the Elah Valley and Bethlehem. **2 Chronicles 24.23-24** tells the rest of the story. The year was about 813 B.C. 9-1 c

The constant pressure from Hazael not only reached the International Coastal Highway and the western approaches to Jerusalem. It also fulfilled the dream of Damascus — control of the Transjordanian Highway. During that long ninth century its leaders had no doubt encouraged liberation movements in Moab and even in Edom. In Moab's *back door* campaign via En-gedi the attack is said to be coming *from Aram* (not *Edom*, as some propose to translate 2 Chronicles 20.2). Thus, as Hazael increased his control 9-1 d over the country in the late ninth century (especially after 815 B.C.), it is not surprising to find him campaigning along the Transjordanian Highway to the Medeba Plateau and south to Nahal Arnon.   With the Medeba Plateau in his control Hazael was in a position to dominate Moab proper.   The Moabites who had fought to gain their independence from Israel and to settle north of the Nahal Arnon either had an agreement with Damascus or were in for a surprise from their former ally. Their cities, as reflected by later prophets, are printed in black on the Medeba Plateau.

> *During that period the Lord began to trim off parts of Israel. Hazael*
> *attacked Israel's borders from every angle east of the Jordan: throughout*
> *the land of Gilead [comprising the territory of] Gad, Reuben and*
> *Manasseh, even from Aroer on the edge of Nahal Arnon [in the south]*
> *to Gilead and [beyond Nahal Yarmuk] to Bashan [in the north].*
> (2 Kings 10.32-33)

Jehu died in the midst of this difficult period (814 B.C.). The Bible tells us that his son **Jehoahaz** also experienced the wrath of Hazael (2 Kings 13.1-9, 22-23).

MARKING (Map 9-1)

1. **Yellow HL on name with red circle around name**:
   a. Above Nahal Arnon = **Aroer.**

   b. **Gath of the Philistines.** Although it is not known which Gath is intended (Gath of the Philistines or Gittaim/Gath farther north), for the sake of simplicity of marking the former has been chosen.)

2. **Red underlining of name or on dot**: Archeological evidence of the destruction of Level VII at this site during this period = Underline **Hazor** (**Level VII** in parentheses can be added in black under the name Hazor) and red on dot of **Jerusalem** (attack from west by forces of Damascus in 2 Kings 12.17-18 and 2 Chronicles 24.23-24).

3. **Sweeping blue arrow and write-in** (skipping over names, but crossing the route when necessary): Hazael's penetration along the major highways of the country (using a solid-tipped arrow for emphasis) =
   a. From the box around Aram (Syria) to Gath of the Philistines by way of Hazor, Megiddo (avoiding Gath-hepher), Aphek and Gibbethon.

   b. From the box of Aram (Syria) to Aroer above Nahal Arnon, keeping to the E side of the map, skipping Karnaim, running along the Transjordanian Highway, W of Ammon and between Bezer and Heshbon, the cities on the Medeba Plateau.

   c. On each of the blue arrows just drawn = HAZAEL (blue). In black add **815-810 B.C.** (in parentheses) by the word Hazael and write the letters *c* and *d* in small circles by Gath and Aroer to indicate the topics in the *SCS*.

DISCUSSION

Map 9-1 now shows vividly the depth of Aramean (Syrian) penetration into the country. The blue arrow represents the complete reversal of David's campaigns (Map 7-7) and Solomon's fortifications (Gezer, Megiddo and Hazor on Map 7-1). However, the principle was the same: If you controlled these two highways, then the rest of the country was yours.

The implications of these events for Judah were serious indeed. With Aramean forces dominating her western approaches (the Aijalon and/or the Elah Valleys) and the Medeba Plateau (a staging area for an attack on Jericho), the takeover of the Central Benjamin Plateau was possible, if not imminent. This was a natural next step in any plan to subject the central Hill Country and Jerusalem.

Under Joshua the Israelites themselves had entered the country via the Medeba Plateau and Jericho (Maps 5-3 and 5-5). Moab had used this approach to dominate Israel from Jericho during the period of the Judges (marked on Map 6-7). While the Moabite independence movement under Mesha in the mid-eighth century had brought Moabite settlements to this plateau (Map 8-6), they do not appear to have been used as a base against Israel or Judah.   5-3 a c   6-7 a   8-6 c

With the arrival of the troops of Hazael on the Medeba Plateau, a new threat had developed which was far worse than Moabite settlements. Coupled with Aramean control along the International Coastal Highway, this created the possibility of an Aramean thrust into the heart of northern Judah and southern Israel. It must have caused deep concern both in Jerusalem and in Samaria.   9-1 d

During these trying years it appeared that nothing could break Hazael's hold on the country. Fortunately, about this time Assyria began to stir again. Adad-nirari III came to power in 811 B.C. and soon organized a new campaign west of the Euphrates River. Two of his own inscriptions speak for themselves. The year was 806 B.C.   9-1 e

> *In the fifth year [of my official rule] I sat down solemnly on my royal*
> *throne and called up the country [for war]. I ordered the numerous army*
> *of Assyria to march against Palestine. I crossed the Euphrates at its flood . . .*
> *I surrounded . . . Damascus . . . .*   (Sabaa Stela)

> *I shut up . . . the king of Damascus in Damascus, his royal residence.*
> *The terror-inspiring glamour of Ahsur [the chief god of the Assyrian*
> *pantheon] overwhelmed him, and he seized my feet, assuming the posi-*
> *tion of a slave. I received in his palace of Damascus, his royal residence,*
> *2,300 talents of silver [corresponding to] 20 talents of gold, 5,000 talents*
> *of iron, garments of linen with multi-colored trimmings, a bed [inlaid]*
> *with ivory, a 'nimattu' couch mounted and inlaid with ivory, [and]*
> *countless [other objects being] his possessions.*   (Stone Slab from Calah)

The Assyrian king also boasted that he conquered *Tyre, Sidon, Israel, Edom, Palestine as far as the shore of the Great Sea of the Setting Sun* and *made them submit all to my feet, imposing upon them tribute.*

Although these kingdoms paid tribute to Assyria for the next few decades (for example, *Joash the Samarian* in 796 B.C.), they did not bear the brunt of the cruel Assyrian army as Damascus had done. One could say that the Assyrian campaign was both *bad news and good news.* Their arrival in the area was regarded as a type of salvation from Hazael (2 Kings 13.5) — the best evidence of any to illustrate how difficult life was under Damascus toward the end of the ninth century B.C.

MARKING
1. **Blue write-in in blue box**: In the very top left-hand corner of the map above section number = ASSYRIA, ADAD-NIRARI III (in two lines and all caps).

2. **Black write-in in blue box** = Between the section number and the printed title (at very N edge of the page) = **806 B.C.**

3. **Sweeping blue arrow** = From the first blue box drawn, skipping over the second blue box (date) and pointing to the arrow of Damascus. Make this a bold blue arrow with a larger solid tip.

800-740 B.C.: THE REVIVAL AND DECLINE OF ISRAEL AND JUDAH

DISCUSSION AND READING

During the first half of the eighth century B.C. Assyria again became involved in matters at home and in wars with her northern neighbor, Urartu. Damascus rose again but was kept busy defending herself against two of her neighbors, Israel in the south and Hamath in the north. Under these improved conditions Israel and Judah regained their strength and began to expand.

Beginnings were slow, but even the prophet Elisha on his death bed was able to see better days ahead. In the light of Hazael's earlier oppression (through which Elisha had lived) and considering the fact that Israel had not gone out to battle for almost half a century (according to our records), Elisha's object lesson in **2 Kings 13.14-19** is very significant indeed.

9-1 e   It was **Jehoash (Joash)**, grandson of Jehu, who was told by the elderly Elisha to shoot toward the east and to *beat* arrows on the ground. Only the king lived to see this object lesson fulfilled in about 790 B.C.

> *When Hazael, king of Aram, died, his son Ben-hadad [a common name for the king of Damascus] succeeded him. Jehoash, the son of Jehoahaz, then took back from Ben-hadad, Hazael's son, the cities which he [Hazael] had seized from his father Jehoahaz in [earlier] wars. Three times Joash [Jehoash] beat him and thereby recovered Israel's cities.*   (2 Kings 13.24-25)

DISCUSSION

During these decades of expansion (prior to the major Assyrian campaigns which ruined the country), Israel and Judah experienced a remarkable recovery. There is little or no evidence that cooperation (like that which characterized the reigns of Ahab and Jehoshaphat a century before) existed between them. Although their parallel growth occurred in that same *lull before the storm,* their foreign policies were, by and large, independent of each other. One reason may lie in the fact that they did not need each other. Israel had recuperated from Jehu's radical revolution, and the threat of Damascus had been removed. The nation had again become both respectable and independent. While Israel was preoccupied with rebuilding the north, Judah was able to concentrate on matters in the south and in the west. Thus the climate was right for independent growth without infringing on each other's priorities.

9-1 g   The only exception to this policy of *laissez-faire* came after Judah (with Benjamin!) returned from Edom where she had conquered the stronghold of Sela/Joktheel and crushed all resistance to her rule. In his triumph **Amaziah** foolishly challenged J(eh)oash of Israel in order to parade his comeback. In reading the context of this campaign during the reign of Amaziah it is not difficult to perceive his method of *kingdom-building* in Jerusalem.

In the story are interesting hints of strategic regions you have already studied. These include the mention of the tribe of Benjamin, the region of Beth-horon and the area of Beth-shemesh. Amaziah's triumph was soon turned into his ruin — and with it the sacking of Jerusalem, his capital. This event may reflect Israel's continuing interest in the Central Benjamin Plateau, although it should be remembered that Israel did not enter the conflict on her own initiative.

Read the details of this episode in Judah-Israel relations in **2 Chronicles 25**. Some important details are added in **2 Kings 14.7-14**. You may want to complete the following marking before reading these passages.

MARKING (All on Map 9-2 unless otherwise specified)
1. **Transfer all relevant marking** from Map 9-1 to Map 9-2. Reposition certain names (like Judah) if necessary. Draw boxes, circles and arrows, highlight names and write in any other information possible. Routes are highlighted below.

2. **Additional blue write-in**: On the high Transjordanian Plateau SE of Bozrah and NE of Teman = EDOM (in large caps with box around the name).

3. **Yellow HL on route**:
   a. All routes printed in red. Note the Transjordanian Highway on the high plateau (Mt. Seir) which reaches elevations of 1500 meters/or 5000 feet above the Rift Valley to the west.

   b. The route from Elath to Kadesh-barnea, Beer-sheba in the Negev, Hebron and N off the map.

   c. The route from the road just highlighted via Kuntilet Ajrud W toward Egypt.

   d. The route from Hebron to Tamar via Arad. Continue S from the crossroads just E of Tamar to Elath.

4. **Yellow HL on name**:
   a. Along the Transjordanian Highway = **Aroer** (already highlighted), **Kerioth. Bozrah, Sela/Joktheel, Teman** and **Elath**. Also HL **Kerioth** on Map 9-1.

   b. Along the International Coastal Highway = **Gaza** and **Ashkelon**. On Map 9-1 HL these same names plus **Ashdod** and **Ekron**.

   c. In the Shephelah and the Negev = **Lachish** and **Beer-sheba** (on Maps 9-1 and 9-2) and **Beth-shemesh** (on Map 9-1).

5. **Brown write-in in red circle**: In the plain (Aravah) S of the Dead Sea (S of the swamps) = VALLEY OF SALT (three lines) with a red circle around it.

6. **Sweeping green arrow and write-in**:
   a. From Arad in the Negev (located at the crossroads) to the red circle.

b. From the red circle via Ir Nahash ascending NE and pointing toward Bozrah.

c. On the first arrow drawn above = AMAZIAH (green).   In black add *g* in a small circle to represent the topic in the *SCS*.

7. **Red on dot** (only on Map 9-1): Confrontation between Israel and Judah after Amaziah's victory in Edom = **Beth-shemesh**.   In black add the letter *g* by Beth-shemesh to indicate the topic in the *SCS*.

MARKING (Map 9-1)

1. **Yellow HL on name**: On the E shore of the Sea of Galilee = **Aphek**.   The word *(Lower) Aphek* indicates the probable site of the Aphek mentioned in 2 Kings 13.17.   The name itself is preserved in a modern village (Fiq) seven kilometers or four miles farther east on the edge of the Golan Heights (on Maps 8-5 and 1-8 and on the *SMA*).   Some have termed this higher site *(Upper) Aphek*.

2. **Red on dot = Aphek.**

3. **Broken but sweeping orange arrow and write-in**:
   a. The advance of J(eh)oash against Ben-hadad of Damascus = From the region of Beth-shan NE and pointing to Aphek.   Under this arrow = J(EH)OASH (orange).   In black write in **(About 790 B.C.)** under the word J(eh)oash and the letter *e* in a small circle by Aphek to indicate the topic in the *SCS*.

   b. J(eh)oash meets Amaziah's challenge at Beth-shemesh after which he sacks Jerusalem = From the box of Samaria toward Beth-shemesh.   On this arrow = J(EH)OASH (orange).

DISCUSSION

The northern thrust marked on Map 9-1 above was part of a larger trend toward expansion which developed in the early eighth century both in Israel and in Judah.   In Israel it began with J(eh)oash and culminated in **Jeroboam II** (so designated as to distinguish him from Jeroboam, son of Nebat, who originally declared political and religious independence from Jerusalem).   In Judah this period of reconstruction began with Amaziah and reached a peak in the reign of **Uzziah** (or **Azariah** as he is sometimes called).

9-1 e

9-1/2 i

Under these two kings, Jeroboam II and Uzziah, Israel and Judah once again expanded to include much of what was contained in the kingdom of David and Solomon.   In the north the Samaria-based monarchy pressed far beyond the limit of Israelite settlement in Galilee.   Areas like Ramoth-gilead (which had been so bitterly fought over in the days of Ahab) and Karnaim were under Israelite control (the northern Transjordanian plateau east of Beth-shan, the Sea of Galilee and Hazor).   Samaria's rule even reached beyond these areas to the east and to the north — including the city and the territory of Damascus itself!   The borders of Israel touched those of Hamath, the kingdom which earlier threatened Damascus from the north.

In its description of this border the Bible mentions a place about one hundred kilometers or sixty miles north of Damascus called *Lebo-hamath*.   This is probably the name of a city in the great Rift Valley (between the Lebanon and Anti-Lebanon mountain ranges) rather than a geographical term, which some translate as *the entrance of Hamath*.   Lebo-hamath is part of Canaan's northern border (Numbers 34.8).   People from Lebo-hamath, the northern limit of Solomon's absolute rule, attended the king's dedication of the Temple in Jerusalem (1 Kings 8.65).   Even Ezekiel, who lived two centuries after the time of Jeroboam II, considered Lebo-hamath as the northern border of the kingdom he described (Ezekiel 47.15).   It was there that he began his list of Israelite tribal territories (Ezekiel 48.1).

All of this points to the remarkable situation which developed during the reign of Jeroboam II.   The mention of Lebo-hamath indicates that the kingdom of Jeroboam II reached a zenith beyond all other Samaria-based monarchies.   The extent of its influence was rivaled only by the *United Monarchy* under David and Solomon.

MARKING (Map 9-1)
1. **Yellow HL on name** = **Lo-debar** and **Karnaim**.

2. **Red on dot or arrow:** Israel's campaigns alluded to in the Bible = **Lo-debar, Karnaim, Damascus** and **Lebo-hamath.**

3. **Sweeping orange arrows**: A symbolic representation of Israel's expansion during this unusual period (using a solid tipped arrow for emphasis) =
   a. From the region of Samaria to Lo-debar (via Tirzah).

   b. From Lo-debar to Karnaim.

   c. From Karnaim to Damascus.

   d. From Damascus to Lebo-hamath.

   e. From the region of Samaria to Ijon via Jezreel, Chinnereth and Hazor.

4. **Orange and black write-in** on arrows *c* and *e* above = JEROBOAM II (orange).   In black add **(From 780 B.C.)** by the word Jeroboam II and write the letter *e* in a small circle to indicate the topic in the *SCS*.

DISCUSSION, READING AND MARKING (Map 9-1)
With this preparation you are now ready to read the short description of this period in Israel's history in **2 Kings 14.23-29.**   Note the name of the prophet Jonah in this passage.   He lived in the north during this period of affluency.   From his home in Gath-hepher he was not very excited about going on a mission to save Nineveh, the capital of Assyria!   In the context of these times, a quick reading of the **book of Jonah** is   9-1 e
very enlightening.   It speaks of one of the Bible's great examples of repentance, one which would lead to the subsequent restoration of the terrible nation feared by both Israel and Judah, as well as by all other powers in the region.   **In yellow highlight Gath-hepher and in black write Jonah** in parentheses under the city name.

The preaching and teaching of Amos and Hosea occurred toward the end of this period when Israel was in full bloom.   Such passages from these prophets give much more information about this period than do the historical books of the Bible.   **Amos 6** and **Hosea 10-11** characterize the apostasy and the lack of social concern which resulted from this season of prosperity.

Also read **Amos 1.1-2.8** with Maps 9-1/2 in view. As you read and refer to these maps, locate the position of any nation or city mentioned in this passage. Like Damascus, Beth-eden was an Aramean city-state (in Mesopotamia beyond the Euphrates River). According to Amos, Kir was another location in Mesopotamia from which the Arameans (Syrians) had come (Amos 9.7) and to which they would return in bondage to Assyria (Amos 2.5). This opening statement from the prophet Amos summarizes conditions in the country during the difficult late ninth century and on through the eighth century B.C.

These prophets (like Jonah) were aware that the respite from Assyria would not last forever. Their severe words to Israel were expressions of deep concern from minds and hearts which knew their times. As suggested in Chapter Three, a reading of these prophets in the context of the mid-eighth century B.C. can be a rewarding experience. Since Amos came from **Tekoa** in Judah, **highlight the name in yellow and add the name Amos in black** below it in parentheses.

DISCUSSION AND READING
The expansion and resulting affluency of Israel was matched by a similar growth in Judah, both in the west (Philistia) and to the south (the Negev, Edom and Elath on the Red Sea). To the east it is not known who controlled the Transjordanian Highway (Israel or Judah), but the Bible states that *the Ammonites paid tribute to Uzziah* (2 Chronicles 26.8).

The rise of Judah in this period can be attributed to three factors. First, the pressure from Damascus which had reached Jerusalem and its approaches was gone. Secondly, Israel's concerns, by and large, were in the north where her cities and defenses had to be rebuilt after the invasions of Hazael. This meant that the northern approaches to Judah were not under the threat of attack. Thirdly, Egypt at this time was not able to extend her control over the routes south and west of Judah, leaving Judah free to expand in those directions.

The combination of these elements resulted in the development of a strong and prosperous Judah, one which you can read about in **2 Chronicles 26**. It speaks of the rule of the young king Uzziah, who continued the process of enlarging Judah after the assassination of his father, Amaziah.

Archeological evidence from this period, especially in the south of the country, presents a picture of Judah's strong control of important routes and regions. This reflects the same situation as was seen in the days of Solomon (Maps 7-1/2). Thus, both historical and archeological sources reflect Judah's relative greatness in the mid-eighth century B.C.

MARKING (Maps 9-1 and 9-2 where appropriate)
1. **Green on dot**: A known Judean fortress = **Beer-sheba, Aroer, Arad** (near Aroer), **En-gedi, Tamar** and **Kunilet Ajrud** (SW part of Map 9-2).

2. **Green solid square on dot**: A known major Judean fortress in Judah = **Lachish, Arad** (the eastern Arad), **Ramoth** of the Negev, **Kadesh-barnea, Hazar-addar, Ezion-geber.** (Questioned sites should be referred to by their archeological names found under *Modern Name* in the *Index of Main Names* at the end of the *SMM*.)

3. **Green write-in**: In the same position as on Map 7-2 = ISRAELITE AGRICULTUR-
   AL SETTLEMENTS AND FORTRESSES (only on Map 9-2).

4. **Yellow HL on name** = **Joppa** and **Jabneh**.

5. **Sweeping green arrows and green write-in**: Uzziah's expansion beyond the Negev
   in the south and to the International Coastal Highway in the west =
   a. From the word Judah one arrow to the SE and one arrow to the SW (via Beer-
      sheba toward Kadesh-barnea). In green on the second arrow drawn add UZZIAH
      (Map 9-2).

   b. From the region of Ekron to Joppa (Map 9-1).

   c. From the region of Ekron to Jabneh (Map 9-1).

   d. From the region of Gath to Ashdod (Map 9-1).

6. **Black write-in**: By the point of the arrow to Joppa (Map 9-1) and by the word
   Uzziah (Map 9-2) = the letter **i** in a small circle to indicate the topic in the *SCS*.

7. **Yellow HL on write-in** (optional) = You may want to emphasize the expansion
   under **Jeroboam II** and **Uzziah** by highlighting these two names you wrote in on
   Maps 9-1 and 9-2

DISCUSSION

The rapid decline of Israel and Judah in the decade prior to 740 B.C. illustrates the
unstable foundation on which these kingdoms were built — the temporary eclipse of
Assyria's influence in the region.

With the death of Jeroboam II and the assassination of his son **Zechariah**, the House of   9-1 e
Jehu came to an end in Israel. The civil strife which followed is briefly described
in **2 Kings 15.8-22**. It presents a period of internal confusion and external threats
(from *Pul*, another name used for Tiglath-pileser III), and is a sad comparison to the
days of Jeroboam II. Israel was entering a period which could be termed *the beginning
of the end*.

In Judah the turning point was succinctly summarized in the dating of Isaiah's famous
vision, *in the year that King Uzziah died* — 740 B.C. (Isaiah 6.1). **Jotham**, Uzziah's   9-1 i
son, was co-regent with his father for a decade prior to 740 B.C. During that time he
was able to maintain a degree of stability in Judah (2 Chronicles 27). However,
Assyria's threat in the north was forcing the old rivals of Damascus and Samaria
to join forces and to mobilize against their larger enemy. In this hour of crisis (after
740 B.C.) the paramount question was, Would Jerusalem put her lot in with them?   8-5 g
The frenzy of political maneuvering which developed out of this situation should   8-6 d e
remind you of a similar incident a century earlier (841 B.C.) when it also appeared
that the world was falling apart.

740-734 B.C.: THE LEAGUE OF ARAM (SYRIA) AND ISRAEL AGAINST JUDAH

DISCUSSION

Rezin, the king of Damascus in 740 B.C., had every reason to fear for his security.
Only a few months earlier, together with King Menachem of Israel, he had paid a

heavy price to Assyria in order to maintain his throne. However, he knew that this was only a delaying tactic to gain time. A common defense against the greater enemy had to be organized before the Assyrian army returned in force to the area. Over a century before, this strategy had stemmed the tide of Assyrian expansion at the Battle of Qarqar (853 B.C.). If such a strong common front were now realized, Damascus had the most to gain in terms of influence in the entire region. If it did not succeed, she had the most to loose. In her threatened position she would be the first to fall in any Assyrian campaign from the north. Israel would be close behind her, surrounded as she was by international routes. What had been gained under Jeroboam II, and more, would soon be lost if Assyrian troops poured into the country. It is clear that this would be a period of great political maneuvering, local alliances and military threats.

8-5 g

In 740 B.C. another chapter in Israel's sordid history opened. In that year **Pekah**, a resistance leader who, it appears, had gained control of the Israelite territory in Transjordan, assassinated the king of Israel (**Pekahiah**) in Samaria and usurped the throne with *fifty men from Gilead* (2 Kings 15.25). Although it is speculation, it is probable that Rezin of Damascus had something to do with these developments in Israel. Damascus' and Israel's interests in defense were closely alligned. A friend on the throne of Samaria would assure the needed alliance. At the same time unstable conditions in Samaria would allow Damascus to assume the leadership in such an alliance.

Unlike Damascus and Israel, Judah did not lie directly in the path of Assyria. Therefore, she could afford to wait and see what developed in the coming months, without obligating herself to any specific course of action. After all, she was still enjoying the fruits of the mid-eighth century. This was the situation when **Ahaz** came to power in 735 B.C. as co-regent with his father Jotham.

9-1/2 j

Rezin of Damascus, who by this time had entered into a mutual defense pact with Pekah of Israel, now put pressure on Ahaz in Judah to join this alliance. Rezin's first step was to weaken Judah's ties to the south, using Edom on the southern Transjordanian Highway as a means to achieve this end. By encouraging rebellion in Edom, Damascus could achieve two important objectives: weaken Judah in the south and strengthen her own ties with Edom at a time when she needed all the support she could muster against Assyria. (Some feel that the word *Aram* in 2 Kings 16.6 should read *Edom*, which is very similar in Hebrew.)

With this plan of action Damascus and Israel could make a joint attack on Judah and place the unnamed *son of Tabeel* on the throne in Jerusalem. Once this were accomplished there would exist an Israel-Judah-Transjordan/Edom alliance with Damascus at its head. Thus, there was an opportunity in this time of crisis to assure the prominence of Damascus while meeting the Assyrian threat in the north. One must admire the genius of such geopolitical maneuvering.

READING AND DISCUSSION
The details of this important moment in the history of the country are related or inferred in **2 Kings 15.37, 16.1-6, 2 Chronicles 28.1-15** and **Isaiah 7**. This reading should be done with Maps 9-1 and 9-2 in view. The marking below can be completed before or after the reading.

In the passage from Isaiah the discerning prophet advised King Ahaz to calm his troubled spirit in the face of these difficulties. The prophet knew that it was only a matter of time before Tiglath-pileser III returned to the region and that Damascus and Israel would bear the brunt of this attack. The present threat from *these two smouldering ends of a wooden poker* would pass away if Judah just held out a little longer.

MARKING (Map 9-2)
1. **Red underlining**: Revolt in Edom probably encouraged by Damascus = **Edom** (inside the blue box).

2. **Sweeping blue arrows and black write-in**:
   a. From the E edge of the map (NE of Edom) to the box around Edom. Add in black, above and below this arrow, HELP FROM DAMASCUS (in small caps).

   b. From the box of Edom to Elath. Add in black on this arrow **2 Kings 16.6** in parentheses.

   c. A later attack by Edom on Judah = From the box of Edom to Tamar and then splitting into two arrows, one toward Ramoth of the Negev and one toward the Israelite settlements south of the Negev. Add in black on this arrow **2 Chronicles 28.17** in parentheses.

   d. Add the letter *j* in a small circle somewhere by the box around Edom indicating the topic in the *SCS*.

MARKING (Map 9-1)
1. **Sweeping blue arrow and blue write-in**: Damascus' attack (with Israel) against Judah = From the NE (by Tirzah) pointing S toward Bethel (in the direction of Jerusalem). On this arrow add (in blue) REZIN.

2. **Sweeping orange arrow and orange write-in**: Israel's attack (with Damascus) against Judah = From Samaria pointing S toward Bethel (in the direction of Jerusalem). On this arrow add (in blue) PEKAH.

3. **Black write-in** = The letter *j* in a small circle between the two arrows just drawn.

LEGEND (In sea area on Map 9-1. In SE corner of Map 9-2)
On Maps 9-1 and 9-2: **Green box on dot** = Major Judean fortress
Green on dot = Judean fortress
On Map 9-1: Compare with Map 7-1
On Map 9-2: Compare with Map 7-2

S M M   9 – 3

TITLE: WARNINGS IN THE SHEPHELAH: PHILISTINE CONQUESTS AND MICAH
THE PROPHET

DATE: 735-734 B.C.

INTRODUCTION

In the years immediately following 740 B.C. political power plays between Damascus
and Samaria left in question Jerusalem's hold on outlying regions.   Edom had rebelled, and the combined forces of Israel and Damascus threatened Judah's northern
approaches.

Ahaz became king of Judah in 735 B.C. (co-regent with his father Jotham).   He was
faced with a coalition of Israel and Damascus, revolts in the south and rumblings
in Philistia, plus the reality of an ever-expanding Assyria under the able leadership
of Tiglath-pileser III.

The year 735 and the spring of 734 B.C. represent a lull before Assyria's major thrust
into the country which probably occurred in the summer of 734 B.C.   It was a moment when those who had been under Jerusalem's control exerted their independence
and turned on the one who had formerly dominated them.

MARKING

1. **Yellow HL on name** = Jerusalem and **Samaria**.

2. **Orange box around name** = Samaria.

3. **Orange write-in**: In the open area south of the city Samaria = ISRAEL (large caps).

4. **Green write-in**: Between Etam and Peor (SW of Bethlehem) = JUDAH (large caps).

5. **Green box around name** = Jerusalem.

6. **Blue box around name**: Chief Philistine cities on this map = **Ashdod, Gath** and
Ekron.

7. **Blue write-in**: In the open area between Gath and Ashdod = PHILISTINES (large
caps).

8. **Brown write-in**:
a. Between Peor and Beth-zur = HILL COUNTRY.

b. Between Beth-shemesh and Timnah = SHEPHELAH.

c. Along the extreme S edge of the map (written vertically), S of Lachish = NEGEV.

9. **Blue border**: Limit of Philistine control after their invasion of the Shephelah =
From T. Mikhal on the coast, E and then SE crossing the Yarqon River and continuing SE between Aphek and Ono and between Hadid and Lod, turning E/SE

between Hadid and Gimzo, continuing SE (N of Shaalbim) to the Hill Country, just E of Aijalon; S along the base of the Hill Country (just E of Aijalon, Eshtaol and Zanoah) and then curving W (between Socoh and Adullam) via the *a* of Moresheth-gath and just N of Ether, and then curving S (running just W of Lachish) and to the S edge of the map. Shade in the W side of this line.

10. **Green border**: Judah's threatened northern border: From the E edge of the map (above the name Michmash) NW via the *i* of Michmash to the *dd* of Ataroth-addar, then W down the ridge (N of the route) to the *r* of both Beth-horons, and then curving slightly SW to meet the border with the Philistines. Shade in the S side of this line.

11. **Yellow HL on route**:
    a. From Bethel to Hebron via Ramah (on the Central Benjamin Plateau), Jerusalem and Bethlehem.

    b. A branch of the International Coastal Highway from Lachish to Aphek via Gath, Ekron and Gittaim.

    c. All routes connecting Gittaim and Ramah via the strategic Aijalon Valley and the two ascents (Beth-horon and Kiriath-jearim).

    d. From Gath to Socoh via Azekah in the strategic Elah Valley.

    e. The routes from Socoh to the main N-S ridge route in the Hill Country (to Bethlehem and to Halhul by Beth-zur).

    f. From Lachish to Hebron via Beth-tappuah.

    g. The Ekron—Beth-shemesh connection.

    h. The natural N-S route from Aijalon S to the Lachish-Hebron connection (via Eshtaol, Zanoah, Keilah and Nezib) running most of the way in a type of chalk moat between the Hill Country and the Shephelah.

    i. The natural diagonal connection from Aijalon to Lachish via Beth-shemesh in the Sorek Valley and Azekah in the Elah Valley.

PHILISTINE INCURSION AND SETTLEMENT

DISCUSSION AND MARKING
The marking completed above has reminded you of the strategic position of the Shephelah and the importance of connections which link it to the Hill Country. Only twenty-five years earlier Uzziah had used these connections in his western 9-1 i thrust to Joppa, Jabneel and Ashdod (Map 9-1). Now, under his grandson Ahaz, the same area was being invaded by the Philistines.

One verse in **2 Chronicles 28.18** describes this Philistine expansion. **Circle in blue the** 9-3 a **cities mentioned in this verse below.** The location of Gederoth by Lachish or in the area of the Elah Valley is not known. (Cities in the same region are listed in Joshua 15.33-41.)

> *Then the Philistines overran the cities of the Shephelah and the Negev of Judah, taking control of **Beth-shemesh, Aijalon,** Gederoth, **Socoh** and its surrounding villages, **Timnah** and its surrounding villages and **Gimzo** and its surrounding villages – and they settled down there [to stay]!*

The dangerous situation created by this Philistine expansion was not unlike what Saul had faced early in his reign. Once the Philistines gained control of the Shephelah, they could easily threaten the Central Benjamin Plateau or the Hill Country of Judah. The new king Ahaz, who had lost control of Edom, now faced an even worse crisis in the west of Judah and in the Negev just south of Hebron. Add a few **sweeping blue arrows** to your map to indicate Philistine penetration from the word PHILISTINES to the northeast, to the east and to the Negev in the south.

THE SETTING OF THE PROPHECY OF MICAH

DISCUSSION AND MARKING

9-3 b   Isaiah and Micah lived through these days and on into the difficult decades which closed the eighth century B.C. Both men were able to see that the interlude which had allowed *the mice to play* was quickly drawing to a close, and that the *cat* would presently make his appearance again in the form of Tiglath-pileser III.

The seven chapters of the book of Micah reflect conditions of the times and are therefore an appropriate reading for this map if time allows. Read **Micah 1**, which reflects the regional perspectives seen from Moresheth(-gath), Micah's home town. The city is probably situated on the southern end of a ridge overlooking the region of Mareshah and Lachish to the south and the Hill Country to the east, with approaches to Hebron and Bethlehem. **Names in this chapter which also appear on Map 9-3 should be highlighted in yellow.** Identifications of other names in the chapter are unknown or very questionable.

In his pronouncement Micah includes both *bad news and good news.* You have just read some of the more depressing portions of his prophecy which deal with the distressing developments and imminent dangers of the moment. These, together with the geographical perspectives from Moresheth-gath, would certainly have given him reason to reflect upon Judah's history and God's promises to his fathers. The view toward the Hill Country of Judah, west of his home in the Shephelah, reminded Micah of promises made to the patriarchs, who traveled along the Bethel-Hebron ridge route. He realized that it must have been difficult for Jacob to believe the promises made to him by *the God of Bethel*, especially after the death of Rachel, who after many years without children had born Joseph, a favorite son. Rachel died by Ramah while giving birth to Benjamin (alluded to in Jeremiah 31). This tragedy happened along the road from Bethel to Bethlehem, after Jacob had built an altar *to the God who answers me in the day of my distress and has been with me wherever I have gone* (Genesis 35.3). After Rachel's death and burial he and his family traveled on and pitched their tent beyond *the Watchtower of the Flock,* somewhere in the vicinity of Bethlehem, which this passage places by Ephrath (Genesis 35.16-21 and Ruth 4.11).

The writings of Micah characterized this attitude of hope and perserverance in spite of present difficulties. In **Micah 4.1-5.9** the prophet looks back to the days of David, the lowly shepherd of Bethlehem and youngest son of Jesse, who led the nation into the period of its greatest glory. Micah knew that the difficulties of his own day and surrounding threats, though realized, would not be the end. Like the flocks with the good shepherd in the Wilderness, Israel's security and well-being were in God's hand, here in this *Land Between*. With this in mind highlight one last name on Map 9-3.

And you, Watchtower of the flock,
  hill of Zion's daughter,
Yes, to you it will come —
  [all the glory of David's] former rule,
  the kingdom of the daughter of Jerusalem.   (Micah 4.8)

*And you, **Bethlehem** by Ephrath,*
  being insignificant as you are among the clans of Judah,
yet because of Me there shall come forth from you
  One to be ruler in Israel.   (Micah 5.2)

Again, *the weakness of God* proved to be *stronger than men.* (1 Corinthians 1.25)

S M M   9 — 4 and 9 — 5

The events studied on Map 9-1/2 and Map 9-3 above have covered a century of change. The year 841 B.C. signaled a radical change in local politics: the overthrow of govern-   8-7 d e
ments in Damascus and Israel, the assassination of the king of Judah, plus an incur-
sion by Shalmaneser III of Assyria. The rest of that century saw Hazael of Damascus overrun both Israel and Judah until Assyria sacked Damascus in 806 B.C. (Adad-
nirari III).

In the first half of the eighth century B.C., especially after 780 B.C., Israel and Judah   9-1/2 e i
remarkably recovered in a period when Damascus was weak and Assyria was involved in other matters. The reigns of Jeroboam II in Israel and Uzziah in Judah culminated this period. However, by 740 B.C. the combination of internal strife and the threat of Assyria (resulting in local power politics) had left the regional governments prey for an ever-expanding Assyria. Already in 742/1 B.C. the shadow of Assyria had been cast over the region, and tribute had been dutifully paid by local governments. When governments like those in Damascus and Samaria plotted against Assyria, the scene   9-1 j
was set for the arrival of Tiglath-pileser III.

Map 9-4 has been discussed in all previous chapters of the *Guide*. It represents the   9-4
end of a century of change (841-735 B.C.) and the beginning of over three decades of major Assyrian campaigns in the country. Lightning campaigns and a policy of annexation meant that by 732 B.C. the regions from Hamath to Gilead (including Damascus) were part of the Assyrian Empire. Galilee and the coastal region of Dor were also under Assyrian administration.

During the latter part of the eighth century Egypt saw all too well the implication of Assyria's policy of creeping annexation. Although her ability to function on the battlefield was limited, she initiated diplomatic maneuvers aimed at encouraging Israel, Judah and the cities of Philistia to stand firm, promising that she would stand with them (from a position of safety 200 km./120 m. to the southwest beyond the desert of Northern Sinai).

During these days there were certainly mixed feelings and much discussion in the capitals of Samaria and Jerusalem as well as in the cities along the International Coastal Highway like Ashdod and Gaza. Some believed Egypt and became part of a resistance movement against Assyrian aggression. The combination of Assyrian expansion and local resistance together with Egyptian diplomatic support forms the context of Maps 9-4 and 9-5. It takes you down to the closing years of the eighth century, to 705 B.C. in this *Land Between*. In order to complete the sequence of events in these momentous decades, **review the discussion of Map 9-4 in Chapters One and Two of the *Guide* and the discussions of Map 9-5 in Chapter Three.**

9-4
9-5 a

The outcome of Tiglath-pileser's campaigns must have left Ahaz with a certain feeling of satisfaction. He had opted to remain outside the resistance movements and therefore could expect to capitalize on the political field. However, it did not work out that way. His actions are summarized (and condemned) in such passages as **2 Kings 16.6-18** and **2 Chronicles 28.19-25.**

S M M   9 – 6

TITLE: RESISTANCE OF HEZEKIAH OF JUDAH AGAINST SENNACHERIB OF ASSYRIA

DATE: 705-701 B.C.

INTRODUCTION

Following the fall of Samaria in 722 B.C. in the last days of Shalmaneser V of Assyria, his successor, Sargon II, was faced with revolts from Gaza to Hamath. Although these were put down by 720 B.C., uprisings broke out again in and around Ashdod, which had to be dealt with in 713/12 B.C. The region of Ashdod was subsequently made an Assyrian province.

9-5 b

At the death of Sargon II (705 B.C.) rebellion again broke out, this time led by **Hezekiah,** king of Judah. Details of this revolt are given both in the Bible and in the annals of the new and efficient king of Assyria, Sennacherib. Both accounts strongly infer that preparations for this war of liberation were extensive. Hezekiah, who came to the throne in 715 B.C., had seen the Ashdod rebellion fail and this coastal region turned into an Assyrian province. He wanted to be certain that his operation from Judah did not end in the same way. Thus his operation had to be well-planned.

9-6 a

Hezekiah was encouraged by several factors around him and in other parts of the Assyrian Empire. Ashkelon and Ekron along the International Coastal Highway were revolting. Sidon and Tyre in Phoenicia were also throwing off the yoke of Assyrian domination. Babylon, at the other end of the empire, had been taken over by Merodach-baladan, who was busy uniting the region against its long time enemy, Assyria. This takeover culminated almost two decades of intense friction between these two power bases in Mesopotamia. Sennacherib's forces would have to settle this matter before he could turn his attention to the rebellions in Phoenicia and Judah. Egypt, at the same time, realized that she had to act *now or never*. If she did not enter into the struggle on the battlefield, her last chance to stop the Assyrian advance would be lost. Add together all of these factors, and the timing of Hezekiah's operation is better understood.

READING

With this background to the times of Hezekiah, read the following passages:

2 Kings 18.1-8	Hezekiah's thrust onto the Coastal Plain.

2 Chronicles 29-31
Isaiah 31.4-10   Hezekiah's religious reforms to unify his kingdom with the population in *Samaria*, and in other Assyrian provinces which formerly made up Israel. (Skim.)

2 Kings 20.20
2 Chronicles 32.30
Isaiah 22.8-11
2 Chronicles 32.27-31
1 Chronicles 4.39-43   Preparations for the revolt by Hezekiah: a tunnel to bring water inside the city of Jerusalem; the reinforcement of Jerusalem's fortifications; administrative improvements to establish a broader economic base for the country; southern expansion into the Negev. (The name *Gedor* should read *Gerar*, an important city in the Western Negev between Judah and Gaza.)

Isaiah 30.1-5; 31.1-3   Jerusalem's tendency to rely on Egypt.

DISCUSSION

After a series of important stabilizing actions in and around Nineveh (Assyria's capital at this time), Sennacherib marched on Babylon, which fell in 702 B.C. This was the most important single action taken in Sennacherib's reign.

With this accomplished, the might of Assyria could turn toward the west. Following   9-6 b a campaign through Phoenicia and the country's northern coastal plain (red names on the northern edge of Map 9-6), Sennacherib moved south to establish a base of operations in the area represented by a triangle of routes between Joppa, Aphek and Gittaim on Map 9-6. From there he turned his attention to the region of the Shephelah, the all-important approach to the Hill Country of Judah and to Jerusalem.

Hezekiah's intensive preparations meant that a direct attack on Jerusalem via the Aijalon Valley appears to have been impractical (although a possible Assyrian attack via the Central Benjamin Plateau in Isaiah 10.28-32 is discussed below). Instead, Sennacherib systematically destroyed Judah's fortresses in the Shephelah and took control of the Sorek Valley, the strategic Elah Valley and the region of Lachish (including the region of Micah's home town). His strategy was generally to isolate a region from the hills by cutting its supply line and then to complete operations in the valley.

During this process he sent threatening messages to Hezekiah in Jerusalem, pointing out the futility of his actions now that Assyria was in control of the Shephelah. He also no doubt wanted to avoid making an attack into the hills where Hezekiah may have had the advantage. The following marking traces the Assyrian campaign which is described in later reading below.

MARKING

1. **Green write-in**: In the open area between Etam and Peor (W of Bethlehem) = JUDAH.

2. **Brown write-in**:
   a. Between Beth-zur and Peor = HILL COUNTRY.

   b. In the open area E of Gezer = SHEPHELAH.

   c. Between Zorah and Zanoah = SOREK VALLEY (small caps in two lines with a brown arrow pointing W of Beth-shemesh; compare Map 6-4).

   d. Between Zanoah and Adullam = ELAH VALLEY (small caps in two lines with arrow pointing W toward Socoh).

   e. Just E of Eltekeh = PLAIN OF ELTEKEH (small caps in two lines).

   f. Between Michmash and Anathoth = THE PASS (small caps with brown arrow to the N to the point where the route between Michmash and Geba crosses the Wadi Suweinit indicated by the broken blue line).

3. **Yellow HL on name**: Names from the Biblical texts (including Micah 1) and from Sennacherib's annals including an inscription formerly thought to be written in the reign of an earlier Assyrian ruler: **Joppa, Bene-berak/Banai-barqa, Azor/ Azuru, Beth-dagon, Eltekeh, Timnah, Ekron, Azekah, Gath, Lachish, Mareshah, Moresheth-gath, Libnah, Adullam, Beth-leaphrah, Aiath/Ayyah** (by Bethel), **Michmash, Geba, Ramah, Gibeah, Anathoth, Nob** and **Jerusalem**.

4. **Yellow HL on route** =
   a. The International Coastal Highway from N of Aphek to Joppa and via Azor/ Azuru and Eltekeh to Ashdod and S off the map.

   b. The shortest routes between the following points: Aphek to Lachish; Joppa to Gittaim; Ekron to Beth-shemesh; Beth-shemesh to Gath; Azekah to Lachish; Lachish to Hebron (via Beth-tappuah); Azekah to Halhul (via Beth-zur); Azekah to Bethlehem; Hebron to Jerusalem; Aphek to Bethel; Bethel to Aiath/Ayyah; Aiath to Michmash; Michmash to Ramah; Ramah to Jerusalem.

5. **Green box around name** = Jerusalem.

6. **Blue write-in** (with additions):
   a. In the NE corner of the map: The Assyrian province created after the fall of the city of Samaria in 722 B.C. = SAMARIA (with black arrow pointing N off the map).

   b. In the open area between Aphek and Ono = ASSYRIA (large caps enclosed in a blue box).

   c. Between Jerusalem and the Water of Nephtoah = RABSHAKEH (small caps) with a blue arrow pointing to Jerusalem and one approaching the name *Rabshekeh* from the route by Bether.

d. In the open space E of Bethel = ISAIAH 10.28-32 (small caps) in blue box with blue arrow pointing toward Aiath/Ayyah.

7. **Red on dot and arrow**: Cities conquered according to the annals or reliefs of Sennacherib = **Sidon, Uzu, Tyre, Achzib, Acco, Joppa, Azor/Azuru, Bene-berak/Banaibarqa, Beth-dagon, Timnah, Ekron, Azekah, Gath** (implied in the inscription) and **Lachish.**

8. **Red circle around name** = **Plain of Eltekeh.**

9. **Sweeping blue arrows**: Advance of the Assyrian army =
a. From N of Aphek to the blue box around Assyria.

b. From the blue box of Assyria W to Joppa.

c. A series of arrows from the blue box of Assyria to Timnah, from Timnah to Ekron, from Timnah to Azekah (via Shaaraim), from Azekah to Gath, from Gath to Lachish, from Lachish to Libnah. (The identification of Libnah is still a subject of debate. Some feel that it is NW of Mareshah by Ether.)

d. From the region of Ekron back to the Plain of Eltekeh. (This may indicate an Assyrian backtrack from the region of Lachish to meet the Egyptian army at Eltekeh.) Also from Beth-dagon to the Plain of Eltekeh representing Assyrian reserve forces which may have been drawn on for this *showdown* with Egypt.

e. From Aiath to Michmash, from Michmash to Geba (by the route), from Geba to Ramah, from Ramah to Nob.

10. **Orange write-in** between Ashdod and Jabneel: The abortive attempt by Egypt to head off the Assyrians and to come to the aid of Hezekiah = EGYPT: TIRHAKAH, KING OF CUSH (in three lines and in orange box).

11. **Sweeping orange arrows**: Egypt's advance to Eltekeh = From the SW along the Coastal Highway to the orange box, and from the orange box to the red circle around the Plain of Eltekeh.

READING AND DISCUSSION
With Map 9-6 before you, read **2 Kings 18.13-19.37**. This campaign is also described in 2 Chronicles 32.1-23. (2 Kings 20 and 2 Chronicles 32.24-33 add information about Hezekiah's later reign and contacts with Babylon.)

The annals of Sennacherib add details about the Assyrian advance and takeover of   9-6 b
the region around Joppa and the cities of Timnah, Ekron, Azekah and Gath (the latter being implied in the text). Both the Bible and the annals of Sennacherib draw attention to the assault on Lachish, the site which appears to have required the most massive Assyrian assault. It was Judah's main defensive position in the Shephelah. Evidence from recent archeological excavations (Level III) again underscores written records from Assyria which describe Sennacherib as *the king of the Universe, king of Assyria, [who] sat upon a throne [while] the booty of Lachish passed before him* (from reliefs showing the siege of Lachish in Sennacherib's palace in Nineveh).

9-6 c   One of the most dramatic geographical texts in the Bible is **Isaiah 10.28-32**. It presents a *blow by blow account* of a possible Assyrian advance from the strategic area (the *emeq*) between the region of Aiath (by Ai) and Michmash (discussed on Maps 5-4 and 7-4 earlier in this chapter). There is a question if this campaign really happened, or if the mention of this important northern approach to Jerusalem was just Isaiah's way of reminding the people of the impending Assyrian invasion of the country farther north.

The events portrayed on Map 9-6 again illustrate Jerusalem's position in the Hill Country, north of Judah and south of Benjamin. Directly west of the city the difficult *Sorek System* blocks any approach by a major army. The important southern approach to the city via Bethlehem and Hebron is guarded by the valleys of the Shephelah (as well as routes ascending from the Negev). Isaiah's use of the *side door* (via Michmash) to the Central Benjamin Plateau reminded everyone of Jerusalem's vulnerable northern approach which within a matter of a few hours would bring the Assyrians to Nob (on the Mount of Olives east of the city). Even the annals of Sennacherib strongly imply this geographical reality.

> *As to Hezekiah, the Jew, he did not submit to my yoke. I laid siege to forty-six of his strong cities, walled forts and to the countless small villages in their vicinity and conquered them . . . . Himself I made prisoner in Jerusalem, his royal residence, like a bird in a cage . . . .* (Prism of Sennacherib)

The remaining events listed in the *SCS* for Map 9-6 cover another century, this time the seventh century (700-605 B.C.). During this time the *Land Between* saw a number of different armies pass along the International Coastal Highway between Assyria and Egypt. These events are briefly summarized below. More detailed information can be found in the *SCS* itself.

9-6 d e   Assyria's march toward Egypt continued under Esarhaddon and Ashurbanipal, later
f   kings of Assyria. Over a decade of campaigns (671-660 B.C.) culminated in Assyria's subjection of both Lower and Upper Egypt. During this time of Assyrian domination little is known about the local history of Judah when **Manasseh**, Hezekiah's son, ruled. During his reign and toward the middle of the seventh century B.C., unsettled conditions throughout the empire made Manasseh suspect. He appears to have been able to clear himself of the charges as related in **2 Chronicles 33.9-17**.

About the same time a serious crisis developed along the Transjordanian Highway. Invading desert tribes (including Nabateans) made a mockery of Assyrian authority. These incursions and the Assyrian response are reflected in **Isaiah 15 and 16** and in **Jeremiah 48.1-49.6**, represented as black names in Moab on Map 9-1/2.

9-6 g   In the second half of the seventh century Assyrian power began to wane. By the latter part of the century Egypt was able to gain her independence, and Babylon, that ancient religious and political center in southern Mesopotamia, finally rose again to threaten Assyria. In this moment, when the control of the country was *up for grabs*, Judah was again able to expand and achieve her final period of greatness, this time under the
9-6 h i   leadership of **Josiah**, who ruled for thirty-one years (640-609 B.C.). Together with internal reform, he was able to extend Jerusalem's control to include the Assyrian provinces of Samaria and Megiddo (Galilee) as well as northern Philistia where archeo-

logical evidence attests his presence at Mezad Yashavyahu. Again, passages relating to his reign are given in the *SCS* and are interesting reading. Note especially the book of **Nahum**, directed against Nineveh, Assyria's capital, and **Zephaniah 2**, no doubt reflecting renewed military activity along the Coastal and Transjordanian Highways.

It was only twenty years from the liberation of Babylon (626 B.C.) to the final defeat of the Assyrian government-in-exile (605 B.C., at the battle of Carchemish on the Euphrates River). These two decades reflect a period of *wars and rumors of wars* in the country and throughout the empire. During this time Egypt also entered the arena, marching at least three times to the Euphrates River and beyond to assist her former enemy, Assyria, who was battling for her life against Babylonia. Egypt had nothing to lose and everything to gain through such a move. It would allow her to extend Egyptian control once again over the *Land Between* and to reach the Euphrates. In so doing she would go beyond the limits established during the heyday of Egyptian power in the days of the Eighteenth and Nineteenth Dynasties.

King Josiah of Judah fully realized the threat which Judah's former ally and Assyria's former enemy posed to his kingdom. In 609 B.C. Josiah was killed at Megiddo in a brave attempt to block Pharaoh Neco II's advance through the country to Carchemish and Haran in northern Mesopotamia. This Egyptian victory (which brought to an end the last period of Judah's greatness) echoes that of Thutmose III over the Canaanites who had attempted to stop an Egyptian army at the same place almost a millennium earlier.

The sad story of Josiah's death is described in **2 Chronicles 35.20-25**. In Judah there must have been many unanswered questions and a certain sense of disillusionment in the minds of those who had participated in Josiah's earlier reforms. To add to the shock, Josiah's son **Jehoahaz/Shallum,** who had been summoned north by the Pharaoh Neco, was deported to Egypt, leaving **Jehoiakim/Eliakim,** another son of Josiah, to rule a Judah now subject to Egypt (**2 Chronicles 36.1-4**).   _{9-7 a}

Jeremiah had little good to say about this period (609-605 B.C.), the first four years of the reign of Jehoiakim. **Jeremiah 7 and 26** address those who felt a false sense of security because of their privileged positions in the holy city of Jerusalem. Such passages as **Jeremiah 22.13-19** scorn the extravagence of the upper classes who appear to have ignored the plight of the disadvantaged around them and the realities of the Babylonian threat from the north.

In 605 B.C., *in the fourth year of Jehoiakim*, the final confrontation between the joint Assyrian/Egyptian armies and Babylonian forces at Carchemish on the Euphrates resulted in total disaster for the Egyptian army. **Jeremiah 46** provides a graphic and frightening description of conditions at that moment in the history of Judah and Jerusalem. As a result of this battle Babylonian forces were posed for an invasion of the *Land Between*, along highways which lead to Egypt via Mt. Tabor and Mt. Carmel, those same highways which had been used by Hazael of Damascus in the late ninth century and Tiglath-pileser III of Assyria in the late eighth century. These conditions provide the context for Jeremiah's preaching at this time, recorded in **Jeremiah 25**. In some ways it is similar to that of Isaiah over a century earlier (Isaiah 8). Jeremiah 36 adds more details about the prophet's actions during these momentous years (605 and 604 B.C.). Like Isaiah's *large tablet* (Isaiah 8.1), Jeremiah's *scroll* supplied his audience with the message of the hour.   _{9-7 b}

With the arrival of the Babylonian army in the *Land Between* (604 B.C., sometime *in the fifth year of Jehoiakim*), a new phase of the history of Judah began. The period of Assyrian dominance was over. Egypt's brief rule in the country ceased. 2 Kings 24.7 tells the state of affairs a few years later.

The king of Egypt no longer extended his control beyond the borders of his own country, for the king of Babylon took control of all that had belonged to the king of Egypt — from the Brook (Nahal) of Egypt to the Euphrates River [and all the 'Land Between']!

Again, Isaiah's words concerning the rise and fall of great empires are appropriate.

They are only just planted, only just sown; their stem has only just taken root, And He puffs on them and they dry up; the storm carries them off like chaff.
(Isaiah 40.24)

S M M   9 — 7

TITLE: **THE RISE OF BABYLON, JUDAH'S CLOSING YEARS AND THE FALL OF JERUSALEM**

DATE: **604-582 B.C.**

INTRODUCTION

This map is the last to be studied in Chapter Four of the *Guide*. It represents two decades of tension between Babylon and Egypt in which Judah, although somewhat on the sidelines, was again caught in the middle. Egyptian military presence in the *Land Between* (which had emerged as Assyrian control was dissolving) was now reduced to diplomatic maneuvers. Egypt again encouraged rebellion in Judah — this time against Babylon and the Chaldean dynasty which reigned there in this period.

Had the kings of Judah been satisfied with keeping a low profile during this period (as Manasseh had done under Assyria), a showdown with Babylon probably would not have occurred. However, they recalled the days of Josiah and yearned for total independence. They failed to take into account that times had changed and that Babylon, which now ruled much of the former Assyrian Empire, would not tolerate this *thorn in the flesh*. Repeated warnings from Babylon and from the prophet Jeremiah went unheeded.

The systematic dismemberment of Judah and its population finally culminated in the fall of Jerusalem in 587 B.C. Even after this disaster some zealots still felt that there was hope and murdered the local administrator whom the Babylonians had installed at Mizpah. Out of fear of a reprisal many local families left for Egypt where Jewish colonies were established. The year 582 B.C. brought more deportations. The simple list of deportees at the close of the book of Jeremiah (52.28-30) is a sad and silent witness to the futile rebellions put down in 598, 587 and 582 B.C.

DISCUSSION AND READING

The list of kings and confrontations between the years 605 and 582 B.C. are given in the *SCS* for this map. **Read the subjects listed there for a summary of the period.** 9-7 b-e
When time allows, you may want to read the references (*Primary Sources*) for these topics in order to understand the sequence of events during these closing years of the Judean monarchy.

One campaign stands out above all others, that of 588/87 B.C., which resulted in the 9-7 d
fall of Jerusalem and the destruction of the Temple. Details leading up to the rebellion and Babylon's expedition to Judah are not known. 2 Kings 24.20 simply states that **Zedekiah** *rebelled against the king of Babylon* (or *King Nebuchadnezzar* in 2 Chronicles 36.13).

Most information about this specific period comes from the book of Jeremiah the prophet. Jeremiah was born at the height of the Assyrian expansion and greatness. As 9-6 f
a man in his forties he lived through the turbulent years when Babylon expanded at Assyria's expense, from the fall of Nineveh (612 B.C.) to the final Assyrian defeat at 9-6 i
Carchemish (605 B.C.). He had watched Josiah march out of Jerusalem across the Central Benjamin Plateau to meet the Egyptian army at Megiddo. He had also participated in Jerusalem's great lament for the fallen king (609 B.C.) only to see Jehoahaz, 9-7 a
Josiah's son, deported to Egypt shortly thereafter.

The prophet contemplated these developments from Jerusalem and from Anathoth, his own village just northeast of Jerusalem overlooking the Wilderness and the Transjordanian highlands to the east. He knew that the winds of political change in the north would sooner or later reach the Transjordanian Highway and the International Coastal Highway a few miles west of the Central Benjamin Plateau.

In his earlier ministry, Jeremiah made every attempt to warn the people of Judah of impending doom — the Babylonian threat from the north via Dan (Jeremiah 4.11-31; 8.14-9.3). Like Isaiah a century before (Isaiah 10.28-32), Jeremiah knew the region of Jerusalem well and made good use of it. Object lessons and references taken from the world of the Judean farmer (vines, figs, grains, etc.) and from that of the herdsman (wilderness, shepherds, cisterns, etc.) punctuate the prophet's writings. If time allows, skim **Jeremiah 1-20.** It will give you a dramatic introduction to Jeremiah's style. His opening paragraphs are reminiscent of Moses' call and the preparation of young Samuel of Benjamin to preach repentance to a former fallen generation (1.4-10; 15.1). A play on Hebrew words in 1.11-12 underscores the urgency of his message. The *almond (shaqed)* is the earliest tree to bloom in the country during the winter season when no one expects it, while *to stay awake, keep ready and watch (shoqed)* anticipates the rapid sequence of unexpected events which occurred in Jeremiah's life from the days of prosperity in the reign of Josiah to the fall of Jerusalem and the captivity of Judah. (This was no doubt the same word used by Jesus on the Mt. of Olives in Matthew 26.30-46 when He urged His disciples to remain alert for the unexpected turn of events about to take place.)

Jeremiah used Anathoth's local setting (a village of cisterns with no natural water supply, a few minutes walk from the Mt. of Olives which overlooks Jerusalem) as a background for his message (2.9-13; 13.1-11). (In Jeremiah 13 the usual translation of *Euphrates* should probably be *Pharah/Farah*, a beautiful spring in a rugged limestone canyon an hour's walk northeast of Anathoth — in the same direction as the Euphrates itself.)

9-7 b   After the short period of Egyptian dominance, Jeremiah experienced the Babylonian takeover of the country (604 B.C.). He knew that Egypt was no longer a force in the region. Given the daily view to the east from his village he must also have been keenly aware of the weakening effect which local raids from Transjordan were having on the country (**2 Kings 24.2**; cf. Jeremiah 9.23-26, 27.2). Then in 598 B.C. after Judah's

9-7 c   rebellion under Jehoiakin, Jeremiah looked on as the nobles and skilled laborers were deported to Babylon leaving only *the poorest people of the land* (**2 Kings 24.10-17**).

9-7 d   In light of all of this, Jeremiah questioned the wisdom of yet another plan to throw off the yoke of Babylonian rule, this time under King Zedekiah. At the very outset of his rule, the prophet had received word which made him question the policies of this new ruler (**Jeremiah 24**).

Much information on the short reign of Zedekiah is included in the book of Jeremiah, as a quick glance at *SCS* 9-7 d shows. It would be well to read all of these passages. However, only a few chapters deal directly with the Babylonian campaign of 588/7 B.C. These are **Jeremiah 32-34 and 37-41**. The marking below may be done before this reading.

As you read these chapters in the book of Jeremiah, especially note the following topics:

32.1-5   The campaign of Nebuchadnezzar of Babylon against Zedekiah of Judah
34.1-7   in 588/587 B.C. The few geographical details given are supplemented by passages in 2 Kings 24.20-25.7 and 2 Chronicles 36.13. Jeremiah 34.7 speaks of only two fortified cities left in the Shephelah of Judah, *Lachish and Azekah*. One of a number of ostraca (letters written on potsherds) no doubt sent from the Hill Country of Judah and found in the gate room of Lachish provides this additional sad note concerning the progress of the Babylonian campaign. *We are looking for the signal station's fires of Lachish . . . since we can no longer see those from Azekah* (Lachish Letter No. 4).

37.3-15   The Egyptian abortive attempt to come to Judah's aid (as in the days of Hezekiah over a century before).

39.1-10   The fall of Jerusalem, the destruction of the Temple, and Zedekiah's attempt to escape. The Babylonian approach route is not known, except that the Shephelah was taken prior to the attack on Jerusalem.

40   A Babylonian appointed administration at Mizpah after the fall of Jerusalem; the return of Jews from surrounding countries.

41   The assassination of Gedaliah and the flight of the assassins; Jeremiah's subsequent flight to Egypt with others is described in Jeremiah 42-43.

MARKING

1. **Green write-in**: Between Etam and Peor = JUDAH.

2. **Brown write-in**:
   a. Between Peor and Beth-zur = HILL COUNTRY.

b. In the open area S of Azekah = SHEPHELAH.

c. Between the eastern Arad and Beer-sheba (written vertically along the route) = NEGEV.

3. **Yellow HL on name = Jerusalem, Azekah, Lachish, Anathoth and Mizpah.**

4. **Green box around name = Jerusalem.**

5. **Yellow HL on route =**
a. The International Coastal Highway (printed in red).

b. The shortest route between the following points: From Gath to Lachish; from Lachish to Hebron (via Beth-tappuah); from Lachish to Azekah; from Gath to Socoh; from Socoh to Bethlehem; from Socoh to Halhul (via Beth-zur); from Hebron to Jerusalem.

c. From the eastern Arad SE off the S edge of the map.

6. **Sweeping blue arrows with blue write-in:** Babylonian advance under Nebuchadnezzar in 588/7 B.C. =
a. From the N edge of the map along the International Coastal Highway toward Ekron. Add BABYLONIANS on this arrow and NEBUCHADNEZZAR (in parentheses) below it.

b. From the region of Ekron one arrow to Azekah and another arrow to Lachish.

c. From the region of Socoh E toward the word Judah.

d. From the word Judah to the green box around Jerusalem.

e. From the SE edge of the map (along the highlighted route) an arrow to the eastern Arad and another one branching off to the W toward (Je)Kabzeel. Along this arrow write EDOMITES.

7. **Blue write-in:** In the open area just SE of Lachish = JEREMIAH 34.7, LACHISH LETTER NO. 4 (small caps in two lines).

8. **Red on dot:** Archeological evidence of total destruction in this period = **Timnah, Azekah, Lachish, Arad** (the eastern one), **Beth-zur** and **Jerusalem.**

9. **Black write-in:** Just above Anathoth = JEREMIAH'S HOME TOWN (small caps).

10. **Flight (green) and chase (blue) arrows:** Zedekiah's attempt to escape = A series from Jerusalem to Jericho.

DISCUSSION AND READING

During the final days of Jerusalem, local nations which surrounded Judah took advantage of her weakened position. In the west most of the action centered around the Babylonian advance in the Shephelah. In the south Edom moved quickly to occupy 9-7 e the Negev and its approaches, the first step in fulfilling her dream of reaching the port of Gaza and the Mediterranean Sea. Recalling earlier domination by Judah,

Edom was only too happy to see Jerusalem's control of the Negev eliminated. The Jews who were left in the region after the fall of Jerusalem could no longer look to Judah for their security.

Exile to Babylon via northern Mesopotamia in this period and Edomite invasions in the south provide the setting for **Psalm 137** and the book of **Obadiah**. This attitude toward Edomites (later called *Idumeans* in Greek) would last for centuries to come. The **five chapters of the Lamentations of Jeremiah** stand out as the most poignant of all expressions during this period and should be read now. Of all the verses in this book which could be quoted, one short phrase best summarizes the grief Jeremiah felt in this most difficult hour of Jerusalem's history.

> *The roads to Zion mourn . . . .*   (Lamentations 1.4)

The despair and disillusionment felt during these years of destruction and exile must be tempered by the promises of a remnant and a future for a restored Zion. Passages expressing such hope, though they be few in Jeremiah's writings, stand out against the futility of his ministry during the closing decades of the kingdom of Judah.

In exile in Babylon and separated from Zion, other prophets like Ezekiel and Daniel were given visions of God's glory and power (much like John, the writer of the Apocalypse, in exile on the island of Patmos at the end of the first century A.D.). Far more important than providing details of time and space, these visions looked beyond the difficulties and the hopelessness of the period and underscored the main theme of the *Land Between, to recognize who God is* — in spite of what appears to be. When time allows, read the writings of the prophets Ezekiel and Daniel, especially noting their actions based on this theme.

In the midst of the revelation of these prophets, both Judah's sad past and her hope of redemption are expressed in the prayer of **Daniel 9.1-19**. Again the details which come after the prayer should not overshadow the prayer itself, a focal point of repentance and hope in a period of despair. Like the preaching of Moses, Joshua and Samuel and the prayers of David, it summarizes the heartfelt cry of one who recognized past failings of God's people in the *Land Between*, and yet held fast to the unchanging love and power of God in this time of judgment and difficulty. The writer's understanding of Jeremiah's prophecy and ministry is clear, both in Daniel 9.1-2 (referring to Jeremiah 25.11 and 29.10), and in his use of the word *shoqed (keep ready and watch)* at a certain place in his prayer (Daniel 9.14; Jeremiah 1.11-12; 5.6; 44.27). The concluding lines of this prayer of confession and this plea for restoration bring to a close this part of your study on Judah, the setting of the city of Jerusalem.

> *O my God, bend your ear and listen. Open your eyes and look at our desolations and the city which is called by Your name. For we are not making our plea before You because of our own righteousness, but because of Your great mercy. O Lord, hear! O Lord, forgive! O Lord, take account of what is happening and do something! O my God, for Your own sake do not delay since it is Your city and it is Your people, called by Your name.*
>
> (Daniel 9.18-19)

REVIEW ASSIGNMENT AND CONCLUSION

In this chapter Judah's geographical perspectives have been viewed from all directions and have been illustrated by the region's rich history. These perspectives can be reviewed by glancing again at the *SMA* and locating key sites and approaches to the Hill Country of Judah and Jerusalem.

The chapter began by reminding you of the priority a big power like Egypt placed on the International Coastal Highway. In the eighth and seventh centuries B.C. Assyria's push through the *Land Between* to Egypt illustrated that same priority. In later centuries Nebuchadnezzar of Babylon, Cambyses of Persia and Alexander the Great of Macedonia used this same route to achieve their objectives.

In the Hill Country of Judah, to the east of the International Coastal Highway, the patriarchal narratives were seen to reflect a totally different perspective, that of local travel in a relatively isolated region. In this context those places frequented by the patriarchs were to become prestigious local centers of religious and political power. Hebron in Judah best exemplifies this. Certainly Caleb had more than a purely agricultural interest when he requested the region of Hebron from Joshua. North of Judah, in southern Ephraim, Bethel represented another important center to which patriarchal visits added esteem.

Between Hebron and Bethel only a few sites are mentioned in the patriarchal narratives. One of these is Salem, which has been linked with Jerusalem (Genesis 14.17-24; Psalm 76.2). Other sites, like Ramah and Ephratha (by Bethlehem), are only mentioned in passing in the sad story of Rachel's death and burial (Genesis 35.16-21; Jeremiah 31.15). Their status did not compare with that of Bethel and Hebron. Yet it was in the region of Bethlehem and Jerusalem that God's greatest work was accomplished through common lives and simple trust. It was in this region that David emerged as God's chosen servant, both as a shepherd boy from Bethlehem and as the king of a united Israel at Jerusalem. It should not be surprising, therefore, to find the name of David linked to the promises given to the patriarchs although David's background is not linked to Bethel or Hebron. Even the words of a priest from the Hill Country of Judah in the days of Herod the Great reflect this theme (Luke 1.57-80). John the Baptist, the son of that priest, matured in the same Wilderness in which David had kept his father's sheep. It was John's task to prepare Israel for the coming of *the son of David,* also born in Bethlehem and later declared king in Jerusalem on a Roman cross.

In reading these first century accounts, one is struck by the fact that the names of Bethel and Hebron rarely occur, either in Jewish or in Roman sources. It appears that the region and city of Jerusalem totally eclipsed these earlier prestigious centers. However, in the larger picture it should be remembered that all of these events took place in the Hill Country of Judah, removed from the main stream of world history and international priorities. If one can say that God's choice of the *Land Between* as His *testing ground of faith* represents the principle that His *power is made whole (perfect) through [human] weakness* (2 Corinthians 12.9), then certainly the choice of the Hill Country of Judah, and especially Jerusalem, in this part of the *Land Between* demonstrates this principle. Humanly speaking, no one would have dared suggest the Hill Country of Judah or the city of Jerusalem as the focal point for God's involvement in world history and redemption. Again, we turn to the words of George Adam Smith for an adequate summary of the region.

12-1/4/
10/11

> *Neither Bethlehem nor Hebron, nor any other part of that [Judean] plateau,*
> *bears tokens of civic promise. Throughout Judea these are lacking. She has*
> *no harbors, no river, no trunk-route, no convenient market for the nations on*
> *either side. In their commerce with each other, these pass by Judea, finding*
> *their emporiums in the cities of Philistia [on the International Coastal Highway],*
> *or, as of old, at Petra and Bozrah [in Edom on the Transjordanian Highway]*
> *on the east of the Jordan. Gaza has outdone Hebron as the port of the desert.*
> *Jerusalem is no match for Shechem in fertility or convenience of site. The*
> *whole [Judean] plateau stands aloof, waterless [lacking any river, much less*
> *a natural resource like the Nile or Euphrates], on the road to nowhere. There*
> *are none of the natural conditions of a great city.*
>
> *And yet it was here that She arose who, more than Athens and more than*
> *Rome, taught the nations civic justice, and gave her name to that ideal city*
> *men are ever striving to build on earth, to the City of God that shall one day*
> *descend from heaven — the New Jerusalem. For her builder was not Nature*
> *nor the wisdom of men, but on that secluded and barren site the Word of God,*
> *by her prophets, laid her eternal foundations in righteousness, and reared her*
> *walls in her people's faith in God.*[1]

In this same theme and with the knowledge of the history and setting of Judah, read **Psalm 46.** In it can be found the perspectives of the Hill Country of Judah, the Mediterranean Sea beyond the International Coastal Highway, the nations and kingdoms which surrounded Judah and her own embattled history in this *Land Between*. The psalmist's statements regarding Jerusalem's basis for security, well-being and peace in the future are made against the background of the city's natural weaknesses and insecure position. Prophets in the late eighth and ninth centuries also spoke in these terms (Isaiah 7.1-4; 33.20-22; Zephaniah 3.14-20). In fact, the history of Judah, more than that of any other part of the country, reflects the description of the land presented in the *Introduction* to the *Guide*. Reread the section entitled *The Land Between* in this *Introduction*. Recall that Habbakuk lived through the same difficult years as Jeremiah, when Babylon was poised at the northern gateway to the country. With the background of these events fresh in your mind, also read the book of **Habakkuk.** Note the prophet's proclamation recorded before his prayer which, as Isaiah's call over a century earlier (Isaiah 6), places God and His creation in the proper perspective in times when everything appeared to be out of control and man turned to his own works and ways.

> *The Lord is in His holy temple —*
> *let all the earth be silent before Him!*   (Habakkuk 2.20)

Over five centuries later, in a period when Rome dominated Judea, Jesus also contemplated the future of Jerusalem which was then on the verge of a major revolt. From the Mt. of Olives overlooking Jerusalem, His thoughts must have been similar to those of Jeremiah, who had often viewed the city from some nearby vantage point. Many passages in the Gospels echo Jeremiah's writings. Specific references (like Jeremiah 7.8-11 and 8.13) or just the general tone of the prophet's message can be detected in Jesus' words.

[1]George Adam Smith, *The Historical Geography of the Holy Land*, 25th ed. rev. (London: Hodder and Stoughton, 1931), pp. 318-19.

His teaching about aiding those in need (Matthew 25.31-46) brings to mind Jeremiah's comparison of King Josiah's reign with the carefree, self-centered way of life in the days of Jehoiakim (Jeremiah 22.13-17).   The tears Jesus shed over Jerusalem (Luke 19.41-44) and His words to the *daughters of Jerusalem* on the way of the cross (Luke 23.27-31) find their precedent in the cry of an earlier man of sorrows (Jeremiah 9.1, 17-22; 13.15-17; Lamentations 2.11-18; 3.46-51).

In His many parables concerning the rule (kingdom) of God, Jesus frequently spoke of the unexpected and of the necessity of waiting and remaining alert in spite of the actions of others.   As in the days of Jeremiah, Jesus' message was appropriate to His times, both in terms of the smoldering rebellion which shortly would break out into a full-fledged war with Rome and in terms of His own imminent death, which would catch His own disciples completely off-guard although He had repeatedly warned them about it.

Jeremiah also spoke of resurrection after the coming destruction. Passages like **Jeremiah 23.1-8, 33.1-26 and Lamentations 3.19-57** from the days of Jehoiakim and Zedekiah, as well as **Jeremiah 30 and 31** (especially verses 31 through 34), must have been in Jesus' mind when He spoke to His disciples about things to come (Matthew 24 and 25, and especially the injunction *Watch!* in 25.13).   Beyond the details of time and space for which the disciples were pressing during those unpredictable last days, certain truths emerge in Jesus' teaching. Zealots in Jerusalem were on a collision course with the *big power* of the day, but the need of the hour was still *to recognize who God is* and to live accordingly.   In the context of coming destruction, which was evident during the closing years of both Jeremiah's and Jesus' ministries in Jerusalem, certain words of the prophet take on added meaning.

Thus says the Lord!

> '*Let not the wise glory in his wisdom.*
> *Let not the mighty glory in his might.*
> *Let not the rich glory in his riches.*
>
> *But let him who glories glory in this —*
>   *in discerning and recognizing who I am.*
>
> *I am the Lord, the One who demonstrates*
>   *unchanging love, justice and righteousness in the land,*
>   *for in these things I delight,' affirms the Lord!*   (Jeremiah 9.23-24)

As this chapter comes to a close and with it your assignments, read **Hebrews 10.35-13.21**. These chapters speak of men and women who, in spite of their weaknesses and short-comings, and the unpredictable nature of the *Land Between, God's testing ground of faith, recognized who God is* and acted accordingly. They, together with the faithful of all ages, could well join in these lines from St. Gregory's hymn of prayer and praise of the sixth century A.D.

> *Banish our weakness, health and wholeness sending* . . . .
> *Thine is the glory, gleaming and resounding through all creation.*

APPENDIX I

AN INTRODUCTION TO THE GUIDE AND TO MARKING PROCEDURES

The purpose of this appendix is to aid the student who is beginning this study without an instructor. It is also a helpful reference for teachers to use when introducing the *Guide* and the *SMM* to a class. First the student is introduced to the various sections of the *SMM*. Then follows an important discussion of the marking kit and procedures which must be read carefully before one begins the assignments. After noting the explanation of the relief used on the *SMM* maps and the difference in the chronological and numerical sequence, the student is prepared to begin marking. The *Introduction* at the beginning of the *Guide* should have been read and the relevant charts marked.

DESCRIPTION OF THE *STUDENT MAP MANUAL (SMM)*

This description should be read with a copy of the *SMM* available for viewing. Note terms and abbreviations which come up often in later assignments (*SCS, SMA, Primary Sources,* etc.)

INTRODUCTORY PAGES OF THE *SMM*
East Orientation Map: This new orientation used in the *SMM* may seem strange at the outset. However, after marking a few maps it becomes very natural.

Contents: This important double page outlines the contents of the *SMM* and provides a cross-reference system. These allow one to find the map on which a particular Biblical or apocryphal reference is studied. A glance at the contents shows that a major part of the *SMM* (Sections 3 through 13) is devoted to historical maps, shown inside the gray and the tan areas.

The maps inside the gray area (Sections 3 through 10) represent the Patriarchal through Persian periods of Old Testament history. Events of these periods are presented on 47 individual maps in the *SMM*. These are seen as a whole on *Student Map A (SMA)* in full color. This map is printed in a 1:275,000 scale and presents sites and regions but no roads. It comes in two sheets, a northern sheet (A-N) and a southern sheet (A-S). These should be trimmed so that they can be joined and placed on a wall (preferably in front of a study desk) for quick reference. Many find it helpful to mount this map and to cover it with mylar (or plastic) so that it can be marked with special colored pens during their studies.

The maps shown inside the beige area (Sections 10 through 13) represent the Persian through Byzantine periods, covering the Return and Intertestament, New Testament and Late Roman/Byzantine periods. These are seen as a whole on *Student Map B (SMB)*, again in two full color sheets.

Other sections in the list of contents include Section 1 (Regional Maps), Section 2 (Archeology), Section 14 (Archeology of Jerusalem) and Section 15 (Indexes).

SECTION 1 – REGIONAL MAPS (full color)
These sixteen regional maps are preceded by a key map which shows the areas covered by each map. Overlapping is intentional and allows one to see strategic sites and

regions in relation to a variety of other sites and regions. Historical and archeological names used in Sections 2 through 13 are combined on these sixteen regional maps. (Note the legend at the top right of each map). Since modern roads are also shown, these maps are ideal for historical and archeological field work or touring in the country. Built-up areas around modern cities are shown in gray with the name of the modern city in many cases.

SECTION 2 — ARCHEOLOGY
Ten archeological period maps, showing sites where important remains have been found, make up Section 2 of the *SMM*. These sites will also appear with relevant background names (in black) on the appropriate historical maps in Sections 3 through 13. Dates used for the various archeological periods are listed in the introduction to these maps. They may be transferred to each of the ten maps.

SECTIONS 3 THROUGH 13 (Historical Maps)
The historical sections of the *SMM* begin here. Certain elements common to all of these sections are discussed. It is helpful to compare the following discussion with the double page of contents as you read. The number of each map is printed at the top left (northeast) corner and at the bottom right (southwest) corner of the map.

Titles of sections (3 through 13) appear at the top of each *SCS* and each map. Titles of individual maps are found in the *SCS* but are not printed on each individual map. This provides student involvement in writing in the title and flexibility in the choice of a title by the teacher.

Each section is preceded by a *Summary of Contents and Sources (SCS)* prepared especially for the study of that period of history. The main Biblical reference for the entire section is listed at the top right corner of the *SCS*.

The *SCS* for Section 3 shows that presently very little is known about the history of that period of the country. The *SCS* for Section 7 shows the breakdown of the section into individual maps and the further breakdown of each map into various topics (7-3 a, b, c; 7-4 a to h; etc.). (Relevant *SCS* topics are given in the margin of the *Guide* as they appear in the discussions.)

The column to the right of each topic in the *SCS* is the *Primary Source* column. Here is listed the actual historical text where one can read the events covered on the map. Any name found in that text appears on that map in **red** (an historical source name). All other names on the map are **black** (background names) and represent relevant archeological finds (from Section 2 of the *SMM*) or contemporary historical sites. Glance through the maps of Section 7 and note the changing red names (reflecting various primary sources from the Bible) and the varying scales of the maps (shown at the top of each map).

The *SCS* for Section 12 develops events surrounding the New Testament by outlining the history of the period preserved in the writings of Josephus Flavius. Both the new and the old systems of numbering of his works are listed under primary sources. New Testament references appear in bold type.

One last word on primary sources must be included here. When the source is extra-Biblical (from outside the Bible), frequently it can be found in certain collections of primary sources. The initials for such collections are given in the column for primary sources in the *SCS* (note the *SCS* reference of 9-4 or 12-13). The abbreviations are explained on the page preceding Section 1. Many libraries contain these reference works.

The next column to the right in each *SCS* lists any relevant full color Regional Map (in Section 1 of the *SMM*) to which reference may be made if one desires to see the full context of the region. The next column lists the relevant map and text from *The Macmillan Bible Atlas*, a very useful tool in this type of study. In the final column on the right space is available for other references and notes (assignments, readings, etc.). The space to the far left can be used for dates of events which the teacher considers important.

In Maps 3-1 through 11-12 natural communication links are printed on each map (international in red and local in black). These links represent the most convenient natural connection between important points on the map. They give a general idea of the movement of commerce and armies. From Map 11-13 through Map 13-5 a later Roman road system has been used, linking important new centers in those periods. Details on routes are given on the page of introduction in the *SMM* following *Contents*.

SECTION 14 — ARCHEOLOGY OF JERUSALEM
In this section much new and valuable information on the City of Jerusalem during three important periods is presented.

SECTION 15 — INDEXES
The indexes are explained in an introductory page. A glance at the *Index of Main Names* shows that red squares in this index match with red names on historical maps, while black squares match black names. Thus the line following each name presents a summary of much of the known history of each site. This particular history can be studied in detail from the *Primary Sources* by referring back to the relevant *SCS*.

THE MARKING KIT AND PROCEDURES

The assignments in the *SMM* consist of instructions for marking, interspersed with discussions and reading assignments from the Bible. **Biblical passages printed in bold should be read with the map in view.** The discussions serve as a commentary on the graphics the student is drawing on the map. Each completed map becomes a type of geographical/ historical building block. First of all, it is a statement in and of itself about a particular historical event. Secondly, it serves to illustrate the expressed goal of the chapter of the *Guide* in which it is found. Finally, the same map has a wide variety of uses in later study as it is linked to other maps in the *SMM*. The more *SMM* maps (building blocks) marked, the more variety of uses are found for each individual map. This is an important concept to remember as each map is marked. The marking is relevant not only to the immediate assignment but also to wider applications later. The procedure for the actual marking of each *SMM* map is discussed here.

1. **Colors and code used for marking.**
   The following is a list of pens and pencils which are needed to complete the map assignments in the *SMM* as outlined in the *Guide*. The use of each color is explained. Items marked with an asterisk (*) are provided by the Institute of Holy Land Studies to students enrolled in its courses.

a. Yellow broad tip felt pen for highlighting important names.

*b. Yellow felt tip pen (fine, not broad tip) for highlighting important routes. (The same pen can be used for highlighting names.)

*c. Brown felt tip pen (not too dark) for writing in geographical information which may or may not be mentioned in the text assigned to the map.

*d. Green felt tip pen (a bright, medium color) for information relating to Israel (except in the study of Israel, the Northern Kingdom).

*e. Light blue felt tip pen (turquoise) for information relating to Non-Israelite nations.

*f. Red felt tip pen to show confrontation of some type.

*g. Orange felt tip pen (bright and not too dark) for a variety of uses.

h. Black ultra-flair or fine ball point pen for writing in titles, dates, notes and legends. The same type pen in red is sometimes needed, but the red felt tip can also be used.

i. Three colored pencils (green, blue and orange) for shading in borders.

2. **Highlighting and color-coding names and routes:**
   In order to avoid mistakes in marking the first few *SMM* maps, the following practice marking may be helpful. It provides the most common types of instructions with examples to mark. The abbreviation *HL* means to highlight the route or name in yellow. This brings out something especially relevant to the topic being studied on the map.

   a. **Yellow HL on route** (Use fine tip yellow pen.)

   b. **Yellow HL on name**   • Megiddo
      Avoid covering the dot with yellow since it may be colored with a different color later.

   c. **Yellow HL on name and blue on the dot**   • Megiddo
      Be careful! Blue and yellow make green.

   d. **Yellow HL on name and blue box around name**   • Ashdod
      Always include the dot inside the box or circle. A circle need not be round.

   e. **Yellow HL on name and orange on dot**   • Beth-shan
      Do not go over a dot so many times that it becomes too dark and may be confused with red.

   f. **Yellow HL on name and name underlined in red**   • Gezer

   g. **Yellow HL on name and red on arrow**   ← Sidon
      Arrows printed by names indicate that the site is off the *SMM* map being studied. Since there is no dot for such a name, the arrow must be colored instead.

Various other marking instructions will be explained as they appear in the assignments. Instructions usually begin by stating which color is being used and what is being colored (route or name). Then there may be a brief phrase to help locate the route or name on the map. An equal sign (=) signals that marking begins although it is not always included. It is a good practice to read to the end of each individual instruction paragraph before marking in case there is an additional explanation.

3. **Writing in information:**
   There are various items which must be written in on each map. The first is the map title, which should be printed (in black capitals) at the top left center of each map. Secondly, the date can be written in (again in black) at the top center under the title. At the end of most assignments a legend is given. This can be written (in small black capitals) in the larger open area of the Mediterranean Sea or in some other convenient place on the map.

4. **Drawing free hand** (sweeping arrows and borders):
   This is perhaps the most difficult part of the assignments. It is done after most other marking is completed. The action on the map is brought to life by blue (non-Israelite), green (Israelite) and orange (miscellaneous) **sweeping arrows**. These arrows graphically show movement and direction. The flow of action is drawn alongside relevant routes (not directly on them), making the map much more attractive and meaningful. These arrows should skip over city names, leaving them intact. The arrows can pass through hilly regions and run into sea areas if necessary. The points of these arrows must be large enough to show definite direction. Do not hesitate to be artistic. Practice with the dry end of the pen before attempting to mark the map. The following example may help to demonstrate the type of arrow required.

The **flight-chase arrow** is a special type of arrow. Forces which are fleeing from a battle are shown graphically with short arrows in the appropriate color. A small, double pointed arrow (directly behind the first arrow) shows the pursuing forces. It is drawn in its own color. The combination would appear like the following example, except in two colors. Try making some yourself.

Free drawn **borders** also present a problem for the less adventurous student. It is difficult to write clear instructions for such borders. The only suggestion is to read the instructions through once before marking. Then make an initial attempt with a colored pencil of the proper color (blue, green or orange). Finally, draw the border with the felt tip pen and add the shading (in pencil) on the appropriate side of the border. Most of these borders are subjective at best. The exact location of the border is not your main concern. If specific information exists, it appears in the instructions.

5. **Helpful tips on marking** (Review these before beginning Chapter One.):
   a. Some students find that marking is easier in a group with one person reading the instructions and discussions. This allows those in the group to keep their eyes on the map as they mark.

   b. The work on the map should be done with good lighting and at a time when your mind is alert. Think while marking. It is not necessary to memorize the information in the discussions. However, a certain involvement in the map while reading the discussions or the passages from the Bible will enhance your learning experience.

c. Students claim that eastern orientation is not difficult to get used to if it is not resisted. The sun rises in the east (top of the *SMM* map). The Mediterranean Sea is in the west (bottom of the *SMM* map). The Jordan River runs from north to south (left to right). On the first few maps it may help to write in abbreviations for the directions on each side of the map (E, W, N and S).

d. Some students press too hard on the pens when they begin to mark. This dulls the point and makes it more difficult to produce free-flowing graphics. If a thicker line is needed, use the side of the pen. New pens sometimes have an excess of ink. Try them out first. It may be necessary to use up some of the excess ink on a sheet of paper. Be careful not to mix blue and yellow or it will come out green. Do not run a red marking over a red name or the name will disappear.

e. Read each separate marking instruction through to the end before marking. In the opening maps of Chapter One it may be helpful to read through the entire assignment prior to marking in order to become acquainted with the system. Some students underline the lead phrase in the required color for later review. Before beginning, check to see if you are marking the correct map.

f. When a new type of marking is required, review instructions in this appendix. Also experiment on a separate piece of paper and run through the marking with the dry end of the pen or with a colored pencil on the map itself. Pay attention to the directions for the flight and chase arrows to be sure that the right color is used for each arrow. When all else fails, have a bottle of white-out handy to make corrections.

g. In drawing sweeping arrows or borders, remember to skip over city names leaving them intact. Avoid straight lines. The flow of the action should be evident by the sweeping arrows. In general, follow along the natural routes unless there are none in the area.

h. In drawing borders it is a good idea to begin with a pencil of the proper color before marking in pen. The borders should then be shaded with a colored pencil on the proper side as indicated in the directions.

i. Add your own notes to the map as you read, but do not overcrowd. An overcrowded map is very difficult to review and to explain to someone else. It may be very helpful to glance over the topics listed in the *SCS (Summary of Contents and Sources)* for each map prior to marking or after the assignment is finished. This serves as a preview or review of the events of the map in a chronological order. In doing this do not attempt to memorize the events. Familiarization is adequate.

j. For those who have the time and the interest, it is possible to purchase a piece of plastic or mylar to go over the unmarked *SMM* map (or the larger *Student Map A*) for experimental marking with wax pencils or special pens. Markings can be created by reading selected parts of the references in the *Primary Source* column in the *SCS*. This exercise is time-consuming and is optional. Before beginning the assignment it is good to get into the habit of glancing at the red names on the map to be marked. These point to where the action will be.

UNDERSTANDING THE RELIEF MAPS IN THE *SMM*

Some people are not accustomed to using relief maps. For that reason the following explanation using Map 5-5 in the *SMM* is given. Keep this map open before you as you read the following explanation.

1. The thin, broken blue lines on the map indicate dry stream beds where water runs during heavy winter rains. (A river is shown by a solid blue line.) Such a stream bed is called a *nahal* in Hebrew or a *wadi* in Arabic. The word *nahal* is used in the assignments of the *Guide* since the English translation *brook* is misleading.

   When looking at a new map in the *SMM* remember that these blue lines indicate the lowest point in the region, a canyon or valley to which water flows. The small blue dots which can be seen on some maps indicate springs, while the small blue circles show cisterns important enough to appear on the map.

2. If the sides of these stream beds are steep, this is shown by shading as can be easily seen in the center of Map 5-5. Note that the stream beds on the western side of this map are not deep since there is little shading along them. Along the western edge of the Dead Sea (on the eastern side of the map) steep cliffs can be seen (geological faults).

3. Above the shading and between the dry stream beds there are higher ridges, seen in the northern center of the map. The top of the ridge usually is not shaded and appears lighter than the surrounding areas. In hilly regions, routes along these ridges are normally much more convenient for travel.

CHRONOLOGICAL AND NUMERICAL ORDER

Chronology is one of the most thoroughly discussed topics in Biblical studies. The *SMM* does not attempt to present any particular view in this regard but simply follows the apparent *Biblical order* of events. This is the point at which all students of the subject begin. Subsequent studies by each teacher can help the student evaluate internal evidence (within the Bible itself) and other disciplines which may clarify actual chronological order. Discussions in the *Guide* on the period of the Divided Kingdom use the chronological synchronization so well developed in Edwin R. Thiele, *The Mysterious Numbers of the Hebrew Kings* (Grand Rapids: Wm. B. Eerdmans, 1965). A handy paperback condensation of major issues is presented by the same author in *A Chronology of the Hebrew Kings* (Grand Rapids: Zondervan, 1977).

Due to limit on the number of maps in the *SMM*, overview maps (which open each historical section of the *SMM*) have also been used to portray historical events. Sometimes the Biblical order and the numerical order in the *SMM* could not be the same. Therefore, some overview maps (4-1, 7-1/2 and 8-1) are out of order when used for historical purposes. This can be clearly seen in the *Index to SMM Maps in the Guide*. It is also stated in all notes in the *SCS* for each relevant map. Within the four chapters of the *Guide*, discussions related to *SCS* subjects are noted by a system of cross-references in the outside column of each page. On the *SCS* itself, the blank space to the left of each subject may be used for relevant dates.

APPENDIX II

THE LAND BETWEEN: A BASIC OUTLINE OF
OLD TESTAMENT HISTORY

INTRODUCTION

The purpose of the *Guide* is to teach the *Land Between* through discussions of regional history. However, as students begin their work in the *Guide*, many come to realize that they have little historical background. These students either become discouraged or are tempted to concentrate on learning history rather than allowing history to teach the *dynamic* of the land. The purpose of this appendix is to provide a basic historical framework in chart form which can serve as a reference throughout this study. Thus, it is not included here to teach history but to help the student achieve the primary goal of the *Guide*, to understand the land itself.

In the *Introduction* to the *Guide*, the *Introductory Schematic: Periods from 1500 to 500 B.C.* was marked and briefly discussed. This schematic provided a basic introduction to the major themes of a millennium of history in the land. The chart discussed in Appendix II (enclosed at the back of the *Guide*) is meant to carry that process a step further. The following marking and discussion will make this chart more meaningful. After marking the chart, keep it in view and refer to it often as you read the discussion below and begin your work in Chapter One. Information or marking may be added as the study develops. The approximate dates listed in the margin are all B.C. and are selected to help you gain control of the basic flow of history.

MARKING

The main body of the chart presents the period from 1500 B.C. (Late Bronze I period) through 500 B.C. (Iron Age III/Persian period). Three geographical divisions are shown on the left hand margin of the chart: Egypt, The Land Between, and Northern Mesopotamia, names which you may want to highlight in yellow. Shading represents control by big powers. Some students prefer to use pencils for marking blue, orange and green.

1. **Yellow HL on numbers:**
   a. Along both the upper and lower time lines = **1500, 1000** and **500.**

   b. In the middle of the chart = **930, 722** and **587.**

2. **Yellow HL on names** = EGYPTIAN DOMINANCE (NEW KINGDOM), ASSYRIAN DOMINANCE, BABYLON, PERSIA, **David** and **Solomon.**

3. **Blue along all arrows with large points:** Major campaigns in or through the *Land Between* =
   a. From EGYPTIAN DOMINANCE (NEW KINGDOM) to the KINGDOM OF MITANNI and the HITTITE EMPIRE.

   b. All arrows (including their continuation below the Divided Kingdom) pointing down, beginning with Shalmaneser III and Adad-nirari III and on through ASSYRIAN DOMINANCE (Tiglath-pileser III, Shalmaneser V, etc.), BABYLON and PERSIA.

    c. Arrows from Shishak, Tirhaqa and Neco in Egypt pointing toward the *Land Between* and northern Mesopotamia.

5. **Orange box around name**: In Divided Monarchy = ISRAEL.

6. **Green box around name**: In Divided Monarchy = JUDAH.

DISCUSSION (Refer to the chart while reading.)

The blue arrows you have just marked represent the activity of major non-Israelite international powers in and through the *Land Between*. The arrows provide more detail about the periods of Egyptian and Assyrian dominance than the simple circles in the *Introductory Schematic* discussed in the *Introduction* to the *Guide*. However, even these arrows reflect only a few of the many campaigns by international powers in these two periods. They have been chosen since they have a direct relationship to events discussed in the *Guide*.

Between these periods of domination by foreign big powers, the Israelite tribes developed into a monarchy (united and divided) portrayed in the middle of the chart. During these centuries, other nationalistic movements vied with the Israelites for control of strategic routes and regions in the land. As noted in the *Introduction* to the *Guide*, these centuries between Egyptian and Assyrian dominance were centuries when *the mice could play while the cat was away.*

1550-
1150
The period of Egyptian dominance in the land in the Late Bronze Period lasted for some four centuries. By the fifteenth century B.C., major campaigns in and through the land were aimed at keeping the country under Egyptian control and engaging the forces of the Kingdom of Mitanni in northern Mesopotamia. These campaigns were led by the pharaohs of the **Eighteenth Dynasty**.

As the Hittite Empire expanded into northern Mesopotamia from Asia Minor, the Kingdom of Mitanni was subdued. At the same time, Egypt became occupied with internal religious and political issues. This allowed stronger leaders in the *Land Between* to expand at the expense of their neighbors who appealed to Egypt for some type of official action. These decades have been termed the *Amarna Period*, after the modern name of Egypt's capital at the time, to which Canaanite leaders filed their complaints.

In the late fourteenth century the Hittite Empire stood at the northern gateway to the *Land Between*. The pharaohs of the **Nineteenth Dynasty** rallied to meet this threat, campaigning in and through the country. The famous peace treaty of 1275 B.C. terminated this costly war between Egypt and the Hittite Empire and established a recognized border. In the twelfth century both of these big powers were faced with the onslaught of the so-called *Sea Peoples*, peoples from the region of the Aegean seeking new homelands throughout the eastern Mediterranean. Unlike the Hittite Empire, Egypt survived their attack. However, control of the *Land Between* slipped out of her hands.

The dating of Biblical events (like the Israelite Conquest) during these centuries of Egyptian dominance in the land is a lively debated subject. Historical and archeological arguments are beyond the scope of this brief introduction and do not serve the specific goal of the *Guide*. They are best left to scholarly articles and classroom discussions. However, it should be remembered that these Biblical events have their setting in the period when Egypt, to a greater or lesser degree, controlled strategic routes through the *Land Between*.

The disappearance of Egyptian authority in the land and the absence of any major power to the north increased the potential for hostilities among local powers in the country. Canaanite centers, an expanding Philistine presence and various emerging peoples like the Israelites all sought to achieve their own interests. Some of the accounts in the book of Judges (one of the most colorful chapters in Israelite history) have their setting in this period. Later, Samuel's ministry and the reign of Saul both reflect attempts to meet the basic security needs of the Israelite tribes, especially in face of the ever-increasing Philistine control of the land and its major highways. `1150-930`

Around 1000 B.C. the Israelite tribes were united under **David** of the tribe of Judah. From his new capital at Jerusalem, David extended his control over most of the *Land Between*. In the absence of international pressures, his son **Solomon** was able to exploit the natural routes of the country and to develop trade links in all directions. However, with the division of this kingdom (930 B.C.), internal tribal tensions, which had been contained by David and Solomon, exploded into an armed struggle between Israel in the north and Judah in the south. At the same time, a major invasion by Pharaoh Shishak of Egypt left the country in a weakened position.

The fifty years following the division of Solomon's kingdom could be termed the *battle for Benjamin*. In this half century, Israel and Judah fought bitterly over this small but strategic tribal territory which, with its approaches, was located between the two kingdoms. The rising power of Aramean Damascus (Syria) made good use of this internal Israelite conflict to bargain for financial and political advantages, waiting for the day when she would be strong enough to take control of the Transjordanian Highway and routes which led through the *Land Between* to the International Coastal Highway. `930-880`

Following the *battle for Benjamin*, Israel and Judah appear to have resolved their differences and entered a period of cooperation. This ushered in a time of affluency for both kingdoms which culminated in the reigns of **Ahab** and **Jehoshaphat**. It was in these decades that Elijah preached against the spiritual apostasy and affluency in the north which was augmented by Ahab's wife, Jezebel of Phoenicia, and her followers. Expansion in Transjordan brought Moab under Israel's control while Judah was able to hold on to the region of Edom and the Red Sea and received tribute from Philistia. `880-840`

In spite of a serious conflict of interests in Transjordan between Israel and Damascus, forces from both nations are listed as allies (with others) against Assyrian forces led by **Shalmaneser III** which had moved into northern Mesopotamia (Battle of Qarqar in 853 B.C.). The years preceding 841 B.C. saw many changes in the *Land Between*. Revolts in Moab against Israel and in Edom and Philistia against Judah, the overthrow of ruling houses in Damascus and in Israel, and the resulting internal strife in Judah were only a prelude to a campaign by Shalmaneser III through the north of the country. Shalmaneser's *Black Obelisk* found in Assyria characterizes this dark moment in Israel's history. It shows Jehu, the new king of Israel, prostrating himself before the king of Assyria, followed by his servants carrying tribute.

When the dust had settled after 841 B.C., Assyria again became occupied with matters in Mesopotamia. Jehu's bloody revolution had left Israel crippled and Judah weakened `840-800` by internal strife. **Hazael**, the new king of Damascus, knew that it was his moment to exploit these weaknesses. Both the Transjordanian and International Coastal Highways (with Galilee and the Jezreel Valley) came under the control of Damascus in those difficult closing decades of the ninth century B.C. It was then that Elisha's ministry took place.

800-740

Damascus' domination of the *Land Between* ended abruptly just before 800 B.C. when **Adad-nirari III** of Assyria sacked the city. This allowed Israel and Judah to recover their former power and to expand again, even beyond the limits of Ahab's and Jehoshaphat's kingdoms a century before. This political and economic revival reached its zenith in Israel under **Jeroboam II** and in Judah under **Uzziah**. Again, prophets arose (Amos and Hosea) who preached against the affluence and resulting spiritual apostasy which characterized this period, especially in Israel.

740-700

The late eighth century B.C. saw the return of Assyria to the *Land Between*, this time to annex it systematically as a prelude to an invasion of Egypt. In response, Egypt feverishly attempted to encourage revolts in the land through diplomatic maneuvers, promising assistance to those who followed her advice. To meet the Assyrian threat, local leaders formed alliances (as they had done in 853 B.C.), hoping that Assyria could be contained. Refusing to join with Israel and Damascus, King Ahaz of Judah requested aid from Assyria. Swift and effective action by **Tiglath-pileser III** brought the major highways of the *Land Between* under the control of Assyria (734-732 B.C.). By 722/1, the city of Samaria fell to **Shalmaneser V**, and what remained of the northern kingdom of Israel was annexed into the Assyrian Empire by **Sargon II**. The region became the province of Samaria, and its inhabitants were replaced by foreigners.

The next two turbulent decades saw more Egyptian inspired revolts against Assyria in Philistia and in Judah. Assyrian annexation continued, leaving only Judah in the Hill Country after an abortive revolt by **Hezekiah** against **Sennacherib**, who also failed in his attempt to capture Jerusalem. Both Micah and Isaiah lived and ministered during these troubled times.

700-640

In the seventh century, under **Esarhaddon** and **Ashurbanipal**, Assyria realized her century old dream of controlling Lower and Upper Egypt. While some revolts broke out along the International Coastal and Transjordanian Highways, little is known about events in the *Land Between* during this period.

640-600

In the last half of the seventh century, the great Assyrian Empire showed signs of decline. Egypt again gained her independence, and much of the *Land Between* came under the control of **Josiah**, who ruled Judah during her last period of greatness. The last three decades of the century saw a quick succession of violent events which resulted in the demise of the Assyrian Empire and its takeover by Babylon, the ancient religious and political capital of southern Mesopotamia.

During this period the forces of Egypt marched through the land in order to assist Assyria as she battled for her life against Babylonia. For a few years after 609 B.C., Pharaoh Neco was able to reassert Egyptian dominance in the *Land Between*. However, in 605 B.C. the tables turned again at the great battle of Carchemish in northern Mesopotamia. The defeat of the Egyptian army in that year opened the doors of the north to **Nebuchadnezzar** of Babylonia, the new master of northern Mesopotamia, who soon entered and occupied the former Assyrian provinces in the *Land Between*.

During the sixth century, Babylon made several attacks on Egypt with limited success. There is also some evidence that Egypt attempted to gain a foothold again in Phoenicia. However, Egyptian activity was mainly on the diplomatic level. Again she encouraged Judah to revolt, this time against Babylon. The closing years of Judah's history are filled with intrigue and turmoil. Jeremiah, the major prophet of the period, witnessed revolts and deportations and, in 587 B.C., the fall of Jerusalem itself before he was taken to Egypt by his own people. In addition to Jeremiah, the promise of a return to Zion is heard in the writings of prophets Ezekiel and Daniel living in exile in Babylon during the sixth century.

600-540

With the fall of Babylon to **Cyrus** of Persia in 539 B.C., a small number of Jews did return to the *Land Between*, to the region of Jerusalem. In 525 B.C. **Cambyses** of Persia took control of Egypt, sealing the fate of the country for the two centuries to come. Shortly thereafter, Jeshua and Zerubbabel *began to rebuild the house of God which is in Jerusalem, together with the prophets of God [Haggai and Zechariah] who were with them to help* (Ezra 5.2). It was in the following century (about 450 B.C.) that Ezra and Nehemiah returned to the *Land Between* to rebuild Jerusalem, both physically and spiritually.

540-440

INDEX TO BIBLICAL REFERENCES

Biblical texts noted in *The Land Between* are listed below. Passages required to be read or translated in the text itself appear in bold. For reference the pages of the four chapters of the *Guide* are as follows: I = 18-38; II = 39-87; III = 88-146; IV = 147-271.

INDEX TO SMM MAPS IN THE GUIDE

The following list of *SMM* maps is arranged in chronological rather than numerical order. A page number in bold indicates that the discussion and marking of that map begins on that page. A number in medium typeface signifies that the map is discussed in a separate section of that chapter but is not marked in that chapter. A number in italics denotes that the map is only discussed as background to another map in the *Guide*. It is possible to study the *SMM* maps chronologically by reading all of the discussions in the *Guide* for each map (in Chapters I, II, III and IV) before proceeding to the next map.